A GUIDE TO THE
WORLD'S RADIO STATIONS

OTHER TITLES OF INTEREST

A GUIDE TO THE WORLD'S RADIO STATIONS

by
PETER SHORE

BERNARD BABANI (publishing) LTD
THE GRAMPIANS
SHEPHERDS BUSH ROAD
LONDON W6 7NF
ENGLAND

PLEASE NOTE

© 1988, © 1991 and © 1995 BERNARD BABANI (publishing) LTD

First Published
(as *International Radio Stations Guide*) – June 1988
Revised Edition – July 1991

First Published
(as *A Guide to the World's Radio Stations*) – March 1995

British Library Cataloguing in Publication Data:
Shore, Peter
Guide to the World's Radio Stations
I. Title
621.38416

ISBN 0 85934 355 3

Set from disk by G C Arnold Partners, Broadstone, Dorset
Printed and bound in Great Britain by Cox & Wyman Ltd, Reading

CONTENTS

Preface

In the air all around us are tens of thousands of radio signals. Along with the myriad of transmissions from mobile telephones, emergency services, the military and other users of the electronic radio frequency spectrum are programmes from every corner of our planet. With a short wave radio, you can tune in to any of them, choosing perhaps Moscow or Beijing, Washington or Delhi. The choice is yours!

This latest edition of *A Guide to the World's Radio Stations* offers a useful map to help the radio listener find his or her way around the short wave broadcast bands. It details which station operates on what frequency and when to tune in to broadcasts in English. There is also useful data such as a world time chart and translations to use when writing to foreign radio stations.

Listening to far off radio signals (or DXing, as it is known to many hobbyists worldwide) is a great pastime, and whether you spend twenty minutes or twenty hours in front of your set this edition of *A Guide to the World's Radio Stations* will prove an invaluable companion as you travel around the globe – all without having to leave the comfort of your armchair.

Good listening!

Peter Shore*
September 1994

*Peter Shore is a pseudonym.

1

Translation Table

	Station Site	Country	Frequency (kHz or MHz)	Wavelength (metres)	Effective Radiated Power ERP (kW)	State	Call	Province
Français	Poste D'emetteur	Pays	Fréquence	Longeur D'onde	Puissance Effective Reyonement	Etat	Indicatif D'appel	Province
Deutsch	Standort der Sendestation	Land	Frequenz	Wellenlänge	Ausgangsleistung	Staat	Rufzeichen	Provinz
Nederlands	Lokatie van Zender	Land	Frequentie	Golfengte	Effectief Stralingvermogen	Staat	Oproepen	Gewest
Espanol	Sitio De Transmisor	Páis	Frecuencia	Longitud De Onda	Potencia Irradiada Efectiva	Estado	Indicativo De Llamada	Provincia
Portugues	Sitio De Transmissor	Pais	Frequencia	Comprimento De Onda	Potencia Irradiacao Efectivo	Estado	Sinal De Chamada	Provincia
Italiano	Sito De Transmettitore	Paese	Frequenza	Lunghezza D'onda	Potenza Radiazione Effettiva	Stato	Segnale Di Chiamata	Provincia
Dansk	Stationsbe-liggenhed	Land	Frekvens	Bølgelængde	Udstrålet Effekt	Stat	Kaldesingnal	Provins
Svenska	Stationsläga	Land	Frekvens	Våglängd	Utstrålad Effekt	Stat	Anropssignal	Provins
Norsk	Stasjonsplasering	Land	Frekvens	Bølgelengde	Utstrålad Effekt	Stat	Kaldesignal	Provins

Section 1

LISTENING TO SHORT WAVE RADIO

Most people in the developed world are oblivious of short wave radio, and yet all around us, throughout the day and night, radio signals from almost every country on the planet are sent through the ether in dozens of languages. For those living in western Europe and North America, radio is something on in the background at breakfast time, or used for entertainment on the move in cars. Research shows that the radio audience declines steadily from an early morning peak to a very low – sometimes unmeasurable – figure in the evening when television takes over as the prime provider of entertainment.

It has also been found that radios mostly stay tuned to one station, with listeners reluctant to fiddle with the tuning knob in case they cannot find their favourite radio station again. But to leave a radio receiver tuned to one station is to miss out on so much; it is almost like reading the books of just one author.

While we all expect news to be brought to us from around the world by our local radio and television stations, few people in the western world know that they could tune in to the radio stations in countries where the news is being made. That is not the case in many parts of the world where huge numbers of people listen to overseas radio broadcasts on a daily basis.

Broadcasts from other countries offer a lifeline of news free from the censorship which affects domestic broadcasting in many countries. In Burma, a country where the news media is controlled entirely by the government, many people listen to the BBC World Service. If discovered, they may face punishment.

If you turn on a short wave radio receiver and tune along the broadcast bands, you can hear broadcasts from every continent in a multiplicity of languages as diverse as English, Chinese, Spanish, Arabic, Farsi, Indonesian and Korean.

How radio waves travel

All radio waves travel at the speed of light, 300 million metres a second. Not all radio waves behave in the same way, however. Short wave, or high frequency, radio signals make use of a part of the earth's atmosphere which has been ionised by the ultra violet and soft X-rays emitted by the sun and is therefore known as the ionosphere. A transmitted signal travels up to the ionosphere where it is effectively bounced back to earth. A short wave signal is able to travel many thousands of kilometres by bouncing between the earth and the

3

ionosphere several times. Signals from Australia routinely reach northern Europe, and vice-versa.

Several factors affect how well short wave signals can travel. Higher short wave frequencies travel during the day, whilst during the night, lower frequencies work best. And the ionosphere changes in relation to the number of sun spots. The sun has a cycle, with periods of high solar activity, and therefore the greatest number of sun spots, occurring each 11 years. As this book goes to press, the number of sun spots is falling which means that broadcasters are moving down the frequency bands to the 11, 9 and 7 MHz [25, 31 and 41 metre bands] At the times when sun spot numbers are high, higher frequencies in the 13, 15, 17 and 21 MHz bands [21, 19, 16 and 13 metre bands] can be used for long distance broadcasting.

To make sure of good reception in the area to which a broadcaster is transmitting, engineers use several frequencies in a number of parts of the short wave broadcast bands. Listeners are encouraged to try each frequency that is being transmitted to find which works best. And listeners should remember that unlike on medium wave or VHF-FM, one frequency will not work for all of the day!

What is on the air?
The choice for the listener is immense, with a huge range of programmes from many stations to choose from. The peak listening times are at local dawn and mid-evening when stations vie for your attention. The principal players in international broadcasting are the BBC World Service, which has a twenty-four hour a day English service and highly respected news on the hour; Radio Australia, in English twenty-four hours a day with news on the hour and the Pacific as the main target area; Radio France International, with a French world service on twenty-four hours a day and English bulletins regularly through the day; and the Voice of America which is on the air for most of the day, but directed to specific regions. There are many smaller stations which are on the air for much less time, but nonetheless have large followings – Radio Netherlands, Swiss Radio International, the Monitor Radio International from the United States and Deutsche Welle from Germany.

Details of the English schedules of all of these stations are included in *A Guide to the World's Radio Stations*. Short wave radio offers an unique way of following international news stories as they unfold. The BBC Monitoring service in England keeps a well tuned ear to the world's airwaves to report what domestic and international radio stations are broadcasting. From a mansion above the town of Reading, teams of language monitors have flashed news around the world within moments of its broadcast: the ending of Prague Spring,

Chernobyl, the invasion of Kuwait, the situation in the former Yugoslavia – all of which short wave listeners with a good radio receiver have heard too. There is much that can be written about international radio, but there is no substitute for tuning around the short wave bands and discovering what is there.

The short wave broadcast bands

Broadcasting is not the sole user of the short wave radio spectrum. There are many other forms of communication, including the military, maritime mobile, aviation, news agencies, radio amateurs and others. The short wave frequency range (3 to 30 MHz) has been divided by World Administrative Radio Conferences in order to meet the requirements of all users. The broadcast bands are the most crowded of the short wave spectrum, and although there are certain areas designated for radio broadcasting, many stations now operate on frequencies outside these official areas to avoid the overcrowding.

The table below indicates the currently sanctioned bands, and the extensions agreed in WARC 1979. Listeners will find that many stations, such as the BBC, Voice of America, China Radio International operate outside these bands in order to ensure that their programmes can be heard by their audiences around the world.

Frequencies in kilohertz (kHz)	Agreed extensions (at WARC 1979)	Metre bands
2300–2495		120 metre band
3200–3400		90 metre band
3900–4000		75 metre band
4750–5060		60 metre band
5950–6200		49 metre band
7100–7300		41 metre band
9500–9775	9780–9900	31 metre band
11700–11975	11950–12050	25 metre band
13600–13800		21 metre band
15100–15450	15455–15600	19 metre band
17700–17900	17550–17895	16 metre band
21450–21750	21755–21850	13 metre band
25600–26100	*25670–26100*	11 metre band

[WARC 1979 agreed that the 11 metre band should be reduced in range]

The 120, 90 and 60 metre bands are allocated to tropical domestic broadcasting where the effectiveness of medium wave broadcasting is severely impaired as a result of high atmospheric noise levels.

Section 2

CHOOSING A SHORT WAVE RADIO RECEIVER

There is a staggeringly wide range of audio equipment available in the developed world, but little of it offers short wave frequencies. In the most part, short wave radio is an unknown quantity for radio shop staff. Large retail chains may offer a limited selection of short wave receivers, but the staff are unlikely to have much expertise in listening, or know what makes one set better than another.

It is essential to decide how much you can afford to spend on a new receiver. Prices start from around £40 in the United Kingdom and go up to more than £2,000 for a top of the range communications receiver. The majority of short wave listeners are likely to look at sets costing up to, say, £200, and there is a good choice available from the main makers of short wave sets. It is better to buy a dedicated short wave set, rather than a multipurpose radio which may have a cassette player built in. Here are some suggestions for what to look for in a new short wave receiver:

Frequency coverage
Short wave frequencies range from 3 to 30 megahertz (3000 to 30 000 kilohertz) and a good set will cover as many of those as possible. Many modern radios offer continuous coverage, and this is to be recommended to enable listeners to tune in to frequencies outside the official broadcast bands (detailed in Section 1) which many stations use to escape the worst overcrowding. Some sets will offer a range of short wave frequency bands, which cover the main bands, with some frequencies either side. Check to see whether main BBC World Service frequencies such as 9410 or 12 095 kHz are included in the range.

Frequency display
It is helpful for a set to give an accurate indication of the frequency it is tuned to. Analogue displays (where a needle moves along the frequencies printed on a dial) are most common, but are not always accurate. Many more sets now have a digital display of the frequency, either in kilohertz or megahertz. This enables easy identification of a station using frequency lists in the *GWRS*.

Tuning
Radios are usually tuned by a rotary knob which causes the frequency to be moved up or down the bands. There may be a selector switch to enable a different short wave range to be chosen if the set has divided

the short wave spectrum in to different bands. More common amongst radios with a digital display is a keypad which enables frequencies to be entered directly. Manual tuning in sets with a keypad is generally possible using a rotary tuning knob, or by arrow keys which increase or decrease the frequency in the same manner as a rotary knob.

Other facilities

Radio receivers which are digitally tuned (in other words with a keypad) usually offer a number of memories into which regularly used frequencies may be stored. This eliminates the need to remember a large number of separate frequencies, and allows almost instantaneous tuning.

Make sure that your set has a socket for the connection of headphones. It is more comfortable to listen to short wave broadcasts through headsets since interference can make listening difficult through a loudspeaker.

Ensure that there is a connection for a tape recorder if you think that you might want to record programmes in the future.

An external aerial socket is highly useful.

Some sets offer single side band [ssb] reception. This is a form of transmission used by radio amateurs, and by broadcast stations for experimental purposes.

Short wave on the move

Many of the short wave radio sets made today are designed for travelling, and so are small (around the size of a paperback book) and light weight. The benefit of frequency memories and digital tuning are obvious for frequent travellers. Bear in mind the size of the set you are looking at if you travel a great deal.

Short wave radio is available in the car, although the choice of receivers is limited. Three European manufacturers make car radio-cassette players with short wave: Blaupunkt, Grundig and Philips.

Several of the DX programmes broadcast by international radio stations carry reviews of new equipment – details are included in this book. The main manufacturers of short wave radios are Grundig, Panasonic, Philips, Sangean (found in the UK under the Roberts brand name and in Germany under Siemens) and Sony. All offer a range of receivers with a wide variety of different features.

Improving reception

The most important part of a radio is the aerial, and yet most people rely solely on the telescopic antenna provided with the set. The advice is to use an outdoor aerial if at all possible. The simplest aerial will generally improve reception greatly. Invest in a piece of copper wire (insulated if possible) and sling it between the house and a convenient tree in the garden, and connect it to the radio. Make sure that the copper wire does not touch any building or tree as this will cause the incoming signal to earth. Also ensure that it does not pass near any exposed electrical cables. More complicated aerials will help to overcome any particular local interference problems, or to pull in signals from a particular direction.

If you are not able to use an outdoor aerial, keep your set next to a window or an outside wall, and away from televisions or electrical motors which may cause very heavy electrical interference.

Section 3

HOW TO USE A GUIDE TO THE WORLD'S RADIO STATIONS

This latest edition of *A Guide to the World's Radio Stations* is an essential reference work for the casual listener and the professional radio monitor. It has been designed to help listeners steer around the constantly changing face of the international broadcast bands.

The *GWRS* has been revised in full and includes the most up-to-date data.

There is a complete listing of the whole short wave spectrum, including the officially designated broadcast bands, and frequencies which, although not allocated to broadcasting, are used by domestic and international radio stations in different parts of the world.

The information contained in the main short wave section has been compiled from registrations lodged with the International Telecommunication Union in Geneva, coupled with extensive monitoring research carried out in the United Kingdom and overseas. This edition of the *GWRS* has been devised so that the reader can tell at a glance whether a particular entry denotes whether a user has registered it with the ITU [the location of the transmitting site is shown in capitals] or it details an off-air observation [the transmitter is in lower case].

For example:
```
7225      MEYERTON        250     AFS       Channel Africa
```
indicates that South Africa has registered a 250 kW transmitter at Meyerton, whereas
```
11850     Sveio           500     NOR       R Norway Intl
```
shows that the Norwegians are using the frequency although it has not been registered with the ITU.

In some cases, countries will submit registrations with the ITU which they have no real intention of using. During compilation of this edition it became clear that Bangladesh, for example, registers tens of frequencies but in practice uses only a handful. However, by including both registrations actually used, as well as those not apparently on the air, the *GWRS* is as complete as possible, as some registrations are brought in to operation at a later date.

The country shown is that where the transmitter is located, but if another country is shown as well [e.g. HKG/G or CHN/E] this shows that a programme from another international broadcaster is being carried as part of a relay agreement – in the cases shown the BBC

11

from its relay station in Hong Kong, and Radio Exterior de Espana from Chinese transmitters.

The number of relay arrangements and hire agreements has increased enormously since the last edition of the *GWRS*. The world's largest international broadcasters are now doing what, just a few years ago, would have been unthinkable: hiring time on transmitters in the former Soviet Union to beam programmes in to China, the Indian subcontinent and other parts of Asia. Deutsche Welle, the BBC World Service, Voice of America and Radio Netherlands are all making use of the new freedom in the Republics which constituted the old Soviet Empire to improve reception for listeners in many parts of the world.

The table of English broadcasts in the *GWRS* shows times for summer, but some stations will alter their transmission times in the autumn to take account of local clock changes and changes in propagation conditions. If the broadcast listed cannot be traced at the time shown, try an hour either side. Alterations to times and frequencies are generally announced at the start of transmissions.

Section 4

ABBREVIATIONS USED IN THIS BOOK

ABC	Australian Broadcasting Corporation
AFN	American Forces Network
AIR	All India Radio
AM	amplitude modulation
AWR	Adventist World Radio
BBC	British Broadcasting Corporation
BBCWS	British Broadcasting Corporation World Service
BC	Broadcast, Broadcasting
BSKSA	Broadcasting System of the Kingdom of Saudi Arabia
CBS	Central Broadcasting System, Taiwan
CNR	China National Radio
DAB	Digital Audio Broadcasting
Dem	Democratic
DLF	Deutschlandfunk, Cologne
DW	Deutsche Welle, Cologne
Dom	Domestic
ELWA	Cultural Missionary Broadcasting Service of Sudan Interior Mission
ERT	Elliniki Radiophonia Tileorassis, Athens
ERTT	Etablissement de la Radiodiffusion Television Tunisienne
Ext	External
FEBA	Far East Broadcasting Association
FEBC	Far East Broadcasting Company
FM	frequency modulation
HCJB	Hail Christ Jesus Blessings, Ecuador
ICRC	International Committee of the Red Cross
Intl	International
ISB	Iceland State Broadcasting
kHz	kilohertz
kW	kilowatt
LSB	lower side band
LW	long wave
MHz	megahertz
MW	medium wave
N, Natl	National
NHK	Nippon Hoso Kyokai
ORF	Osterreichischer Rundfunk, Vienna
ORT	Office de Radiodiffusion et Television
OAS	Organisation of American States
R	Radio

RAE	Radiodifusion Argentina al Exterior
RAI	Radiotelevisione Italiana, Rome
RCI	Radio Canada International
RDP	Radiodifusao Portugesa, Lisbon
REE	Radio Exterior de Espana
Rev	Revolution, Revolutionary
RFE	Radio Free Europe
RFI	Radio France International
RFO	Radiodiffusion Francaise d'Outre Mer
RIAS	Radio in the American Sector, Berlin
RL	Radio Liberty
RRI	Radio Republik Indonesia
RSA	Republic of South Africa
RTBF	Radio-Television Belge de la Communaute Francaise, Brussels
RTM	Radiodiffusion Television Marocaine
SBC	Singapore Broadcasting Corporation
SDR	Suddeutscher Rundfunk, Stuttgart
SFB	Sender Freies Berlin
SLBC	Sri Lanka Broadcasting Corporation
SSB	single side band
SW	short wave
SWF	Sudwestfunk
TRT	Turkish Radio-Television Corporation, Ankara
TWR	Trans World Radio
UAE	United Arab Emirates
USB	upper side band
v	variable
V	Voice
VHF	very high frequency
VO	Voice of
VoA	Voice of America
VoFC	Voice of Free China, Taiwan
VOIRI	Voice of the Islamic Republic of Iran
WCSN	Monitor Radio Intl, Boston, transmitting station in Maine
WHRI	World Harvest Radio International, South Bend
WINB	World international Broadcasters Inc, Red Lion
WMLK	Assemblies of Yahweh, Bethel
WRNO	WRNO New Orleans
WS	World Service
WSHB	Monitor Radio Intl, Boston, transmitting station in South Carolina
WYFR	Family Radio, Oakland
YLE	Yleisradio, Finland

Section 5

COUNTRY CODES USED IN THIS BOOK

Listed in alphabetical order

AFG	Afghanistan	CBG	Cambodia
AFS	South Africa	CHL	Chile
AGL	Angola	CHN	People's Republic of China
ALB	Albania		
ALG	Algeria	CHR	Christmas Island
ALS	Alaska	CKH	Cook Islands
AND	Andorra	CLM	Colombia
ANG	Anguilla	CLN	Sri Lanka
ARG	Argentina	CME	Cameroon
ARM	Armenia	CNR	Canary Islands
ARS	Saudi Arabia	COG	Congo
ARU	Aruba	COM	Comoro Republic
ASC	Ascension Island	CPV	Cape Verde
ATG	Antigua	CTI	Ivory Coast
ATN	Netherlands Antilles	CTR	Costa Rica
AUS	Australia	CUB	Cuba
AUT	Austria	CVA	Vatican City
AZE	Azerbaijan	CYP	Cyprus
AZR	Azores	D	Germany
B	Brazil	DJI	Djibouti
BAH	Bahamas	DNK	Denmark
BDI	Burundi	DOM	Dominican Republic
BEL	Belgium	E	Spain
BEN	Benin	EGY	Egypt
BFA	Burkina Faso	EQA	Ecuador
BHR	Bahrain	EST	Estonia
BGD	Bangladesh	ETH	Ethiopia
BLR	Belarus	F	France
BLZ	Belize	FJI	Fiji
BOL	Bolivia	FLK	Falkland Islands
BOS	Bosnia-Hercegovina	FNL	Finland
BOT	Botswana	G	United Kingdom
BRB	Barbados	GAB	Gabon
BRM	Burma	GDL	Guadeloupe
BRU	Brunei	GEO	Georgia
BUL	Bulgaria	GHA	Ghana
CAF	Central African Republic	GIB	Gibraltar
CAN	Canada	GMB	Gambia

GNB	Guinea Bissau	MAC	Macau
GNE	Equatorial Guinea	MAU	Mauritius
GRC	Greece	MCO	Monaco
GRD	Grenada	MDA	Moldova
GRL	Greenland	MDG	Madagascar
GTM	Guatemala	MDN	Macedonia
GUF	French Guiana	MDR	Madeira
GUI	Guinea	MEX	Mexico
GUM	Guam	MLA	Malaysia
GUY	Guyana	MLD	Maldives
HKG	Hong Kong	MLI	Mali
HND	Honduras	MLT	Malta
HNG	Hungary	MNG	Mongolia
HOL	Netherlands	MOZ	Mozambique
HRV	Croatia	MRA	Northern Marianas
HTI	Haiti	MRC	Morocco
HWA	Hawaii	MRT	Martinique
I	Italy	MSR	Montserrat
ICO	Cocos Island	MTN	Mauritania
IND	India	MWI	Malawi
INS	Indonesia	MYT	Mayotte
IRL	Ireland	NCG	Nicaragua
IRN	Iran	NCL	New Caledonia
IRQ	Iraq	NGR	Niger
ISL	Iceland	NIG	Nigeria
ISR	Israel	NIU	Niue Island
J	Japan	NMB	Namibia
JMC	Jamaica	NOR	Norway
JOR	Jordan	NPL	Nepal
KAZ	Kazakhstan	NRU	Nauru
KEN	Kenya	NZL	New Zealand
KGZ	Kyrgystan	OCE	French Polynesia
KIR	Kiribati	OMA	Oman
KOR	South Korea	PAK	Pakistan
KRE	North Korea	PHL	Philippines
KWT	Kuwait	PNG	Papua New Guinea
LAO	Laos	PNR	Panama
LBN	Lebanon	POL	Poland
LBR	Liberia	POR	Portugal
LBY	Libya	PRG	Paraguay
LSO	Lesotho	PRU	Peru
LTU	Lithuania	PTR	Puerto Rico
LUX	Luxembourg	QAT	Qatar
LVA	Latvia	REU	Reunion

ROU	Romania	VUT	Vanuatu
RRW	Rwanda	WAL	Wallis Island
RUS	Russia	YEM	Yemen
S	Sweden	YUG	Yugoslavia
SDN	Sudan	ZAI	Zaire
SEN	Senegal	ZMB	Zambia
SEY	Seychelles	ZWE	Zimbabwe
SHN	St Helena		
SLM	Solomon Isles		
SLO	Slovenia		
SLV	El Salvador		
SMA	American Samoa		
SMO	Western Samoa		
SNG	Singapore		
SOM	Somalia		
SRL	Sierra Leone		
STP	Sao Tome et Principe		
SUI	Switzerland		
SUR	Surinam		
SVK	Slovakia		
SWZ	Swaziland		
SYR	Syria		
TCH	Chad		
TCH	Czech Republic		
TGO	Togo		
THA	Thailand		
TJK	Tajikistan		
TKM	Turkmenistan		
TON	Tonga		
TRD	Trinidad		
TUN	Tunisia		
TUR	Turkey		
TUV	Tuvalu		
TWN	Taiwan		
TZA	Tanzania		
UAE	United Arab Emirates		
UGA	Uganda		
UKR	Ukraine		
URG	Uruguay		
USA	United States of America		
UZB	Uzbekistan		
VEN	Venezuela		
VIR	American Virgin Isles		
VTN	Vietnam		

Section 6

WORLDWIDE SHORT WAVE RADIO STATIONS

Freq. [kHz]	Transmitter site	Power [kW]	Country	Station name
2310	Alice Springs	50	AUS	ABC Alice Springs
2325	Tennant Creek	50	AUS	ABC Tennant Creek
2340	Fuzhou	10	CHN	Fujian 1
2350	Sariwon	10	KRE	Regional station
2360	Huehuelenango	0.5	GTM	R Maya de Barillas
2380	Limeira	0.25	B	R Educadora
2390	Santiago	1	GTM	La Voz de Atitlan
	Huayacocotla	0.5	MEX	R Huayacocotla
2410	Senr Guiomard	1	B	R Transamazonica
	Wabag	10	PNG	R Enga
2415	Wenzhou	10	CHN	Wenzhou 1
2420	Sao Carlos	0.5	B	R Sao Carlos
2445	Nanchang	10	CHN	Jiangxi 1
2460	Rio Branco	1	B	R Alvorado
	Kunming	10	CHN	Yunnan
2475	Hangzhou	20	CHN	Zhejiang
2485	Katherine	50	AUS	ABC Katherine
2490	Descalvado	0.25	B	R 8 Setembro
	Ujung Padang	0.5	INS	RRI
2560	Urumqui	15	CHN	Xinjiang
2850	Pyongyang	120	KRE	Korean Central BS
2905	Tenggara	0.5	INS	RPDT Ngada
2960	Ruteng	0.3	INS	RKPDT Manggaraj
3000	Bengkalis	0.25	INS	RPDT2 Bengkalis
3143	Tanjung Pandan	0.3	INS	RPKDT2 Belitung
3178	Bima	0.3	INS	RKPDT2
3200	Manzini	25	SWZ	TWR
	Bolivia	0.5	BOL	R 9 de Abril
3205	Ribeirao Preto	1	B	R Ribeirao Preto
	Humaita	5	B	R Vale Rio Madeira
	Vanimo	10	PNG	R West Sepik
3210	Maputo	100	MOZ	R Mozambique

Freq. [kHz]	Transmitter site	Power [kW]	Country	Station name
3215	Sulawesi	10	INS	RRI Manado
3220	Beijing	50	CHN	CNR 1
	Quito	10	EQA	HCJB
	Lae	10	PNG	R Morobe
3222	Lama Kara	10	TGO	R Lama Kara
3223	Shimla	2.5	IND	AIR
	Lombok	5	INS	RRI Mataram
3230	Kathmandu	100	NPL	R Nepal
	Juliaca	0.5	PRU	R Sol de los Andes
	Meyerton	100	AFS	R Oranje
3232	Bukittingi	10	INS	RRI
3235	Gauhati	20	IND	AIR
	Kimbe	2	PNG	R West New Britain
	Marilia	0.5	B	R Clube
3240	Manzini	25	SWZ	TWR
3240	Esmeraldas	1	EQA	R Antena Libre
3245	Varginha	1	B	R Clube
	Kerema	10	PNG	R Gulf
3250	Pyongyang	120/400	KRE	R Pyongyang + domestic
	Kalin	20	INS	RRI
	Santa Barbara	0.8	HND	R Luz y Vida
3255	Shillong	50	IND	AIR
	Lancers Gap	100	LSO/G	BBC
	Crato	1	B	R Educadora
3260	Niamey	4	NGR	Voix de Sahel
	Guiyang	10	CHN	Guizhou 1
	Calceta	3	EQA	La Voz de Rio Carrizal
	Xapampa	2.5	PRU	La Voz de Oxapampa
	Kupang	1	INS	RRI
	Madang	10	PNG	R Madang
3265	Bengkulu	10	INS	RRI
	Brazzaville	100	COG	R National Congolaise
3268	Srinagar	50	IND	AIR
3270	Windhoek	100	NMB	R Namibia
		1	EQA	R Ecos del Oriente
3275	Mendi	2	PNG	R South Highlands
3277	Srinagar	50	IND	R Kashmir
3280	Beira	100	MOZ	R Beira

Freq. [kHz]	Transmitter site	Power [kW]	Country	Station name
3280	Ayacucho	1	PRU	R Huari
(cont)	Shanghai	10	CHN	Vo Pujiang
3285	Bidos	1	B	RTV Sentinela
	Cuenca	4	EQA	La Voz del Rio Tarqui
3290	Windhoek	100	NMB	R Namibia
	Port Moresby	10	PNG	R Central
3300	Guatemala	10	GTM	R Cultural
3305	Ranchi	2	IND	AIR
	Daru	10	PNG	R Western
	Dili	10	INS	RRI
3310	Bagua	1	PRU	R Bagua
3315	Bhopal	10	IND	AIR
	Lorengau	2	PNG	R Manus
	Goderich	10	SRL	SLBS
3320	Pyongyang	120	KRE	R Pyongyang
3325	Lagos	50	NIG	R Nigeria
	Belem	5	B	R Liberal
	Sao Paulo	2.5	B	R Tupi
	Huehuetenango	1	GTM	R Maya de Barillas
	Quevedo	1.5	EQA	Ondas Quevedenas
	Palangkaraya	10	INS	RRI
	Kieta	10	PNG	R North Solomons
3330	Moroni	4	COM	R Comoro
	Huallaga	5	PRU	Ondas del Huallaga
3335	Taipei	10	TWN	Central BC System
	Wewak	10	PNG	R East Sepik
	Londrina	5	B	R Alvorada
3340	Maputo	10	MOZ	R Mozambique
	Viloco	1	BOL	R Viloco
3345	Lusaka	50	ZMB	R Zambia
	Ternate	10	INS	RRI
	Jammu	2	IND	R Kashmir
	Popondetta	2	PNG	R Northern
	Mindoro	1	PHL	DZB-2
3350	Pyongyang	120	KRE	R Pyongyang
3355	Cazenga	10	AGL	R Nacional
	Gabarone	50	BOT	R Botswana
	Kureseong	20	IND	AIR
	Jambi	1	INS	RRI

Freq. [kHz]	Transmitter site	Power [kW]	Country	Station name
3355	Kundiawa	10	INS	R Simbu
(cont)	Noumea	20	NCL	RFO New Caledonie
3360	Sucua	10	EQA	R Federacion
	Nahuala	1	GTM	La Voz de Nahuala
	Antanarivo	10	MDG	R Madagasikara
3365	Accra	50	GHA	Ghana BC Corp
	Delhi	10	IND	AIR
	Alotau	10	PNG	R Milne Bay
	Araraquara	1	B	R Cultura
	Havana	50	CUB	R Rebelde
3370	Caban	5	GTM	R Tezulutlan
	Samaipata	1	BOL	R Florida
3375	Luanda	10	AGL	R Nacional
	Guajara Mirim	5	B	R Educadora
	S Gabriel	5	B	R Nacional
	Mount Hagen	10	PNG	R Western Highland
	Sumatera	7.5	INS	RRI
3380	Limbe	100	MWI	Malawi BC
	Jocotan	1	GTM	R Chortis
	Java	1	INS	RRI
3385	Tefe	1	B	R Educacao Rural
	Miri	10	MLA	RTM Sarawak
	Timur	10	INS	RRI
	Rabaul	10	PNG	R East New Britain
3390	Bunia	1	ZAI	R Candip
	Camargo	1	BOL	R Camargo
3395	Gweru	100	ZMB	Zimbabwe BC Corp
	Santa Domingo	5	EQA	R Catolica
	Tanjung Karang	10	INS	RRI
	Goroka	2	PNG	R Eastern Highlands
3400	Xapuri	2	B	R 6 de Agosto
3475	Padilla	0.5	BOL	R Padilla
3500	Puerto Inirida	5	CLM	La Voz del Guainia
3570	Brasilia	15	B	R 3 de Julho
3645	Irian Jaya	0.5	INS	RRI Fak Fak
3800	Oyon	1	PRU	R Oyon
3815	Beijing	10	CHN	CNR Taiwan 1
3900	Hailar	2	CHN	Haixia 1

Freq. [kHz]	Transmitter site	Power [kW]	Country	Station name
3905	Kavieng	2	PNG	R New Ireland
	Jaya	1	INS	RRI
3915	Kranji	100	SNG/G	BBC
3920	Sinuiju	100	KRE	North Pyongyang PS
3925	Tokyo Yamata	50	J	RCI
	Tokyo Nagara	50	J	R Tanpa
3930	Seoul	5	KOR	Korean BC System
	Transkei	20	AFS	Capital R
	Hohhot	50	CHN	Nei Menggu-Mo Mongolia
3935	Levin	1	NZL	Print Disabled R
	Java	5	INS	RRI
3940	Wuhan	1	CHN	Hubei 1
	Kowloon	2	HKG	RTV Hong Kong
3945	Tokyo Nagara	10	J	R Tanpa
	Efate Island	10	VUT	R Vanuatu
	Gorakphur	50	IND	AIR
	Bali	10	INS	RRI
3950	Xining	10	CHN	Qinghai 1
3955	Skelton	250	G	BBC
	Jaszbereny	100	HNG	R Budapest
	Novosibirsk	50	RUS	Kazakh R
	Palu	10	INS	RRI
3960	Lampertheim	100	D/USA	RFE/RL
	Ulan Bator	12	MNG	R Ulan Bator/R Moscow
	Urumqi	50	CHN	Xinjiang
	Sulawesi	10	INS	RRI
3965	Allouis	500	F	RFI
3970	Biblis	100	D/USA	RFE/RL
	Buea	4	CME	Cameroon BC Corp
	Nagoya	0.3	J	NHK
	Sapporo	0.6	J	NHK
	Hohhot	100	CHN	Nei Menggu
	Enugu	100	NIG	R Nigeria
3975	Skelton	250	G	BBC
	Java	10	INS	RRI
3980	Ismaning	100	D/USA	VoA
	Ch'ongjin	10	KRE	Regional station
3985	Lenk	250	SUI	China R Intl

Freq. [kHz]	Transmitter site	Power [kW]	Country	Station name
3985 (cont)	Beromunster	250	SUI	SRI
	Biblis	100	D/USA	RFE/RL
3990	Biblis	100	D/USA	RFE/RL
	Urumqi	50	CHN	Xinjiang-Ug
3995	Julich	100	D	DW
	Khabarovsk	50	RUS	Domestic/External
4000	Bafoussam	20	CME	Cameroon RTV Corp
	Kendari	5	INS	RRI
4003	Padang	5	INS	RRI
4010	Biskek	50	KGZ	Biskek 1
	Vladivostok	100	RUS	Domestic/external
4020	Beijing	500	CHN	China R Intl
4035	Lhasa	500/120	CHN	China R Intl/Xizang dom
4040	Yerevan	15	ARM	R Yerevan
	Tura	1.5	RUS	Domestic
	Vladivostok	50	RUS	Domestic/external
	Tocache	1	PRU	R Marginal
4050	Frunze	50	KGZ	R Frunze
	Sakhalinsk	50	RUS	Domestic/External
4055	Moscow	60	RUS	Domestic/External
4080	Ulan Bator	50	MNG	R Ulan Bator/R Moscow
4120	Sena Madureira	0.25	B	R Difusora
4190	Beijing	50	CHN	Domestic
4200	Beijing	500	CHN	China R Intl
4220	Urumqi	15	CHN	Xijiang Mongolian
4270	Gonzanama	1	EQA	R Gonzanama
4300	Naylamp	3/0.25	PRU	R Naylamp
4330	Urumqi	50	CHN	Xinjiang Kazakh
4395	Yakutsk	2	RUS	Kazakh R
4410	Reyes	1	BOL	R Eco
4420	Reyes	0.35	BOL	Radioemisora Reyes
	Bambamarca	0.85	PRU	Frecuencia Lider
4455	Haeju	100	KRE	Vo National Salvation
4460	Beijing	10	CHN	CNR 1
4472	Santa Ana	1	BOL	R Movima
4485	Petropavlovsk	50	RUS	Domestic/External
	Ufa	50	RUS	Domestic

24

Freq. [kHz]	Transmitter site	Power [kW]	Country	Station name
4500	Urumqi	50	CHN	Xinjiang
4510	Fergana	15	UZB	Fergana R
4520	Khanty-Mansiysk	50	RUS	Domestic
4545	Alma Ata	50	KAZ	Kazakh R
4550		3	BOL	R Diff Tropico
4605	Irian Jaya	0.5	INS	RRI
4610	Komsomolsk	15	RUS	R Vostock
4635	Dushanbe	50	TJK	Tadzhik R
4650	Santa Ana	1	BOL	R Santa Ana
4680	Guayaramerin	5	BOL	R Paititi
4700	Java	2	INS	R K Informasi Pern
	Chota	1	PRU	R Waira
4705	Rioja	0.25	PRU	Laser
4725	Yangon	50	BRM	Burma BC Service
4735	Urumqi	50	CHN	Xinjiang
4740	Ashkhabad	100	TKM	Domestic
4747	Huanta	0.5	PRU	R Huanta 2000
4750	Bertoua	20	CME	Cameroon RTV Corp
	Ulan Bator	12	MNG	R Ulan Bator/R Moscow
	Lhasa	50	CHN	Xizang
4755	Campo Grande	10	B	R Educacao Rural
	Puerto Lempira	10	HND	Sani R
	Ujung Pandang	50	INS	RRI
4760	Monrovia	10	LBR	ELWA
	Manzini	25	SWZ	TWR
	Port Blair	10	IND	AIR
	Leh	10	IND	AIR
	Kunming	50	CHN	Yunnan
4765	Brazzaville	50	COG	RTV Congolaise
	Cruzeiro do Sul	10	B	R Integracao
4770	Kaduna	50	NIG	R Nigeria
	Bolivar	1	VEN	R Mundial Bolivar
4775	Gauhati	20	IND	AIR
	Cuiaba	1	B	Portal da Amazonia
	Congonhas	1	B	R Congonhas
4777	Moyabi	100	GAB	Radiodiffusion Gabonaise
	Jakarta	7.5	INS	RRI

Freq. [kHz]	Transmitter site	Power [kW]	Country	Station name
4780	Djibouti	20	DJI	RTV de Djibouti
	Pyongyang	400/100	KRE	R Pyongyang
4785	Bamako	18	MLI	RTV Malienne
	Dar es Salaam	50	TZA	R Tanzania
	Baku	50	AZE	Azerbaijani R
	San Borja	0.5	BOL	R Ballivan
	Campinas	1	B	R Brasil
	Porto Velho	1	B	R Caiari
	Hangzhou	20	CHN	Zhejiang
	Ibague	5	CLM	Ecos del Combeima
	Satipo	1	PRU	R Chincheros
4790	Manzini	25	SWZ	TWR
	Shillong	50	IND	AIR
	Irian Jaya	1	INS	RRI Fak Fak
	Rawalpindi	100	PAK	Azad Kashmir R
	Iquitos	3	PRU	R Atlantida
4795	Ulan Ude	50	RUS	Domestic
	Douala	100	CME	Cameroon RTV Corp
	Aquidauana	1	B	R Nova Difusora
	Bahia Caraquez	5	EQA	La Voz de los Caras
4800	Maseru	100	LSO	R Lesotho
	Alma Ata	50	KAZ	R Alma Ata
	Hyderabad	10	IND	AIR
	Urumqi	2/50	CHN	CNR 2
	Puno	1.5	PRU	R Onda Azul
	Cuenca	5	EQA	R Popular
4805	Timor	0.3	INS	RRI
	Manaus	5	B	Difusora Amazonas
4810	Yerevan	50	ARM	Armenian R
	Meyerton	100	AFS	R Orion/R Afrikaans
	Tarapoto	3	PRU	R San Martin
	Vladivostock	100	RUS	Domestic/external
4815	Ouagadougou	50	BFA	RTV Burkina
	Togtoh	500	CHN	China R Intl
	Karachi	100	PAK	R Pakistan
	Londrina	10	B	R Difusora
	Taabatinga	10	B	R Caboclaas
4820	Khanty-Mansiysk	50	RUS	Domestic
	Tegucigalpa	5	HND	La Voz Evangelica
	Cajamarca	1	PRU	R Atahualpa
4825	Ashkhabad	50	TKM	Turkmen R
	Kiev	500	UKR	R Ukraine Intl

Freq. [kHz]	Transmitter site	Power [kW]	Country	Station name
4825	Cabrican	0.5	GTM	Radio Mam
(cont)	Braganca	10	B	R Educadora
4830	Gabarone	50	BOT	R Botswana
	Altai	12	MNG	R Ulan Bator/R Moscow
	Pathum Thani	10	THA	R Thailand
	San Cristobal	10	VEN	R Tachira
	Santa Cruz	5	BOL	R Grigota
4832	San Jose	3	CTR	R Reloj
4835	Bamako	100	MLI	RTV Malienne
	Coban	3	GTM	R Tezulutlan
	Corumba	5	B	R Atalaia
	Kuching-Stapol	10	MLA	RTM Sarawak
	Alice Springs	50	AUS	ABC
4840	Bombay	10	IND	AIR
	Harbin	50	CHN	Heilongjiang 1
	Valera	1	VEN	R Valera
	Andahuaylas	2	PRU	R Andahuaylas
	San Cristobal	5	GTM	R K'ekchi
4845	Nouakchott	100	MTN	R Mauritanie
	Ibitinga	1	B	R Meterologica
	Manaus	250	B	R Nacional Brasilia
	La Paz	5	BOL	R Fides
	Bucaramanga	1	CLM	R Caracol
4850	Tashkent	50	UZB	Uzbek R
	Yauonde	100	CME	Cameroon RTV Corp
	Kohima	10	IND	AIR
	Ulan Bator	50	MNG	R Ulan Bator/R Moscow
	Loja	5	EQA	R Luz y Vida
4855	Sana'a	50	YEM	Yemen R
	Santa Curz	1	BOL	R Centenario
	Barra da Garcas	1	B	R Aruana
	Palembang	10	INS	RRI
4860	Tchita	15	RUS	Domestic
	Saurimo	5	AGL	EP do Lunda Sul
	Delhi	50	IND	AIR
4865	Saynshang	12	MNG	R Ulan Bator/R Moscow
	Maputo	20	MOZ	R Mozambique
	Lanzhou	50	CHN	Gansu 1
	Arauca	5	CLM	La Voz del Cinaruco
	Cruzeiro do Sul	5	B	R Verdes Florestas
4870	Cotonou	30	BEN	RT du Benin

Freq. [kHz]	Transmitter site	Power [kW]	Country	Station name
4870 (cont)	Ekala	10	CLN	SLBC
	Macuma	5	EQA	R Rio Amazonias
4875	Tbilisi	2	GEO	Tbilisi 2
	Nanjing	50	CHN	Vo Jinling
	Rio de Janeiro	10	B	R Jornal do Brasil
	Irian Jaya	10	INS	RRI
	La Paz	10	BOL	R la Cruz del Sur
4880	Lucknow	10	IND	AIR
	Dhaka	100	BGD	R Bangladesh
4883	Hohhot	500	CHN	China R Intl
4885	Nairobi	10	KEN	Kenya BC Corp
	Belem	5	B	R Clube do Para
	Villavicencio	5	CLM	Ondas del Meta
4890	Moyabi	250	GAB	RFI
	Dakar	100	SEN	RT du Senegal
	Port Moresby	10	PNG	National BC of PNG
4895	Murun	12	MNG	R Ulan Bator/R Moscow
	Tyumen	15	RUS	Tyumen R
	Islamabad	100	PAK	R Pakistan
	Arauca	10	CLM	La Voz del Rio Arauca
	Kuresong	20	IND	AIR
4900	Conakry	18	GUI	RTV Guineenne
	Haixia	50	CHN	Haixia 2
	Ekala	10	CLN	SLBC
4905	Beijing	10	CHN	CNR 2
	Rio de Janeiro	5	B	R Relogio Federal
4910	Lusaka	50	ZMB	R Zambia
	Tennant Creek	50	AUS	ABC
	Trujillo	1	PRU	R Libertad
4915	Nairobi	100	KEN	Kenya BC Corp
	Accra	50	GHA	Ghana BC Corp
	Goiania	10	B	R Anhanguera
	Islamabad	100	PAK	R Pakistan
4920	Yakutsk	50	RUS	Yakutsk R
	Madras	10	IND	AIR
	Quito	5	EQA	R Quito
	Brisbane	10	AUS	ABC VLM4
4925	Arauca	2.5	CLM	Em Meridiano70
	Taubate	1	B	R Difusora

Freq. [kHz]	Transmitter site	Power [kW]	Country	Station name
4930	Ashkabad	50	TKM	Domestic/External
	Java	10	INS	RRI
4935	Nairobi	100	KEN	Kenya BC Corp
	Jatai	2.5	B	R Difusora
4940	Yakutsk	100	RUS	Yakutsk R
	Kiev	50	UKR	Ukrainian R
	Abidjan	25	CTI	RTV Ivoirienne
	Ekala	10	CLN	SLBC
	Gauhati	50	IND	AIR
4945	Meyerton	250	AFS	Channel Africa
	Port Velho	50	B	R Nacional
4950	Mulenvos	10	AGL	R Nacional
	Shanghai	10	CHN	Vo Pujiang
	Jammu	2	IND	R Kashmir
	Kuching-Stapok	10	MLA	RTM Sarawak
	P. Maldonado	5	PRU	R Madre de Dios
4955	Campos	2.5	B	R Cultura
	Belem	10	B	R Marajoara
	Amauta	5	PRU	R Cultural Amauta
4957	Baku	50	AZE	Azerbaijani R
4960	Delhi	10	IND	AIR
	Sucua	5	EQA	R Federacion
4965	Parintins	5	B	R Alvorada
	Cusco	5	BOL	R San Miguel
	San Ignacio de Velasco	3	BOL	R Juan XXIII
4970	Urumqi	50	CHN	Xinjiang Kazakh
	Kota Kinabalu	10	MLA	RTM Kota Kinabalu
	Tarapoto	1	PRU	R Imagen
	Caracas	10	VEN	R Rumbos
4975	Fuzhou	10	CHN	Fujinan 1
	Sao Paulo	1	B	R Tupi
	Sasco	1	B	R Timbira do Maranhao
4976	Kampala	50	UGA	R Uganda
4980	Urumqi	50	CHN	Xinjiang Mongolian
	San Cristobal	10	VEN	Ecos del Torbes
4985	Goiania	10	B	R Brasil Central
4990	Yerevan	50	ARM	Yerevan R
	Lagos	50	NIG	R Nigeria
	Madras	100	IND	AIR
	Changsha	10	CHN	Hunan 1

Freq. [kHz]	Transmitter site	Power [kW]	Country	Station name
4990	Sulawesi	10	INS	RRI
(cont)	Chocaya	1	BOL	R Animas
4995	Choybalsan	12	MNG	R Ulan Bator/R Moscow
	Huancayo	1	PRU	R Andina
5004	Bata	100	GNE	R Nacional
5005	Sibu	10	MLA	RTM Sarawak
	Harriharpur	100	NPL	R Nepal
	La Paz	1	BOL	R Libertad
	Paramaribo	0.35	SUR	R Apintie
5010	Garoua	100	CME	Cameroon RTV Corp
	Antananarivo	100	MDG	R Madagascar
	Nanning	10	CHN	Guangxi 1
5015	Archangelsk	50	RUS	Archangelsk R
	Vladivostok	50	RUS	Domestic/External
	Cuiaba	5	B	R Brasil Tropical
5020	Niamey	20/100	NGR	La Voix du Sahel
	Honiara	10	SLM	Solomon Islands BC
	Ekala	10	CLN	SLBC
	Nanchang	10	CHN	Jiangxi 1
	Quibdo	2	CLM	Ecos del Atrato
	Hanoi	10	VTN	Vo Vietnam
	Macas	10	EQA	Voz del Upano
5025	Parakou	20	BEN	RT du Benin
	Thimpu	50	BHU	Bhutan BS
	Kampala	50/250	UGA	R Uganda
	Katherine	50	AUS	ABC
	Altamira	5	B	R Transamazonica
	Quillabamba	5	PRU	R Quillabamba
	Havana	50	CUB	R Rebelde
5030	Costa Rica	20	CTR	AWR Latin America
	Kuching-Stapok	10	MLA	RTM Sarawak
	Nukualofa	1	TON	Tonga BC Commission
	Quito	9	EQA	R Catolica
	Huamachuco	1	PRU	R Los Andes
	Caracas	10	VEN	R Continente
5035	Bangui	100	CAF	RTV Centrafricaine
	Alma Ata	50	KAZ	R Alma Ata
	Aparecida	10	B	R Aparecida
5040	Tbilisi	50	GEO	Georgian R
	Benguela	1	AGL	Er de Benguela
	Fuzhou	10	CHN	Fujian 1

Freq. [kHz]	Transmitter site	Power [kW]	Country	Station name
5040	Macas	10	EQA	La Voz del Upano
(cont)	Java	20	INS	RRI
5045	Belem	10	B	R Cultura do Para
5047	Lome	100	TGO	R Lome
5050	Minsk	50	BLR	Domestic
	Dar es Salaam	10	TZA	R Tanzania
	Aizawl	50	IND	AIR
	Nanning	50	CHN	Guangxi FBS
	Cangallo	0.5	PRU	R Municipal
	Yopal	1	CLM	La Voz de Yopal
5052	Jurong	50	SNG	SBC
5055	Cayenne	10	GUF	RFO Guyane
	Manzini	25	SWZ	TWR
	Caceres	1	B	R Difusora
	Irian Jaya	1	INS	RRI
5057	Gjirokaster	50	ALB	RTV Shqiptar
5060	Changji	10	CHN	Xinjiang Mongolian
	Loja	5	EQA	R Nac Progreso
5065	Bunia	1	ZAI	R Candip
5075	Bogota	50	CLM	Caracol Bogota
5090	Xian	50	CHN	CNR Taiwan 2
5125	Beijing	10	CHN	CNR Taiwan 1
5163	Xian	50	CHN	CNR 2
5240	Lhasa	10	CHN	Xizang Chinese
5250	Beijing	120	CHN	China R Intl
5260	Alma Ata	50	KAZ	Kazakh R
5271	S R Huayabamba	0.5	PRU	R Nororiental
5286	Moundou	5	TCD	R Moundou
5290	Krasnoyarsk	100	RUS	Krasnoyarsk R
5320	Beijing	15	CHN	CNR 1
5420	Beijing	10	CHN	CNR Minority Progs
5440	Urumqi	50	CHN	Xinjiang Kazakh
5570	Tibu	0.2	CLM	R Nueva Vida
5582	S J Chiquitos	0.5	BOL	R San Jose
5660	Cutervo	0.7	PRU	La Voz de Cutervo
5800	Urumqi	50	CHN	Xinjiang Uighur
	Cajamarca	0.25	PRU	R Nuevo Cajamarca

Freq. [kHz]	Transmitter site	Power [kW]	Country	Station name
5810	Nashville	100	USA	WWCR
5825	Birmingham	500	USA	WEWN
5850	Cypress Creek	500	USA	Monitor R Intl
5860	Shijiazhuang	50	CHN	CPBS
5875	Rampisham	500	G	BBC
	Monaco	100	MCO	Trans World R
5880	Cypress Creek	500	USA	Monitor R Intl
	Scotts Corners	500	USA	WCSN
5882	SM Galeria	500	CVA	Vatican R
5885	Monaco	500	MCO	TWR
5890	Carnarvon	300	AUS	R Australia
	Plovdiv	500	BUL	R Bulgaria
5895	Plovdiv	500	BUL	R Bulgaria
5900	Chengdu	120	CHN	Sichuan 2
	Allouis	500	F	RFI
	Jerusalem	20	ISR	Kol Israel
	Moscow	20	RUS	Domestic
5910	Wavre	250	BEL	R Vlaanderen Intl
5915	Jerusalem	500	ISR	Kol Israel
	Alma Ata	100	KAZ	R Alma Ata
	Volgograd	20	RUS	R Vedo
	Irkutsk	1000	RUS	VoA
	Novosibirsk	200	RUS	VoA
	Rimavska Sobota	250	SVK	R Prague/Slovak R Intl
	Tashkent	200	UZB	R Tashkent
5920	Allouis	500	F	RFI
	Yekaterinburg	200	RUS	BBCWS
	Yakutsk	20	RUS	Domestic
5925	Tallin	100	EST	R Tallin
5930	Erevan	250	ARM	R Yerevan
	Monchegorsk	100	RUS	Domestic
	Rimavska Sobota	250	SVK	R Prague/Slovak R Intl
5935	Lhasa	100	CHN	Xizang
	Riga	100	LAT	R Riga
	Nashville	100	USA	WWCR
5940	Arman	50	RUS	Domestic
	Yekaterinburg	200	RUS	R Pamyat
5945	Moosbrunn	500	AUT	R Austria Intl
	Allouis	500	F	RFI

Freq. [kHz]	Transmitter site	Power [kW]	Country	Station name
5945	Alma Ata	20	KAZ	R Alma Ata
(cont)	Irkutsk	1000	RUS	VoA
	Tashkent	100	UZB	R Tashkent
5950	Lhasa	50	CHN	Xizang Tibetan
	Georgetown	10	GUY	Vo Guyana
	Okeechobee	100	USA	WYFR/VoFC
5955	MEYERTON	100	AFS	Channel Africa
	S.PAULO	10	B	R Gazeta, Sao Paulo
	LLALLAGUA	5	BOL	
	SEBELE	50	BOT	R Botswana
	SANTIAGO	1	CHL	
	HARBIN	50	CHN	CNR 1
	LHASA	50	CHN	CNR 1
	HABANA	500	CUB	R Havana Cuba
	BIBLIS	100	D/USA	RFE/RL
	HOLZKIRCHEN	250	D/USA	RFE/RL
	ALLOUIS	500	F	RFI
	KAVALLA	250	GRC	VoA
	GUATEMALA	10	GTM	R Cultural
	FLEVO	500	HOL	R Netherlands
	SURAKARTA	50	INS	RRI
	HUANCAYO	1	PRU	R Huancayo
	BUCURESTI	250	ROU	R Romania Intl
	KRASNOIARSK	20	RUS	Russian domestic
	LUBUMBASHI	10	ZAI	
	Rampisham	500	G	BBCWS
	Maxoquiera	500	POR/USA	RFE/RL
5960	SACKVILLE	250	CAN	RCI
	KUNMING	50	CHN	Yunnan
	JUELICH	100	D	Deutsche Welle
	SKELTON	250	G	BBCWS
	JAMMU	1	IND	AIR
	SISOGUICHI	0	MEX	
	ULAN BATOR	50	MNG	China domestic
	FREDRIKSTAD	350	NOR	R Norway Intl
	ISLAMABAD	213	PAK	R Pakistan Intl
	UDORN	500	THA/USA	VoA
	ALMA ATA	100	KAZ	R Moscow
	SERPUKHOV	100	RUS	R Moscow
	TBILISI	100	GEO	R Moscow
5965	MEYERTON	250	AFS	Channel Africa
	ST.MARIA	8	B	R Transamerica
	ORCHA	20	BLR	Mahileu

Freq. [kHz]	Transmitter site	Power [kW]	Country	Station name
5965	HUANUNI	3	BOL	
(cont)	SACKVILLE	250	CAN/G	RCI
	SHIJIAZHUANG	50	CHN	China domestic
	HABANA	250	CUB	R Havana Cuba
	LIMASSOL	250	CYP/G	BBCWS
	WERTACHTAL	500	D/USA	DW; VoA
	SKELTON	300	G	BBCWS
	RHODOS	50	GRC	VoA
	TSANG TSUI	250	HKG/G	BBCWS
	KAJANG	100	MLA	RTM M1
	MASIRAH	100	OMA/G	BBCWS
	MALOLOS	8	PHL	
	MT HAGEN	10	PNG	NBC Mount Hagen
	KALININGRAD	50	RUS	Domestic
	MURMANSK	20	RUS	Domestic
	Jos	10	NIG	R Plateau
5970	SOFIA	100	BUL	R Sofia
	HEZUO	15	CHN	Gannan
	CARIARI	100	CTR/E	REE
	BIBLIS	100	D/USA	RFE/RL
	HOLZKIRCHEN	250	D/USA	RFE/RL
	LAMPERTHEIM	100	D/USA	RFE/RL
	NOBLEJAS	350	E	REE
	ATHINAI	100	GRC	Vo Greece
	DIOSD	100	HNG	R Budapest
	JASZBERENY	250	HNG	R Budapest
	GAUHATI	50	IND	AIR
	BANDJARMASIN	10	INS	RRI
	LIMA	10	PRU	
	ALMA ATA	50	KAZ	Domestic
	BLAGOVECHTCHEN	100	RUS	R Moscow
	ADEN	100	YEM	Yemen R&TV
	Maxoqueira	500	POR/USA	RFE/RL
5975	LUSHNJA	50	ALB	R Tirana
	ANTIGUA	250	ATG	BBCWS
	COCHABAMBA	1	BOL	R Nacional Cochabamba
	BEIJING	120	CHN	CNR Intl
	LIMASSOL	250	CYP/G	BBCWS
	NAUEN	100	D	DW
	RAMPISHAM	500	G	BBCWS
	PT.AU PRINCE	60	HTI	
	SERUI	25	INS	RRI
	HWASUNG	100	KOR	R Korea

Freq. [kHz]	Transmitter site	Power [kW]	Country	Station name
5975	VILLARRICA	3	PRG	
(cont)	KRANJI	250	SNG/G	BBCWS
	LITOMYSL	100	TCH	R Prague
	BETHANY	250	USA/G	BBCWS
	Macarena	5	CLM	R Macarena
5980	FLORIANOPOLIS	10	B	R Guaruja
	HUHHOT	50	CHN	Nei Menggu
	PERKARA	250	CLN	
	JUELICH	100	D	DW
	WERTACHTAL	500	D	DW
	SKELTON	250	G	BBCWS
	GUATEMALA	5	GTM	AWR
	IMPHAL	50	IND	AIR
	KIMJAE	250	KOR	R Korea
	LINARES	1	MEX	R Xeuj Linares
	LIMA	5	PRU	R Programas del Peru
	GODERICH	250	SRL	
	LITOMYSL	100	TCH	R Prague
	ANKARA	250	TUR	Vo Turkey
	RIAZAN	100	RUS	R Moscow
	Quito	5	EQA	R Federacion Shuar
5985	LUSHNJA	50	ALB	R Tirana
	ORURO	3	BOL	
	TEMUCO	10	CHL	
	BRAZZAVILLE	50	COG	R National Congolaise
	HABANA	100	CUB	R Havana Cuba
	BIBLIS	100	D/USA	RFE/RL
	LAMPERTHEIM	100	D/USA	RFE/RL
	PAKANBARU	50	INS	RRI
	MEXICO	10	MEX	R Mexico Internacional
	ISLAMABAD	100	PAK	R Pakistan
	RABAUL	10	PNG	NBC Rabaul
	DAR ES SALAAM	50	TZA	
	TACHKENT	20	UZB	R Tashkent
	TULA	100	RUS	R Moscow
	DELANO	250	USA	VoA
	OKEECHOBEE	50	USA	WYFR
	Kavala	250	GRC	VoA
	Morocco	500	MRC	VoA
	Maxoquiera	500	POR	RFE/RL
5990	RIO DE JANEIRO	10	B	
	SHIJIAZHUANG	50	CHN	China domestic
	GEDJA	100	ETH	Vo Ethiopia
	ALLOUIS	100	F	RFI

Freq. [kHz]	Transmitter site	Power [kW]	Country	Station name
5990	EJURA	10	GHA	
(cont)	ROMA	100	I	RAI
	ALIGARH	250	IND	AIR
	BHOPAL	50	IND	AIR
	MENADO	10	INS	RRI
	TUMBES	2	PRU	
	S.SALVADOR	50	SLV	
	IRKUTSK	100	RUS	R Moscow
	KHABAROVSK	20	RUS	R Moscow
	TBILISI	100	GEO	R Moscow
	Bucharest	250	ROU	R Romania Intl
5995	DHAKA	50	BGD	R Bangladesh
	SUCRE	1	BOL	
	LHASA	50	CHN	Xizang Tibetan
	WERTACHTAL	500	D/USA	RFE/RL
	SKELTON	300	G	RCI
	YOGYAKARTA	100	INS	RRI
	BAMAKO 1	50	MLI	Radiodiffusion TV Malienne
	WARSZAWA	100	POL	Polish R Warsaw
	P J CABALLERO	2	PRG	
	KENGA	50	RUS	Domestic
	TACHKENT	100	UZB	R Tashkent domestic
	TULA	100	RUS	R Moscow
	GREENVILLE	250	USA	VoA
	MBANDAKA	10	ZAI	La Voix du Zaire
	Blantyre	100	MWI	Malawi BC
	Arequipa	1	PRU	R Melodia
6000	PT.ALEGRE	10	B	R Guaiba
	RIO DE JANEIRO	10	B	R Boas Nova
	FUZHOU FJ	50	CHN	Haixia 2
	HABANA	100	CUB	R Havana Cuba
	LIMASSOL	100	CYP/G	BBCWS
	LEH	10	IND	AIR
	PYONGYANG	200	KRE	R Pyongyang
	SEBHA	100	LBY	Libya domestic
	HOERBY	500	S	R Sweden
	SINGAPORE	250	SNG	City Sounds
	MONTEVIDEO	5	URG	
	EKATERINBURG	240	RUS	R Moscow
	Wertachtal	500	D	DW
6005	ASCENSION	250	ASC	BBCWS
	LA PAZ	10	BOL	
	LANZHOU	15	CHN	China domestic

Freq. [kHz]	Transmitter site	Power [kW]	Country	Station name
6005	EKALA	10	CLN	SLBC
(cont)	BERLIN	100	D/USA	RIAS Berlin
	ZAHEDAN	500	IRN	IRIB
	NAGOYA	0.3	J	NHK [ssb]
	SAPPORO	1	J	NHK
	BRIECH	500	MRC/USA	VoA
	MAHE	250	SEY/G	BBCWS
	KHABAROVSK	20	RUS	Domestic
	VLADIVOSTOK	100	RUS	R Moscow
	VOLGOGRAD	20	RUS	Domestic
	ADEN	100	YEM	Yemen R&TV
	BELGRADE	500	YUG	R Yugoslavia
	Rome	100	I	RAI
6010	BELO HORIZONTE	10	B	R Inconfidencia
	ABU HAYAN	60	BHR	R Bahrain
	HABANA	100	CUB	R Havana Cuba
	LIMASSOL	100	CYP/G	BBCWS
	SKELTON	250	G	BBCWS
	KAVALLA	250	GRC	VoA
	CALCUTTA	50	IND	AIR
	MEXICO	5	MEX	R Mil
	ISLAMABAD	100	PAK	R Pakistan
	LIMA	10	PRU	
	MONTEVIDEO	10	URG	
	MOSKVA	20	RUS	R Ukraine Intl
	Gloria	250	POR	VoA
6015	S.CRUZ	10	BOL	R El Mundo
	SACKVILLE	250	CAN	R Austria Intl
	BEIJING	50	CHN	CNR Taiwan Sce
	ABIDJAN	500	CTI	
	LIMASSOL	250	CYP/G	BBCWS
	WERTACHTAL	500	D	DW
	AMBOINA	50	INS	RRI
	LANGATA	20	KEN	KBC
	HWASUNG	100	KOR	Liberty 1
	FREDRIKSTAD	500	NOR	R Norway Intl
	ASUNCION	1	PRG	
	KIGALI	250	RRW	DW
	KALININGRAD	100	RUS	R Moscow
	OKEECHOBEE	100	USA	WYFR
6020	RIYADH	50	ARS	BSKSA
	BONAIRE RNW	250	ATN	R Netherlands
	SHEPPARTON	100	AUS	R Australia
	PT.ALEGRE	10	B	R Gaucha

Freq. [kHz]	Transmitter site	Power [kW]	Country	Station name
6020	SALVADOR	10	B	
(cont)	CALAMA	30	CHL	
	BIBLIS	100	D/USA	RFE/RL
	NOBLEJAS	350	E	REE
	FLEVO	500	HOL	R Netherlands
	SIMLA	3	IND	AIR
	MT.CARLO	500	MCO	R Monte Carlo
	TALATA VOLON	300	MDG	R Netherlands
	VERACRUZ	5	MEX	La Voz de Vera Cruz
	PALAUIG	250	PHL	R Veritas Asia
	KIETA	10	PNG	NBC Kieta
	LIMA	5	PRU	
	UDORN	500	THA/USA	VoA
	KHABAROVSK	100	RUS	R Moscow/R Ukraine Intl
	GWELO	100	ZWE	
6025	LA PAZ	10	BOL	R Illimani
	BAYENHAOTE	15	CHN	Aixa
	KUNMING	50	CHN	CNR
	DIOSD	100	HNG	R Budapest
	SZEKESFEHERVAR	100	HNG	R Budapest
	BANDJARMASIN	50	INS	RRI
	KAMALABAD	500	IRN	IRIB
	KAJANG	100	MLA	RTM R5
	CYCLOPS	250	MLT	DW
	BEIRA	10	MOZ	Beira 1
	TINANG	250	PHL	VoA
	ASUNCION	100	PRG	R Nacional del Paraguay
	IQUITOS	1	PRU	
	MANZINI	100	SWZ	TWR
	Skelton	300	G	RCI
6030	MEYERTON	500	AFS/G	BBCWS
	LUSHNJA	50	ALB	R Tirana
	RIO DE JANEIRO	10	B	R Globo
	COYHAIQUE	1	CHL	R Sta Maria
	HABANA	100	CUB	R Havana Cuba
	MUEHLACKER	20	D	Süddeutscher Rundfunk
	KIMJAE	250	KOR	R Korea; RCI
	MASIRAH	100	OMA/G	BBCWS
	TINANG	250	PHL	VoA
	MOSKVA	100	RUS	AWR
	BETHANY	250	USA	VoA
	GREENVILLE	500	USA	VoA; R Marti
	Rampisham	500	G	BBCWS
	Skelton	250	G	R Japan; R Korea

Freq. [kHz]	Transmitter site	Power [kW]	Country	Station name
6035	WAVRE	100	BEL	R Vlaanderen Intl
	KUNMING	50	CHN	Yunnan BS
	PUTTALAM	13	CLN	TWR
	ITANAGAR	50	IND	AIR
	MEXICO	100	MEX	
	RANGITAIKI	100	NZL	R New Zealand Intl
	PALAUIG	250	PHL	R Veritas Asia
	WARSZAWA	100	POL	Polish R Warsaw
	AREQUIPA	1	PRU	Super R Landa
	KRANJI	250	SNG/G	R Japan
	MONTEVIDEO	1	URG	
	VLADIVOSTOK	100	RUS	R Moscow
	GREENVILLE	500	USA	VoA
	Belgrade	500	YUG	R Yugoslavia
6040	ANTIGUA	250	ATG	DW
	CURITIBA	8	B	R Clube Paranaense
	NANCHANG	50	CHN	Jiangxi 1
	JUELICH	100	D	DW
	NAUEN	500	D	DW
	WERTACHTAL	500	D/USA	VoA
	ALLOUIS	100	F	RFI
	WOOFFERTON	250	G	VoA
	KARACHI	50	PAK	R Pakistan
	ALOTAU	10	PNG	NBC Alotau
	Limassol	250	CYP	BBCWS
	Sines	250	POR	DW
	Taipei	20	TWN	CBS Network 5/1
6045	MEYERTON	100	AFS	BBCWS
	HUHHOT	15	CHN	Nei Menggu
	HABANA	100	CUB	R Havana Cuba
	ALLOUIS	500	F	RFI
	SKELTON	250	G	BBCWS
	ATHINAI	5	GRC	Vo Greece
	DELHI	100	IND	AIR
	KOMA ROCK	250	KEN	Vo Kenya
	S.LUIS POTOSI	0.25	MEX	R Universad de S L Potosi
	LIMA	10	PRU	R Santa Rosa, Lima
	TAMBACOUNDA	4	SEN	
	UDORN	500	THA/USA	VoA
	MONTEVIDEO	3	URG	R Integral Americana
	KINGHISEPP	100	RUS	R Moscow
	KOMSOMOLSKAMUR	100	RUS	R Moscow
	MOSKVA	240	RUS	R Moscow

Freq. [kHz]	Transmitter site	Power [kW]	Country	Station name
6045	GWELO	100	ZWE	
(cont)	Cyclops	250	MLT	DW
6050	BELO HORIZONTE	10	B	R Guarania
	ORCHA	100	BLR	R Moscow
	LHASA	50	CHN	CNR Tibet
	LIMASSOL	250	CYP/G	BBCWS
	QUITO	100	EQA	HCJB
	SKELTON	250	G	BBCWS/RCI/ NHK R Japan
	DELHI	100	IND	AIR
	STAPOK	10	MLA	RTM Sibu
	MAXOQUEIRA	500	POR	RFE/RL
	JIGULEVSK	150	RUS	R Moscow
6055	MINSK	20	BLR	Domestic/external
	POTOSI	1	BOL	
	KUNMING	50	CHN	CNR
	NOBLEJAS	350	E	REE
	ALIGARH	250	IND	AIR
	MEDAN	100	INS	RRI
	PALEMBANG	100	INS	RRI
	TOKYO NAGARA	50	J	R Tanpa
	SULAIBIYAH	500	KWT	R Kuwait
	AREQUIPA	1	PRU	R Continental
	KIGALI	50	RRW	R Rwanda
	VELKEKOSTOLANY	100	SVK	R Prague/Slovak R Intl
	LITOMYSL	300	TCH	R Prague/Slovak R Intl
	MELO	5	URG	
	JIGULEVSK	150	RUS	R Moscow
	VOLGOGRAD	20	RUS	Domestic
	OKEECHOBEE	100	USA	WYFR
	Wertachtal	500	D	DW
6060	SHEPPARTON	100	AUS	R Australia
	CURITIBA	10	B	R Universo
	CONCEPCION	10	CHL	
	XICHANG	15	CHN	Sichuan 1
	HABANA	50	CUB	R Havana Cuba
	WERTACHTAL	500	D/USA	VoA
	SKELTON	250	G	BBCWS
	WOOFFERTON	250	G	VoA
	KAVALLA	250	GRC	VoA
	CALTANISSETTA	25	I	RAI Radio 1
	ROMA	100	I	RAI
	LANGATA	100	KEN	Vo Kenya
	MIRI	10	MLA	RTM Miri

Freq. [kHz]	Transmitter site	Power [kW]	Country	Station name
6060	NIAMEY	4	NGR	La Voix du Sahel
(cont)	HOFFNUNG	100	NMB	Namibian BC
	LIMA	3	PRU	R JSV
	ALMA ATA	20	KAZ	R Alma Ata
	BLAGOVECHTCHEN	20	RUS	Domestic
	LUSAKA	10	ZMB	
	Buenos Aires	30	ARG	RAE
	Poro	250	PHL	VoA
6065	MOEPENG HILL	100	BOT/USA	VoA
	PT.AYSEN	0.1	CHL	
	KOHIMA	2	IND	AIR
	PYONGYANG	200	KRE	R Pyongyan
	TEXMELUCAN	1	MEX	
	HOERBY	500	S	R Sweden
	EREVAN	100	ARM	Domestic/external
	KENGA	100	RUS	R Moscow
	KHABAROVSK	100	RUS	R Moscow
	Bogota	5	CLM	R Super
	Wertachtal	500	D	DW
	Woofferton	250	G	VoA
	Bucharest	250	ROU	R Romania Intl
	Okeechobee	100	USA	WYFR
6070	MEYERTON	500	AFS/G	BBCWS
	RIO DE JANEIRO	8	B	R Capital
	ORURO	1	BOL	
	SOFIA	250	BUL	R Sofia
	CHANGCHUN	15	CHN	CNR
	LAMPERTHEIM	100	D/USA	RFE/RL
	TEMA	100	GHA	Ghana BC
	JAYAPURA	20	INS	RRI
	ISLAMABAD	100	PAK	R Pakistan
	BANGKOK	10	THA	R Thailand P1
	Kiev	500	UKR	R Ukraine Intl
	Toronto	1	CAN	CFRX
6075	ANTIGUA	250	ATG	DW
	BRASILIA	250	B/D	DW
	BEIJING	50	CHN	CNR
	EKALA	10	CLN	SLBC
	WERTACHTAL	500	D	DW
	QUITO	500	EQA	HCJB
	KOMA ROCK	250	KEN	KBC National Service
	CYCLOPS	250	MLT	DW
	SINES	250	POR	DW
	MONTEVIDEO	3	URG	La Voz de Artigas

Freq. [kHz]	Transmitter site	Power [kW]	Country	Station name
6075	ALMA ATA	20	KAZ	R Alma Ata
(cont)	Bucharest	250	ROU	R Romania Intl
	Bethany	250	USA	R Marti
6080	LUSHNJA	100	ALB	R Tirana
	SHEPPARTON	100	AUS	R Australia
	CURITIBA	10	B	R Novas de Paz
	GOIANIA	5	B	R Anhanguera
	LA PAZ	10	BOL	
	COYHAIQUE	1	CHL	R Patagonia
	HAILAR	2	CHN	Hulun Buir Mongolian
	HABANA	100	CUB	R Havana Cuba
	QUITO	10	EQA	HCJB
	YOGYAKARTA	100	INS	RRI
	KAMALABAD	500	IRN	IRIB
	LANGATA	10	KEN	KBC
	DARU	10	PNG	NBC Daru
	LIMA	40	PRU	
	KRANJI	100	SNG/G	BBCWS
	KOMSOMOLSKAMUR	100	RUS	R Moscow
	Brest	20	BLR	Belarus R
6085	SOFIA	100	BUL	R Sofia
	SACKVILLE	250	CAN	DW
	NANNING	15	CHN	CNR
	ISMANING	100	D	Bayerischer RF
	NAUEN	500	D	DW
	SKELTON	250	G	NHK R Japan
	AIZAWL	10	IND	AIR
	DELHI	50	IND	AIR
	CYCLOPS	250	MLT	DW
	SEEB	100	OMA	R Oman
	THUMRAIT	100	OMA	R Oman
	S.SALVADOR	50	SLV	
	KALININGRAD	50	RUS	Domestic
	OKEECHOBEE	100	USA	WYFR
	KISANGANI	10	ZAI	
	La Paz	5	BOL	R San Gabriel
	Kavalla	250	GRC	VoA
	Bucharest	250	ROU	R Romania Intl
6087	Taipei	100	TWN	CBS
6090	S.PAULO	10	B	R Bandeirantes
	TEMUCO	10	CHL	R Esperanzo
	BAODING	120	CHN	CNR Intl
	WERTACHTAL	500	D/USA	VoA

Freq. [kHz]	Transmitter site	Power [kW]	Country	Station name
6090	WOOFFERTON	300	G	VoA
(cont)	JUNGLINSTER	500	LUX	R Luxembourg
	CD.MANTE	1	MEX	
	BEIRA	25	MOZ	
	VOLGOGRAD	240	RUS	R Moscow
	Kaduna	250	NIG	R Nigeria
	Kavalla	250	GRC	VoA
6095	MINSK	20	BLR	
	COCHABAMBA	1	BOL	R Cosmos
	NANCHANG	50	CHN	CNR Taiwan 2
	EKALA	10	CLN	SLBC
	S.M.GALERIA	100	CVA	Vatican R
	RHODOS	50	GRC	Vo Greece
	PONTIANAK	100	INS	RRI
	KIMJAE	250	KOR	R Korea
	PORO	100	PHL	VoA
	WARSZAWA	100	POL	Polish R Warsaw
	LIMA	10	PRU	R Nacional del Peru
	S.SALVADOR	50	SLV	
	MURMANSK	20	RUS	Domestic
	SERPUKHOV	50	RUS	Domestic
	VOLGOGRAD	20	RUS	Domestic
	Woofferton	250	G	VoA
	Kavalla	250	GRC	VoA
6100	KABUL	100	AFG	R Afghanistan
	LUSHNJA	25	ALB	R Tirana
	CALAMA	1	CHL	
	URUMQI	50	CHN	Xinjiang
	HABANA	100	CUB	R Havana Cuba
	WERTACHTAL	500	D	DW
	KOMA ROCK	250	KEN	KBC
	KANGGYE	200	KRE	KCBS
	KAJANG	100	MLA	Vo Malaysia
	KATHMANDU	100	NPL	R Nepal
	MUGE	100	POR	R Renascenca
	KALININGRAD	50	RUS	Domestic
	BELGRADE	500	YUG	R Yugoslavia
	Borno	10	NIG	R Borno
6105	CACHOEIRA PAUL	5	B	R Cancao Nova
	FOZ DO IGUACU	5	B	R Cultura
	LA PAZ	10	BOL	
	HOLZKIRCHEN	250	D/USA	RFE/RL
	LAMPERTHEIM	100	D/USA	RFE/RL
	MERIDA	1	MEX	Tus Panteras

Freq. [kHz]	Transmitter site	Power [kW]	Country	Station name
6105	TACNA	1	PRU	
(cont)	DAR ES SALAAM	50	TZA	R Tanzania domestic
	TVER	100	RUS	R Moscow
	San Jose	5	CTR	R UCR
	Salah el Deen	500	IRQ	R Baghdad
	Bucharest	500	ROU	R Romania Intl
	Okeechobee	100	USA	WYFR
6110	ASCENSION	250	ASC	BBCWS
	ANTIGUA	250	ATG	BBCWS
	BEIJING	50	CHN	CNR Minorities
	QUITO	500	EQA	HCJB
	SKELTON	300	G	BBCWS
	KAVALLA	250	GRC	VoA
	DIOSD	100	HNG	R Budapest
	ALIGARH	250	IND	AIR
	SRINAGAR	50	IND	AIR
	MEXICO	100	MEX	R Universad de Sonora
	TINANG	250	PHL	VoA
	ASUNCION	3	PRG	
	BAKU	200	AZE	Domestic
	Inabab	38	NIG	
	Beromunster	500	SUI	SRI
6115	ORCHA	20	BLR	Belarus R
	FUZHOU FJ	50	CHN	Haixia 1
	BRAZZAVILLE	50	COG	
	K.WUSTERHAUSEN	100	D	DW
	NAUEN	100	D	DW
	BIBLIS	100	D/USA	RFE/RL
	ALIGARH	250	IND	AIR
	MADRAS	100	IND	AIR
	BIAK	100	INS	RRI
	TOKYO NAGARA	50	J	R Tanpa 2
	LANGATA	100	KEN	KBC
	HERMOSILLO	1	MEX	
	MAPUTO	25	MOZ	
	LIMA	10	PRU	R Union
	MONTEVIDEO	5	URG	
	JIGULEVSK	20	RUS	Domestic
	KAZAN	20	RUS	Domestic
	KHABAROVSK	50	RUS	Domestic
	Sveio	500	NOR	R Norway Intl
6120	MEYERTON	250	AFS	Channel Africa
	KRUJA	100	ALB	R Tirana
	S.PAULO	8	B	R Globo

Freq. [kHz]	Transmitter site	Power [kW]	Country	Station name
6120 (cont)	SACKVILLE	250	CAN	RCI/NHK R Japan
	XIAN	120	CHN	CNR Intl
	HABANA	500	CUB	R Havana Cuba
	PORI	100	FIN	YLE R Finland
	GANGTOK	10	IND	AIR
	TAPACHULA	0	MEX	
	SEEB	100	OMA	R Oman
	ISLAMABAD	250	PAK	R Pakistan
	LIMA	1	PRU	
	ARMAVIR	100	RUS	R Moscow
	Sveio	500	NOR	R Norway Intl
6125	LA PAZ	5	BOL	R Diffusion Integracion
	SHIJIAZHUANG	50	CHN	CNR 1
	LIMASSOL	250	CYP/G	BBCWS
	WERTACHTAL	500	D/USA	VoA
	NOBLEJAS	350	E	REE
	QUITO	100	EQA	HCJB
	RAMPISHAM	500	G	BBCWS
	SKELTON	250	G	BBCWS/NHK R Japan
	WOOFFERTON	250	G	BBCWS/VoA
	NABIRE	25	INS	RRI
	PYONGYANG	200	KRE	R Pyongyang
	MONTEVIDEO	10	URG	SODRE
	ARMAVIR	20	RUS	Domestic
	CELINOGRAD	20	RUS	Domestic
	IAKUTSK	20	RUS	Domestc
	ORENBURG	20	RUS	Domestic
	TCHITA	100	RUS	R Moscow
	KANANGA	10	ZAI	La Voix du Zaire
6130	MINSK	20	BLR	Belarus R
	EKALA	10	CLN	SLBC
	NAUEN	100	D	DW
	WERTACHTAL	500	D	DW
	ARGANDA	100	E	REE
	NOBLEJAS	350	E	REE
	ACCRA	50	GHA	GBC R 2/Ext Service
	DELHI	20	IND	AIR
	GAUHATI	50	IND	AIR
	FUKUOKA	1	J	NHK Fukuoka
	PYONGYANG	200	KRE	R Pyongyang
	VIENTIANE	20	LAO	Laotian Nat R
	MEXICO	10	MEX	
	S.GABRIEL	100	POR	R Portugal
	IRKUTSK	20	RUS	Domestic/AWR

Freq. [kHz]	Transmitter site	Power [kW]	Country	Station name
6130	OMSK	20	RUS	Domestic
(cont)	BETHANY	250	USA	VoA
	DELANO	250	USA	BBCWS
	Poro	250	PHL	VoA
	Okeechobee	100	USA	WYFR
6135	MEYERTON	500	AFS/G	BBCWS
	APARECIDA	25	B	R Aparecida
	S.CRUZ	10	BOL	R Santa Cruz
	CONCEPCION	30	CHL	
	SHIJIAZHUANG	500	CHN	CNR Intl
	BIBLIS	100	D/USA	RFE/RL
	HOLZKIRCHEN	250	D/USA	RFE/RL
	LAMPERTHEIM	100	D/USA	RFE/RL
	SAMARINDA	8	INS	RRI
	HWASUNG	10	KOR	R Korea Liberty 2
	FENOARIVO	30	MDG	R Madagasikara
	PAPEETE	20	OCE	RFO Tahiti
	WARSZAWA	100	POL	Polish R Warsaw
	MAHE	250	SEY/G	BBCWS
	SCHWARZENBURG	150	SUI	SRI
	ARMAVIR	100	RUS	R Moscow
	ADEN	50	YEM	Yemen Republic R
	Gyanca	100	AZE	Azerbaijan R
	Alma Ata	100	KAZ	Alma Ata R
6140	GITEGA	5	BDI	R National Burundi
	BAODING	120	CHN	CNR Intl
	KUNMING	50	CHN	CNR Intl
	PUTTALAM	13	CLN	SLBC
	HABANA	100	CUB	R Havana Cuba
	K.WUSTERHAUSEN	100	D	DW
	WERTACHTAL	500	D	DW
	NOBLEJAS	350	E	REE
	WOOFFERTON	300	G	VoA
	KAVALLA	250	GRC	VoA
	DELHI	50	IND	AIR
	RANCHI	2	IND	AIR
	CHIHUAHUA	0	MEX	
	BRIECH	500	MRC/USA	VoA
	KATHMANDU	100	NPL	R Nepal
	WEWAK	10	PNG	NBC Wewak
	KRANJI	250	SNG/G	BBCWS
	ANKARA	250	TUR	TRT Vo Turkey
	MONTEVIDEO	10	URG	

Freq. [kHz]	Transmitter site	Power [kW]	Country	Station name
6140	KAZAN	20	RUS	Domestic
(cont)	Wanneroo	10	AUS	VLW6
6145	LUSHNJA	50	ALB	R Tirana
	OULED FAYET	50	ALG	RTV Algerienne
	DHAKA	50	BGD	R Bangladesh
	TARIJA	1	BOL	
	SACKVILLE	250	CAN	R Korea
	BEIJING	50	CHN	CNR Intl
	JUELICH	100	D	DW
	NAUEN	500	D	DW
	WERTACHTAL	500	D	DW
	JAKARTA	120	INS	RRI
	TOKYO YAMATA	300	J	NHK R Japan
	TLAXIACO	0	MEX	
	LA OROYA	1	PRU	
6150	BENGUELA	1	AGL	EP de Benguela
	ANCHOR POINT	100	ALS	KNLS
	S.PAULO	8	B	R Record
	SACKVILLE	250	CAN	RCI
	SANTIAGO	100	CHL	
	QIQIHAR	50	CHN	CNR
	EKALA	10	CLN	SLBC
	ALLOUIS	500	F	RFI
	WOOFFERTON	250	G	VoA
	KAVALLA	250	GRC	VoA
	TOKYO YAMATA	300	J	RCI
	KOMA ROCK	250	KEN	KBC National Sce
	KIMJAE	250	KOR	R Korea
	BRIECH	500	MRC/USA	VoA
	QUETTA	10	PAK	R Pakistan
	PALAUIG	250	PHL	VoA
	SERPUKHOV	20	RUS	Domestic/AWR
	Xian	120	CHN	RCI
	Northern Cyprus	7.5	CYP	R Bayrak II
	Costa Rica	20	CTR	AWR
	SM Galeria	500	CVA	Vatican R
	Sines	250	POR	RCI
6155	ASCENSION	250	ASC	BBCWS
	WIEN	300	AUT	R Austria Intl
	LA PAZ	10	BOL	R Fides
	LANZHOU	15	CHN	Gansu 1
	CONAKRY	100	GUI	Guinea Rep R
	DELHI	100	IND	AIR
	BANDJARMASIN	100	INS	RRI

Freq. [kHz]	Transmitter site	Power [kW]	Country	Station name
6155	TOKYO	10	J /USA	Far East Network
(cont)	TRIPOLI	500	LBY	Libya Jamahiriyah B
	MASIRAH	100	OMA/G	BBCWS
	BUCURESTI	250	ROU	R Romania Intl
	SINGAPORE	250	SNG	SBC R 1
	MONTEVIDEO	10	URG	
	NIKOLAEVSKAMUR	50	RUS	Domestic
6160	OULED FAYET	50	ALG	RTV Algerienne
	ANTIGUA	250	ATG	DW
	MANAUS	8	B	R Rio Mar
	PT.ALEGRE	10	B	R Nova Esperanca
	CHILE CHICO	0	CHL	
	SHIJIAZHUANG	50	CHN	CNR
	BIBLIS	100	D/USA	RFE/RL
	WOOFFERTON	250	G	VoA
	KAVALLA	250	GRC	VoA
	PALAUIG	250	PHL	VoA
	TINANG	250	PHL	VoA
	St John's	0.3	CAN	CKZN
	Vancouver	0.5	CAN	CKZU
	Bogota	50	CLM	RCN Bogota
	Maxoquiera	500	POR	RFE/RL
6165	BONAIRE RNW	250	ATN	R Netherlands
	KUNMING	50	CHN	CNR
	DELHI	100	IND	AIR
	JAIPUR	50	IND	AIR
	UJUNGPANDANG	50	INS	RRI
	AHWAZ	500	IRN	IRIB
	TOKYO YAMATA	300	J	NHK R Japan
	MEXICO	10	MEX	La Voz de America Latina
	PALAUIG	250	PHL	R Veritas Asia
	SARNEN	250	SUI	SRI
	EKATERINBURG	20	RUS	Domestic
	LUSAKA	50	ZMB	ZNBC National R2
6170	KRUJA	100	ALB	R Tirana
	S.PAULO	8	B	R Cultura
	DHAKA	100	BGD	R Bangladesh
	FUZHOU FJ	15	CHN	Domestic
	PERKARA	250	CLN	DW
	WERTACHTAL	500	D	DW
	BIBLIS	100	D/USA	RFE/RL
	LAMPERTHEIM	100	D/USA	RFE/RL
	CAYENNE	10	GUF	RFO Cayenne
	LANGATA	10	KEN	KBC

Freq. [kHz]	Transmitter site	Power [kW]	Country	Station name
6170	FENOARIVO	30	MDG	R Madagasakira
(cont)	MARULAS	10	PHL	
	MONTEVIDEO	1	URG	
	Mogadishu?	1?	SOM	R Manta
6175	POTOSI	1	BOL	
	SACKVILLE	100	CAN/G	BBCWS
	XIAN	15	CHN	China domestic
	ALLOUIS	500	F	RFI
	MOYABI	250	GAB/F	RFI
	MONTSINERY	500	GUF	RFI
	GAUHATI	50	IND	AIR
	SEMARANG	50	INS	RRI
	KAMALABAD	500	IRN	IRIB
	TOKYO SHOBU	1	J	NHK Tokyo
	KIMJAE	100	KOR	R Korea
	KAJANG	50	MLA	Vo Malaysia
	HOFFNUNG	100	NMB	Namibian BC
	ISLAMABAD	100	PAK	R Pakistan
	CUZCO	5	PRU	R Tawantinsuyo
	KHABAROVSK	50	RUS	R Moscow
	OKEECHOBEE	100	USA	WYFR
6180	BRASILIA	250	B	R Nacional da Amazonia
	MINSK	20	BLR	Belarus R
	BAODING	120	CHN	CNR Intl
	HABANA	100	CUB	R Havana Cuba
	LIMASSOL	250	CYP/G	BBCWS
	GUATEMALA	2	GTM	
	KATHMANDU	100	NPL	R Nepal
	ZIGUINCHOR	4	SEN	Senegal R
	ABU DHABI	500	UAE	UAE R Abu Dhabi
	ALMA ATA	100	KAZ	Alma Ata R
	TBILISI	100	GEO	R Moscow
	Woofferton	250	G	VoA
6185	LA PAZ	3	BOL	R Batallon Colorados
	EKALA	10	CLN	SLBC
	S.M.GALERIA	250	CVA	Vatican R
	NAUEN	500	D	DW
	WERTACHTAL	500	D	DW
	BIAK	300	INS	RRI
	MANADO	50	INS	RRI
	MANOKWARI	1	INS	RRI
	TOKYO YAMATA	300	J	NHK R Japan
	TRIPOLI	100	LBY	Libya Jamahiriyah B
	MEXICO	1	MEX	R Educacion

Freq. [kHz]	Transmitter site	Power [kW]	Country	Station name
6185	MAHE	75	SEY	FEBC
(cont)	UDORN	500	THA/USA	VoA
	Ufa	20	RUS	R Shark
	Belgrade	500	YUG	R Belgrade 1
6190	SANTIAGO	100	CHL	
	BAOJI	50	CHN	CNR
	BREMEN	10	D	SFB/R Bremen
	DELHI	50	IND	AIR
	PADANG	10	INS	RRI
	OSAKA	1	J	NHK Osaka
	LANCERS	100	LSO/G	BBCWS
	IQUITOS	3	PRU	R Oriente
	BUCURESTI	250	ROU	R Romania Intl
	BICHKEK	100	RUS	R Moscow
	GREENVILLE	250	USA	VoA
	Belgrade	500	YUG	R Yugoslavia
6195	ANTIGUA	250	ATG	BBCWS
	DHAKA	50	BGD	R Bangladesh
	LA PAZ	6	BOL	R Metropolitana
	HUHHOT	50	CHN	Nei Menggu Mongolian
	RAMPISHAM	500	G	BBCWS
	SKELTON	250	G	BBCWS
	PT.AU PRINCE	60	HTI	
	SURABAJA	50	INS	RRI
	CUZCO	1	PRU	R La Voz de Huamanga
	KRANJI	125	SNG/G	BBCWS
	BAKU	50	ARM	Armenian R
6200	Lhasa	20	CHN	Xizang Tibetan
	Yekaterinburg	50	RUS	Domestic
6205	Quito	500	EQA	HCJB
6210	Sofia	500	BUL	R Bulgaria
6220	Sofia	500	BUL	R Bulgaria
6230	Abis	250	EGY	R Cairo
	Monaco	100	MCO	TWR
6245	SM Galeria	80	CVA	Vatican R
6280	Beirut	10	LBN	Vo Hope
6480	Kimjae	250	KOR	R Korea
6500	Lhasa	50	CHN	Qinghai Tibetan
6540	Pyongyang	400	KRE	R Pyongyang
6560	Pyongyang	400	KRE	R Pyongyang

Freq. [kHz]	Transmitter site	Power [kW]	Country	Station name
6575	Pyongyang	400	KRE	R Pyongyang
6690	Cutervo	1	PRU	R Cutervo
6920	Xian	500	CHN	CNR Intl
6933	Xian	500	CHN	CNR Intl
6955	Xian	500	CHN	CNR Intl
6974	Hohhot	50	CHN	CNR Mongolian
7090	Xian	500	CHN	China R Intl
7105	LUSHNJA	100	ALB	R Tirana
	ASCENSION	250	ASC	BBCWS
	HUHHOT	50	CHN	Nei Menggu
	BRAZZAVILLE	25	COG	R National Congolaise
	JUELICH	100	D	DW
	BIBLIS	100	D/USA	VoA
	HOLZKIRCHEN	250	D/USA	VoA
	WERTACHTAL	500	D/USA	VoA
	NOBLEJAS	350	E	REE
	RAMPISHAM	500	G	BBCWS
	WOOFFERTON	300	G	VoA
	KAVALLA	250	GRC	VoA
	RHODOS	50	GRC	VoA
	LUCKNOW	50	IND	AIR
	BANDA ACEH	50	INS	RRI
	YOGYAKARTA	8	INS	RRI
	KAMALABAD	500	IRN	IRIB
	BUCURESTI	120	ROU	R Romania Intl
	KRANJI	100	SNG/G	BBCWS
	UDORN	500	THA/USA	VoA
	SERPUKHOV	100	RUS	R Moscow
	Taipei	300	TWN	CBS 2
7110	LUSHNJA	50	ALB	R Tirana
	LHASA	50	CHN	Xizang Tibetan
	XIAN	150	CHN	China R Intl
	GEDJA	100	ETH	Vo Ethiopia
	KAVALLA	250	GRC	VoA
	ROMA	100	I	RAI
	DELHI	50	IND	AIR
	UJUNGPANDANG	100	INS	RRI
	PYONGYANG	200	KRE	R Pyongyang
	MAPUTO	25	MOZ	Em Interprovincial Maputo
	PESHAWAR	10	PAK	R Pakistan
	HOERBY	500	S	R Sweden

Freq. [kHz]	Transmitter site	Power [kW]	Country	Station name
7110	KRANJI	250	SNG/G	BBCWS
(cont)	ANKARA	250	TUR	TRT Vo Turkey
	KAMPALA	20	UGA	R Uganda
	Poro	250	PHL	VoA
7115	DHAKA	100	BGD	R Bangladesh
	BEIJING	50	CHN	Vo Pujiang
	COLOMBO	10	CLN	SLBC
	BIBLIS	100	D/USA	RFE/RL
	WERTACHTAL	500	D/USA	RFE/RL
	ITANAGAR	50	IND	AIR
	SURAKARTA	50	INS	RRI
	LISBON	250	POR	RFE/RL
	MAXOQUEIRA	500	POR	RFE/RL
	RIMAVSKA	250	SVK	R Prague
	BANGKOK	10	THA	R Thailand 1
	BICHKEK	20	KAZ	R Alma Ata
	JIGULEVSK	100	RUS	R Moscow
	ORENBURG	20	RUS	Domestic
	BANDUNDU	10	ZAI	R Zaire
7120	SOFIA	100	BUL	R Sofia
	HUHHOT	50	CHN	China R
	ATHINAI	100	GRC	Vo Greece
	DELHI	100	IND	AIR
	TRIPOLI	500	LBY	Libya Jamahiriyah B
	TALATA VOLON	300	MDG	
	KATHMANDU	100	NPL	R Nepal
	MANZINI	50	SWZ	TWR
	N DJAMENA	100	TCD	Radiodiff Nat Tchadienne
	TULA	150	RUS	R Moscow
7125	BAODING	120	CHN	China R Intl
	XIAN	150	CHN	China R Intl
	COLOMBO	10	CLN	SLBC
	WOOFFERTON	300	G	VoA
	CONAKRY	100	GUI	R Conakry
	BANGALORE	500	IND	AIR
	RANCHI	2	IND	AIR
	BENGKULU	50	INS	RRI
	JAKARTA	3	INS	RRI
	PADANG CERMIN	250	INS	RRI
	TOKYO YAMATA	300	J	NHK R Japan
	LANGATA	10	KEN	KBC
	BRIECH	500	MRC/USA	VoA
	ISLAMABAD	100	PAK	R Pakistan

Freq. [kHz]	Transmitter site	Power [kW]	Country	Station name
7125	PORO	50	PHL	VoA
(cont)	MOSKVA	20	RUS	Domestic
7130	DHAKA	250	BGD	R Bangladesh
	JUELICH	100	D	DW
	NAUEN	100	D	DW
	WERTACHTAL	500	D	DW
	NOBLEJAS	350	E	REE
	KAVALLA	250	GRC	VoA
	FLEVO	500	HOL	R Netherlands
	MT.CARLO	500	MCO	TWR
	STAPOK	10	MLA	RTM Kuching
	S.PETERSBURG	200	RUS	R Moscow
	Woofferton	250	G	VoA
7135	LINGSHI	50	CHN	China R Intl
	LIMASSOL	250	CYP/G	BBCWS
	JUELICH	100	D	DW
	ALLOUIS	500	F	RFI
	MOYABI	250	GAB/F	RFI
	FLEVO	500	HOL	R Netherlands
	BUCURESTI	250	ROU	R Romania Intl
	ANKARA	250	TUR	TRT Vo Turkey
	NOVOSIBIRSK	50	RUS	R Moscow
	Lampertheim	100	D	RFE/RL
7140	LOBITO	1	AGL	R Nac Angola
	MINSK	20	BLR	Belarus R
	XIAN	150	CHN	China R Intl
	LIMASSOL	100	CYP/G	BBCWS
	DELHI	50	IND	AIR
	HYDERABAD	50	IND	AIR
	AMBOINA	100	INS	RRI
	TOKYO YAMATA	300	J	NHK R Japan
	KOMA ROCK	250	KEN	KBC National Sce
	KAZAN	100	RUS	R Moscow
	TACHKENT	100	AZE	R Moscow
7145	BOUCHAOUI	100	ALG	RTV Algerienne
	ORCHA	20	BLR	Belarus R
	BEIJING	50	CHN	China R
	BIBLIS	100	D/USA	RFE/RL
	HOLZKIRCHEN	250	D/USA	RFE/RL
	NOBLEJAS	350	E	REE
	ALLOUIS	500	F	RFI
	DELHI	50	IND	AIR
	VIENTIANE	50	LAO	Laotian R External

Freq. [kHz]	Transmitter site	Power [kW]	Country	Station name
7145	STAPOK	10	MLA	RTM Kuching
(cont)	QUELIMANE	0	MOZ	
	WARSZAWA	100	POL	Polish R Warsaw
	MAXOQUEIRA	500	POR	RFE/RL
	BUCURESTI	250	ROU	R Romania
	NOVOSIBIRSK	100	RUS	R Moscow
7150	UMTATA	50	AFS	Capital R Transkei
	LUSHNJA	50	ALB	R Tirana
	DARWIN	250	AUS	R Australia
	LINGSHI	50	CHN	China R Intl
	XIAN	120	CHN	China R Intl
	PERKARA	250	CLN	SLBC
	JUELICH	100	D	DW
	RAMPISHAM	500	G	BBCWS
	RHODOS	50	GRC	Vo Greece
	ALIGARH	250	IND	AIR
	GAUHATI	50	IND	AIR
	LANGATA	10	KEN	KBC
	PYONGYANG	200	KRE	R Pyongyang
	TRIPOLI	500	LBY	Libya Jamahiriyah B
	MAPUTO	0	MOZ	R Moxambique
	KRASNOIARSK	100	RUS	R Vilnius
	Sofia	500	BUL	R Sofia
	Douala	100	CME	Cameroon RTV
	Poro	50	PHL	VoA
	Taipei	300	TWN	CBS 1
7155	LUSHNJA	100	ALB	R Tirana
	BIBLIS	100	D/USA	RFE/RL
	HOLZKIRCHEN	250	D/USA	RFE/RL
	JAYAPURA	50	INS	RRI
	KAMALABAD	500	IRN	IRIB
	AL KARANAH	500	JOR	R Jordan
	KIMJAE	250	KOR	R Korea
	FENOARIVO	10	MDG	R Madagasikara
	NIAMEY	4	NGR	La Voix du Sahel
	KVITSOY	500	NOR	R Norway Intl
	KINGHISEPP	200	RUS	R Moscow
7160	MEYERTON	500	AFS/G	BBCWS
	SHIJIAZHUANG	500	CHN	China R Intl
	ALLOUIS	500	F	RFI
	MOYABI	250	GAB/F	RFI
	KAVALLA	250	GRC	VoA
	MADRAS	10	IND	AIR
	MT.CARLO	100	MCO	TWR

Freq. [kHz]	Transmitter site	Power [kW]	Country	Station name
7160	STAPOK	10	MLA	RTM Kuching
(cont)	MASIRAH	100	OMA/G	BBCWS
	PALAUIG	250	PHL	VoA
	KRANJI	250	SNG/G	BBCWS
	KAZAN	240	RUS	R Moscow
	OMSK	100	RUS	R Moscow
	TACHKENT	100	UZB	R Moscow
7165	BEIJING	120	CHN	China R Intl
	BIBLIS	100	D/USA	RFE/RL
	WERTACHTAL	500	D/USA	RFE/RL
	GEDJA	100	ETH	Vo Ethiopia
	JAMBI	50	INS	RRI
	TRIPOLI	500	LBY	Libya Jamahiriyah B
	KVITSOY	500	NOR	R Norway Intl
	KATHMANDU	100	NPL	R Nepal
	MAXOQUEIRA	500	POR	RFE/RL
	DAR ES SALAAM	10	TZA	R Tanzania Nat Sce
	KIEV	1000	UKR	R Ukraine Intl
	KINGHISEPP	100	RUS	R Moscow
	SERPUKHOV	50	RUS	R Moscow
	BELGRADE	250	YUG	R Yugoslavia
	Tokyo Yamata	300	J	RFI
7170	LUSHNJA	50	ALB	R Tirana
	BEIJING	120	CHN	China R Intl
	LHASA	50	CHN	Xizang
	NAUEN	500	D	DW
	WOOFFERTON	300	G	VoA
	DELHI	100	IND	AIR
	NOUMEA	20	NCL	RFO
	SEEB	100	OMA	R Oman
	QUETTA	10	PAK	R Pakistan
	TINANG	250	PHL	VoA
	DAKAR	100	SEN	
	SINGAPORE	100	SNG	SBC
7175	XIAN	150	CHN	China R Intl
	BRAZZAVILLE	25	COG	
	LIMASSOL	100	CYP/G	BBCWS
	WERTACHTAL	500	D	DW
	WOOFFERTON	300	G	VoA
	CALTANISSETTA	5	I	RAI Radio Due
	DILI	50	INS	RRI Serui
	KHABAROVSK	240	RUS	R Moscow
	NIJNIINOVGOROD	20	RUS	Armenian R
	Kigali	250	RRW	DW

Freq. [kHz]	Transmitter site	Power [kW]	Country	Station name
7180	DHAKA	50	BGD	R Bangladesh
	BEIJING	120	CHN	China R Intl
	LIMASSOL	100	CYP/G	BBCWS
	BIBLIS	100	D/USA	RFE/RL
	LAMPERTHEIM	100	D/USA	RFE/RL
	NOBLEJAS	350	E	REE
	WOOFFERTON	300	G	VoA
	MOYABI	500	GAB	NHK R Japan
	TSANG TSUI	250	HKG/G	BBCWS
	PT. BLAIR	10	IND	AIR
	KRANJI	100	SNG/G	BBCWS
	RIMAVSKA	250	SVK	R Prague
	MANZINI	50	SWZ	TWR
	ANKARA	250	TUR	TRT Vo Turkey
	SIMFEROPOL	1000	UKR	R Ukraine Intl
	KAZAN	150	RUS	R Moscow
	MOSKVA	100	RUS	R Moscow
7185	MEYERTON	250	AFS	Channel Africa
	DHAKA	250	BGD	R Bangladesh
	MINSK	20	BLR	Belarus R
	BAODING	120	CHN	China R Intl
	JUELICH	100	D	DW
	TANJUNGKARANG	50	INS	RRI
	KIGALI	250	RRW	DW
	ANKARA	250	TUR	TRT VoTurkey
	EKATERINBURG	20	RUS	Domestic
	TACHKENT	100	UZB	R Moscow
	VOLGOGRAD	20	RUS	R Vedo
	Yangon	50	BRM	R Myanmar
7190	PARAKOU	20	BEN	
	DHAKA	250	BGD	R Bangladesh
	KUNMING	50	CHN	China R
	EKALA	10	CLN	SLBC
	BIBLIS	100	D/USA	RFE/RL
	LAMPERTHEIM	100	D/USA	RFE/RL
	KAVALLA	250	GRC	Vo Greece
	SHILLONG	50	IND	AIR
	KAMALABAD	500	IRN	IRIB
	LANGATA	100	KEN	KBC
	LISBON	250	POR	RFE/RL
	ALMA ATA	100	KAZ	R Alma Ata
	TACHKENT	240	UZB	R Moscow
	Aden	100	YEM	Yemen Republic R
7195	DHAKA	50	BGD	R Bangladesh

Freq. [kHz]	Transmitter site	Power [kW]	Country	Station name
7195	URUMQI	15	CHN	Xinjiang
(cont)	SKELTON	300	G	RCI
	SEMARANG	50	INS	RRI
	BUCURESTI	250	ROU	R Romania Intl
	KAMPALA	10	UGA	R Uganda
	Kiev	500	UKR	R Ukraine Intl
7200	MINSK	20	BLR	Belarus R
	LAMPERTHEIM	100	D/USA	RFE/RL
	WOOFFERTON	300	G	VoA
	TRIVANDRUM	50	IND	AIR
	TOKYO YAMATA	300	J	NHK R Japan
	KIMJAE	250	KOR	R Korea
	PYONGYANG	200	KRE	R Pyongyang
	PORO	100	PHL	VoA
	MANZINI	25	SWZ	TWR
	IAKUTSK	100	RUS	R Moscow
	JIGULEVSK	20	RUS	Domestic
	BELGRADE	100	YUG	R Yugoslavia
	Kabul	100	AFG	R Afghanistan
	Salah el Deen	500	IRQ	R Iraq Intl
	Omdurman	100	SDN	R Sudan
7205	CARNARVON	250	AUS	R Australia
	XIAN	150	CHN	China R Intl
	LIMASSOL	250	CYP/G	BBCWS
	KAVALLA	250	GRC	VoA
	DELHI	100	IND	AIR
	MEDAN	50	INS	RRI
	KIMJAE	250	KOR	R Korea
	WARSZAWA	1	POL	Rozglosina Harcerska
	ARMAVIR	1000	RUS	R Moscow
	S.PETERSBURG	100	RUS	R Moscow
	VOLGOGRAD	100	RUS	R Moscow
	LUBUMBASHI	10	ZAI	La Voix du Zaire
7210	DHAKA	250	BGD	R Bangladesh
	MINSK	20	BLR	Belarus R
	KUNMING	15	CHN	Yunnan G
	LIMASSOL	250	CYP/G	BBCWS
	RAMPISHAM	500	G	BBCWS
	WOOFFERTON	300	G	VoA
	CALCUTTA	50	IND	AIR
	DELHI	100	IND	AIR
	TOKYO YAMATA	100	J	NHK R Japan
	LANGATA	100	KEN	KBC
	PYONGYANG	200	KRE	R Pyongyang

Freq. [kHz]	Transmitter site	Power [kW]	Country	Station name
7210 (cont)	KHABAROVSK	50	RUS	R Vostok
	Sottens	250	SUI	RCBS
	Kavalla	250	GRC	VoA
	Sines	250	POR	RCI
	Forli	10	I	AWR
7215	LUANDA	1	AGL	R Nacional
	BAOJI	50	CHN	CNR
	NANJING	50	CHN	Vo Jinling
	ABIDJAN	20	CTI	Radiodiff TV Ivoirienne
	MATARAM	50	INS	RRI
	SVEIO	500	NOR	R Norway Intl
	MASIRAH	100	OMA/G	BBCWS
	ISLAMABAD	250	PAK	R Pakistan
	TINANG	50	PHL	R Veritas Asia
	MAHE	100	SEY	FEBA
	MANZINI	100	SWZ	TWR
	UDORN	500	THA/USA	VoA
	ABU DHABI	500	UAE	UAE R Abu Dhabi
	BELGRADE	250	YUG	R Yugoslavia
7220	BANGUI	20	CAF	RTV Centrafricaine
	LINGSHI	50	CHN	China R
	HOLZKIRCHEN	250	D/USA	RFE/RL
	LAMPERTHEIM	100	D/USA	RFE/RL
	PLAYA DE PALS	500	E	REE
	DIOSD	100	HNG	R Budapest
	JASZBERENY	250	HNG	R Budapest
	SZEKESFEHERVAR	20	HNG	R Budapest
	EKATERINBURG	240	RUS	R Moscow
	TCHITA	240	RUS	R Moscow
	BELGRADE	250	YUG	R Yugoslavia
	LUSAKA	50	ZMB	ZNBC R1
7225	MEYERTON	250	AFS	Channel Africa
	CHENGDU	15	CHN	Sichuan 1
	PERKARA	250	CLN	DW
	ALIGARH	250	IND	AIR
	DELHI	100	IND	AIR
	BUKITTINGGI	50	INS	RRI
	PADANG CERMIN	250	INS	RRI
	ISLAMABAD	250	PAK	R Pakistan
	BUCURESTI	250	ROU	R Romania
	KIGALI	250	RRW	DW
	KRANJI	100	SNG/G	BBCWS
	UDORN	500	THA/USA	VoA
	SFAX	100	TUN	

Freq. [kHz]	Transmitter site	Power [kW]	Country	Station name
7225	TULA	240	RUS	R Moscow
(cont)	Wertachtal	500	D	DW
	Cyclops	250	MLT	IBRA R
7230	MEYERTON	250	AFS/G	BBCWS/Channel Africa
	WAVRE	100	BEL	R Vlaanderen Intl
	SKELTON	250	G	RCI/NHK R Japan
	KURSEONG	20	IND	AIR
	PYONGYANG	200	KRE	R Pyongyang
	SEEB	50	OMA	R Oman
	PALAUIG	250	PHL	VoA
	NIKOLAEVSKAMUR	100	RUS	R Moscow
	S.PETERSBURG	100	RUS	R Moscow
	Ougadougou	50	BFA	R Burkina
	Forli	10	I	AWR
	Gloria	250	POR	RFE/RL
7235	KUNMING	50	CHN	China R Intl
	LIMASSOL	100	CYP/G	BBCWS
	WERTACHTAL	500	D	DW
	SKELTON	300	G	RCI
	ROMA	100	I	RAI
	FAKFAK	25	INS	RRI
	KAMALABAD	500	IRN	IRIB
	KIMJAE	250	KOR	RCI
	ULAN BATOR	250	MNG	R Moscow
	PALAUIG	250	PHL	R Veritas Asia
	UDORN	250	THA/USA	VoA
	ALMA ATA	20	KAZ	R Alma Ata
	KALATCH	20	UKR	Domestic
	Tokyo Yamata	300	J	RCI
	Bucharest	250	ROU	R Moldova Intl
7240	BRANDON	10	AUS	R Australia
	BOMBAY	10	IND	AIR
	MAPUTO	100	MOZ	Em Nacional
	KATHMANDU	100	NPL	R Nepal
	KOMSOMOLSKAMUR	100	RUS	R Moscow
	VOLGOGRAD	20	RUS	Domestic
7245	LUSHNJA	100	ALB	R Tirana
	OULED FAYET	50	ALG	RTV Algerienne
	DHAKA	250	BGD	R Bangladesh
	XIAN	150	CHN	China R Intl
	BIBLIS	100	D/USA	RFE/RL
	HOLZKIRCHEN	250	D/USA	RFE/RL
	LAMPERTHEIM	100	D/USA	RFE/RL

Freq. [kHz]	Transmitter site	Power [kW]	Country	Station name
7245	BANDUNG	50	INS	RRI
(cont)	KIMJAE	250	KOR	R Korea
	TRIPOLI	500	LBY	Libya Jamahiriyah B
	NOUAKCHOTT	100	MTN	Nouakchott
	PALAUIG	250	PHL	R Veritas Asia
	MAXOQUEIRA	500	POR	RFE/RL
	UDORN	500	THA/USA	VoA
	ALMA ATA	100	KAZ	R Moscow
	DUCHANBE	20	TJK	R Dushanbe
	KHABAROVSK	240	RUS	R Moscow
	Mulenvos	10	AGL	R Nacional
	Kavalla	250	GRC	VoA
	Bucharest	120	ROU	R Moldova Intl
7250	DHAKA	100	BGD	R Bangladesh
	BEIJING	120	CHN	China R Intl
	KUNMING	120	CHN	China R Intl
	S.M.GALERIA	100	CVA	Vatican R
	GORAKHPUR	50	IND	AIR
	UJUNGPANDANG	300	INS	RRI
	PYONGYANG	200	KRE	R Pyongyang
	SINGAPORE	250	SNG	SBC
	KAZAN	100	RUS	R Moscow
	TACHKENT	100	UZB	R Tashkent
7255	ORCHA	150	BLR	Belarus R
	SEBELE	50	BOT	R Botswana
	BEIJING	500	CHN	China R Intl
	WERTACHTAL	500	D	DW
	BIBLIS	100	D/USA	RFE/RL
	SKELTON	250	G	BBCWS
	KAVALLA	250	GRC	VoA
	ALIGARH	250	IND	AIR
	KIMJAE	250	KOR	R Korea
	CYCLOPS	250	MLT	DW
	NAMPULA	3	MOZ	
	BRIECH	500	MRC/USA	VoA
	IKORODU	500	NIG	Vo Nigeria
	UDORN	500	THA/USA	VoA
	ALMA ATA	100	KAZ	R Moscow
	KINSHASA	10	ZAI	Voix du Zaire
7260	SUMBE	1	AGL	R Nacional Angola
	KRUJA	100	ALB	R Tirana
	LUSHNJA	100	ALB	R Tirana
	CARNARVON	300	AUS	R Australia
	MINSK	20	BLR	Belarus R

Freq. [kHz]	Transmitter site	Power [kW]	Country	Station name
7260	BAODING	120	CHN	China R Intl
(cont)	MORONI	4	COM	R Comoro
	RAMPISHAM	500	G	BBCWS
	BOMBAY	100	IND	AIR
	KOHIMA	2	IND	AIR
	MASHHAD	500	IRN	IRIB
	KIMJAE	250	KOR	R Korea
	ULAN BATOR	50	MNG	R Ulan Bator
	TINANG	250	PHL	VoA
	EKATERINBURG	100	RUS	R Moscow
	PORT VILA	10	VUT	R Vanuatu
	Skelton	300	G	RCI
7265	ORCHA	20	BLR	Belarus R
	MOEPENG HILL	100	BOT/USA	VoA
	BEIJING	120	CHN	China R Intl
	ROHRDORF	20	D	Sudwestfunk
	ALIGARH	250	IND	AIR
	SURABAJA	50	INS	RRI
	KIMJAE	250	KOR	R Korea
	CYCLOPS	250	MLT	DW
	ISLAMABAD	100	PAK	R Pakistan
	KIGALI	250	RRW	DW
	HOERBY	500	S	R Sweden
	UDORN	500	THA/USA	VoA
	IAKUTSK	20	RUS	Domestic
	KAZAN	200	RUS	R Moscow
	BELGRADE	500	YUG	R Yugoslavia
	Litomysl	250	TCH	R Prague
	Lome	100	TGO	Radiodiff Togolaise
7270	MEYERTON	100	AFS	R Oranje
	KRUJA	100	ALB	R Tirana
	LUSHNJA	100	ALB	R Tirana
	HUHHOT	50	CHN	Nei Menggu Mongolian
	RAMPISHAM	500	G	BBCWS
	WOOFFERTON	300	G	VoA
	KOMA ROCK	250	KEN	KBC
	STAPOK	10	MLA	RTM Kuching
	WARSZAWA	100	POL	Polish R Warsaw
	LISBON	250	POR	DW
	SINES	250	POR	DW
	DAKAR	100	SEN	
	MAHE	100	SEY	FEBA
	RIMAVSKA	250	SVK	R Slovakia
	MOSKVA	100	RUS	R Moscow

Freq. [kHz]	Transmitter site	Power [kW]	Country	Station name
7270	Gabon	100	GAB	Radiodiff Gabonaise
(cont)	Kavalla	250	GRC	VoA
	Yogyakarta	50	INS	RRI
7275	KABUL	100	AFG	R Afghanistan
	GUIYANG	8	CHN	Guizhou 1
	JUELICH	100	D	DW
	ARGANDA	100	E	REE
	NOBLEJAS	350	E	REE
	ROMA	100	I	RAI
	BIAK	300	INS	RRI
	KIMJAE	250	KOR	R Korea
	KVITSOY	500	NOR	R Norway Intl
	LISBON	250	POR	R Portugal
	Riyadh	500	ARS	BSKSA
	Kaduna	100	NIG	R Nigeria
7280	DHAKA	250	BGD	R Bangladesh
	MOEPENG HILL	100	BOT/USA	VoA
	BEIJING	500	CHN	China R Intl
	FUZHOU FJ	50	CHN	Haixia 1
	WERTACHTAL	500	D/USA	RFE/RL
	NOBLEJAS	350	E	REE
	ALLOUIS	500	F	RFI
	KAVALLA	250	GRC	VoA
	ALIGARH	250	IND	AIR
	GAUHATI	50	IND	AIR
	FENOARIVO	10	MDG	R Madagasakira
	SFAX	100	TUN	
	DAR ES SALAAM	30	TZA	R Tanzania
	KOMSOMOLSKAMUR	200	RUS	R Moscow
	OMSK	20	RUS	Domestic
	S.PETERSBURG	240	RUS	R Moscow
7285	MEYERTON	100	AFS	Afrikaans Stereo
	LANZHOU	15	CHN	China R domestic
	XIAN	150	CHN	China R Intl
	JUELICH	100	D	DW
	K.WUSTERHAUSEN	100	D	DW
	WERTACHTAL	500	D	VoA
	BIBLIS	100	D/USA	RFE/Rl
	RAMPISHAM	500	G	BBCWS
	WOOFFERTON	300	G	BBCWS
	FAKFAK	1	INS	RRI
	KIMJAE	250	KOR	R Korea
	TALATA VOLON	300	MDG	R Netherlands
	BAMAKO 2	100	MLI	Radiodiff Malienne

Freq. [kHz]	Transmitter site	Power [kW]	Country	Station name
7285	WARSZAWA	100	POL	Polish R Warsaw
(cont)	LISBON	250	POR	DW
	KIGALI	250	RRW	DW
	TACHKENT	100	UZB	R Moscow
	GWELO	100	ZWE	
7290	KUNMING	50	CHN	China R Intl
	ROMA	100	I	RAI
	DELHI	100	IND	AIR
	LANGATA	20	KEN	KBC
	MT.CARLO	100	MCO	TWR
	ISLAMABAD	250	PAK	R Pakistan
	KARACHI	50	PAK	R Pakistan
	ANKARA	250	TUR	TRT Vo Turkey
	KENGA	100	RUS	R Moscow
	Levin	0.25	NZL	Print Disabled R
7295	BAODING	120	CHN	China R Intl
	XIAN	150	CHN	China R Intl
	BIBLIS	100	D/USA	RFE/RL
	LAMPERTHEIM	100	D/USA	RFE/RL
	RAMPISHAM	500	G	BBCWS
	SKELTON	300	G	BBCWS
	ACCRA	50	GHA	GBC R 2
	BHOPAL	50	IND	AIR
	MENADO	50	INS	RRI
	KAJANG	100	MLA	RTM R4
	BRIECH	500	MRC/USA	VoA
	SVEIO	500	NOR	R Norway Intl
	MOSKVA	100	RUS	R Moscow
	TACHKENT	240	AZE	R Moscow
	MBUJIMAYI	10	ZAI	
7300	Balashihka	20	RUS	Azerbaijan R
	Samara	250	RUS	R Netherlands
	Petropavl	250	RUS	VoA
7305	SM Galeria	500	CVA	Vatican R
	Allouis	500	F	RFI
	Budapest	250	HNG	RFI
	Alma Ata	500	KAZ	R Netherlands
	Novosibirsk	1000	RUS	DW
7310	SM Galeria	500	CVA	Vatican R
	Velke Kostlany	100	SVK	Slovak R
7315	Allouis	500	F	RFI
	Samara	250	RUS	DW

Freq. [kHz]	Transmitter site	Power [kW]	Country	Station name
7315 (cont)	Noblesville	100	USA	WHRI
	Tashkent	200	UZB	BBCWS
7320	Rampisham	500	G	BBCWS
	Arman	50	RUS	Domestic
7325	Skelton	250	G	BBCWS
	Rampisham	500	G	BBCWS
	Woofferton	300	G	VoA
	Islamabad	100	PAK	R Pakistan
	Tashkent	200	UZB	BBCWS
7330	Tchita	500	RUS	BBCWS
7335	Allouis	500	F	RFI
	Islamabad	100	PAK	R Pakistan
7340	Moepeng Hill	100	BOT	VoA
	Madras	100	IND	AIR
	Novosibirsk	1000	RUS	DW
7345	Islamabad	250	PAK	R Pakistan
	Velke Kostolany	100	SVK	R Prague/Slovak R Intl
7355	Anchor Point	100	ALS	KNLS
	SM Galeria	500	CVA	Vatican R
	Noblesville	100	USA	WHRI
	New Orleans	100	USA	WRNO
	Okeechobee	100	USA	WYFR
7360	Xian	500	CHN	China R Intl
	SM Galeria	100	CVA	Vatican R
7365	Anchor Point	100	ALS	KNLS
	Alma Ata	500	KAZ	R Netherlands
	Cypress Creek	500	USA	Monitor R Intl
7370	Wavre	250	BEL	R Vlaanderen Intl
7375	Sofia	500	BUL	R Bulgaria
	Xian	500	CHN	China R Intl
	Costa Rica	5	CTR	R for Peace Intl
7380	Yekaterinburg	200	RUS	BBCWS
	Irkutsk	250	RUS	DW
	Kiev	500	UKR	R Ukraine Intl
7385	Xian	500	CHN	China R Intl
	Costa Rica	30	CTR	R for Peace Intl
	Monte Carlo	500	MCO	TWR
7390	Novosibirsk	200	RUS	DW
7395	New Orleans	100	USA	WRNO
	Cypress Creek	500	USA	Monitor R Intl

Freq. [kHz]	Transmitter site	Power [kW]	Country	Station name
7405	Xian	500	CHN	China R Intl
	Bethany	250	USA	VoA
	Greenville	250	USA	VoA
7412	Aligarh	250	IND	AIR
7415	Moepeng Hill	100	BOT	VoA
	Vietnam	100	VTN	Vo Vietnam
7420	Urumqi	500	CHN	China R Intl
	Irkutsk	250	RUS	BBCWS
7425	Hawaii	100	HWI	KWHR
	Birmingham	500	USA	WEWN
7435	Nashville	100	USA	WWCR
7440	Beijing	10	CHN	CNR 2
7455	Sofia	500	BUL	R Bulgaria
	Guam	100	GUM	KSDA
	Cypress Creek	500	USA	Monitor R Intl
7465	Jerusalem	500	ISR	Kol Israel
	Cypress Creek	500	USA	Monitor R Intl
7470	Xian	500	CHN	China R Intl
7475	Tunis	100	TUN	ERTT
7480	Beijing	120	CHN	Swiss R Intl
7490	Millerstown	100	USA	WJCR
7510	Salt Lake City	100	USA	KTBN
	Scotts Corners	500	USA	
7520	Birmingham	500	USA	WEWM
	Okeechobee	100	USA	WYFR
7550	Kimjae	100	KOR	R Korea
7580	Pyongyang	400	KRE	R Pyongyang
7660	Xian	120	CHN	China R Intl
7670	Solnik	15	BUL	Domestic
7780	Xian	500	CHN	China R Intl
7820	Urumqi	500	CHN	China R Intl
9022	Tehran	500	IRN	IRIB
9080	Xian	50	CHN	CNR 1
9280	Taipei	100	TWN	WYFR
9325	Pyongyang	400	KRE	R Pyongyang
9345	Pyongyang	400	KRE	R Pyongyang

Freq. [kHz]	Transmitter site	Power [kW]	Country	Station name
9350	Birmingham	500	USA	WEWN
9355	SM Galeria	500	CVA	Vatican R
	Saipan	100	MRA	Monitor R Intl
	Cypress Creek	500	USA	Monitor R Intl
9365	Urumqi	500	CHN	China R Intl
9370	Islamabad	100	PAK	R Pakistan
	Birmingham	500	USA	WEWN
9388	Jerusalem	500	ISR	Kol Israel
9400	Vilnius	5	LTU	R Centras
9405	Litomysl	100	TCH	R Prague Intl
9410	Rampisham	500	G	BBCWS
	Skelton	300	G	BBCWS
9420	Athens	100	GRC	Vo Greece
	Islamabad	100	PAK	R Pakistan
9425	Kavala	250	GRC	ERT Thessaloniki
	Athens	100	GRC	Vo Greece
	Saipan	100	MRA	Monitor R Intl
9430	Saipan	100	MRA	Monitor R Intl
	Birmingham	500	USA	WEWN
	Cypress Creek	500	USA	Monitor R Intl
9435	Jerusalem	500	ISR	Kol Israel
9440	Urumqi	500	CHN	China R Intl
	Velke Kostolany	100	SVK	Slovak R Intl
9445	Monte Carlo	500	MCO	TWR
	Ankara	500	TUR	TRT Vo Turkey
9455	Sofia	500	BUL	R Sofia
	Sottens	500	SUI	Swiss R Intl
	Greenville	500	USA	VoA
	Scotts Corners	500	USA	
	Cypress Creek	500	USA	Monitor R Intl
9460	Islamabad	10	PAK	R Pakistan
	Ankara	500	TUR	TRT VoTurkey
9465	Saipan	100	MRA	KFBS
	Taipei	100	TWN	WYFR
	Delano	250	USA	VoA
	Noblesville	100	USA	WHRI
	Bethel	50	USA	WMLK
	Cypress Creek	500	USA	Monitor R Intl
9475	Abis	250	EGY	R Cairo

Freq. [kHz]	Transmitter site	Power [kW]	Country	Station name
9475	Guam	100	GUM	KTWR
(cont)	Saipan	100	MRA	Monitor R Intl
9480	Xian	500	CHN	China R Intl
9485	Islamabad	100	PAK	R Pakistan
9490	Urumqi	500	CHN	China R Intl
	Monte Carlo	100	MCO	TWR
	Litomysl	100	TCH	R Prague
9495	Allouis	500	F	RFI
	Guam	100	GUM	KSDA
	Monte Carlo	500	MCO	TWR
	Saipan	100	MRA	Monitor R Intl
	Islamabad	100	PAK	R Pakistan
	Manila	100	PHL	FEBC
	Noblesville	100	USA	WHRI
	Cypress Creek	500	USA	Monitor R Intl
9500	Bogota	20	CLM	R Diffusion Nacional
	S M Galeria	500	CVA	Vatican R
	Palauig	250	PHL	R Veritas Asia
	Blagoveschensk	3	RUS	Domestic
9505	S.PAULO	8	B	R Record
	FUZHOU FJ	50	CHN	Haixia 2
	JINHUA	500	CHN	China R Intl
	BIBLIS	100	D/USA	RFE/RL
	KAVALLA	250	GRC	VoA
	MEDAN	100	INS	RRI
	PYONGYANG	400	KRE	R Pyongyang
	PALAUIG	50	PHL	VoA
	MAXOQUEIRA	500	POR	RFE/RL
	TACNA	1	PRU	R Tacna
	VELKEKOSTOLANY	100	SVK	Slovak R Intl/R Prague
	ALMA ATA	100	KAZ	R Moscow
	TULA	240	RUS	R Moscow
	OKEECHOBEE	100	USA	WYFR
	BELGRADE	500	YUG	R Yugoslavia
	LUSAKA	50	ZMB	R Zambia
	Moosbrunn	300	AUT	RCI
	Wertachtal	500	D	RCI
	Kiev	500	UKR	R Ukraine Intl
9510	OULED FAYET	50	ALG	RTV Algerienne
	CARNARVON	250	AUS	R Australia
	DHAKA	100	BGD	R Bangladesh
	SANTIAGO	100	CHL	

Freq. [kHz]	Transmitter site	Power [kW]	Country	Station name
9510	BEIJING	50	CHN	China R Intl
(cont)	HABANA	500	CUB	R Havana Cuba
	RAMPISHAM	500	G	BBCWS
	SKELTON	250	G	R Korea
	MADRAS	100	IND	AIR
	PYONGYANG	200	KRE	R Pyongyang
	RANGITAIKI	100	NZL	R New Zealand
	TINANG	250	PHL	VoA
	LIMA	5	PRU	
	BUCURESTI	250	ROU	R Romania Intl
	UDORN	500	THA/USA	VoA
	ARMAVIR	100	RUS	R Moscow
	IRKUTSK	250	RUS	R Moscow
	Trincomalee	250	CLN	DW
	Cyclops	250	MLT	IBRA R
	Taipei	250	TWN	VoFC
9515	MEYERTON	500	AFS/G	BBCWS
	BONAIRE TWR	50	ATN	TWR
	CURITIBA	10	B	R Novas de Paz
	OUAGADOUGOU	50	BFA	R Ouagadougou
	SACKVILLE	250	CAN/G	BBCWS
	BEIJING	50	CHN	China R
	JUELICH	100	D	DW
	WERTACHTAL	500	D	DW
	QUITO	100	EQA	HCJB
	ATHINAI	100	GRC	Vo Greece
	CALTANISSETTA	5	I	RAI Radio Uno
	KUPANG	50	INS	RRI
	KIMJAE	100	KOR	R Korea
	FENOARIVO	30	MDG	R Madagasikara
	MEXICO	20	MEX	La Voz de America Latina
	CYCLOPS	250	MLT	DW
	ISLAMABAD	100	PAK	R Pakistan
	PALAUIG	250	PHL	R Veritas Asia
	MANZINI	50	SWZ	TWR
	MONTEVIDEO	10	URG	
	ARMAVIR	100	RUS	R Moscow
	SERPUKHOV	100	RUS	R Moscow
	DELANO	250	USA	BBCWS
9520	MEYERTON	250	AFS	Channel Africa
	DHAKA	250	BGD	R Bangladesh
	HUHHOT	50	CHN	China R Intl
	HOLZKIRCHEN	250	D/USA	RFE/RL
	LAMPERTHEIM	100	D/USA	RFE/Rl

Freq. [kHz]	Transmitter site	Power [kW]	Country	Station name
9520	NOBLEJAS	350	E	REE
(cont)	PLAYA DE PALS	500	E	REE
	ALIGARH	250	IND	AIR
	KARACHI	50	PAK	R Pakistan
	PALAUIG	250	PHL	R Veritas Asia
	MAXOQUEIRA	500	POR	RFE/RL
	LIMA	5	PRU	R La Cronica
	MAHE	100	SEY	FEBA
	S.SALVADOR	50	SLV	
	MANZINI	100	SWZ	TWR
9525	HABANA	100	CUB	R Havana Cuba
	NOBLEJAS	350	E	REE
	JAKARTA	100	INS	RRI
	KIMJAE	250	KOR	R Korea
	MAPUTO	25	MOZ	Em Interprovincial
	ISLAMABAD	250	PAK	R Pakistan
	PORO	100	PHL	VoA
	WARSZAWA	100	POL	Polish R Warsaw
	SERPUKHOV	100	RUS	R Moscow
	BETHANY	250	USA	VoA
	GREENVILLE	250	USA	R Marto
	Tehran	500	IRN	IRIB
9530	XIAN	150	CHN	China R Intl
	LIMASSOL	100	CYP/G	BBCWS
	WERTACHTAL	500	D/USA	RFE/RL
	NOBLEJAS	350	E	REE
	KAVALLA	250	GRC	VoA
	RHODOS	50	GRC	VoA
	AGAT	100	GUM	KSDA
	CALCUTTA	10	IND	AIR
	MARPI	100	MRA	KHBI
	BRIECH	500	MRC/USA	VoA
	TACNA	5	PRU	R Tacna
	BUCURESTI	250	ROU	R Romania
	SINGAPORE	250	SNG	SBC R1
	ARMAVIR	250	RUS	R Moscow
	NOVOSIBIRSK	100	RUS	R Moscow
	OKHOTSK	100	RUS	R Moscow
	BETHANY	250	USA	VoA
9535	LUANDA	100	AGL	R Nacional
	BOUCHAOUI	100	ALG	RTV Algerienne
	BONAIRE TWR	50	ATN	TWR
	SACKVILLE	250	CAN	RCI
	XIAN	150	CHN	RCI

Freq. [kHz]	Transmitter site	Power [kW]	Country	Station name
9535	EKALA	300	CLN	R Japan
(cont)	JUELICH	100	D	DW
	LAMPERTHEIM	100	D/USA	RFE/RL
	ALLOUIS	100	F	RFI
	KAVALLA	250	GRC	VoA
	MONTSINERY	500	GUF	RFI
	ALIGARH	250	IND	AIR
	MADRAS	100	IND	AIR
	BIAK	50	INS	RRI
	FUKUOKA	1	J	NHK Fukuoka
	OSAKA	1	J	NHK Osaka
	SAPPORO	1	J	NHK Sapporo
	TOKYO YAMATA	300	J	NHK R Japan
	PALAUIG	250	PHL	VoA
	PORO	100	PHL	R Veritas Asia
	SINES	250	POR	DW
	LENK	250	SUI	SRI
	ABU DHABI	500	UAE	UAE R Abu Dhabi
	DUCHANBE	100	TJK	R Moscow
	TBILISI	100	GEO	R Moscow
	TULA	250	RUS	R Moscow
9540	SALVADOR	10	B	R Educadora da Bahia
	BEIJING	50	CHN	China R
	NOBLEJAS	350	E	REE
	KAVALLA	250	GRC	VoA
	KATHMANDU	100	NPL	R Nepal
	WARSZAWA	100	POL	Polish R Warsaw
	MOSKVA	100	RUS	R Moscow
	TACHKENT	100	UZB	R Tashkent
9545	BEIJING	50	CHN	China R Intl
	XINING	50	CHN	China R
	JUELICH	100	D	DW
	NAUEN	500	D	DW
	WERTACHTAL	500	D	DW
	TEMA	100	GHA	R Ghana
	PT.AU PRINCE	50	HTI	
	PALANGKARAYA	25	INS	RRI
	VERACRUZ	1	MEX	La Jarocha
	CYCLOPS	250	MLT	DW
	ISLAMABAD	10	PAK	R Pakistan
	TINANG	250	PHL	VoA
	BICHKEK	100	RUS	R Moscow
	KHABAROVSK	50	RUS	R Moscow
	Solomon Islands	10	SLM	SIBC Honiara

Freq. [kHz]	Transmitter site	Power [kW]	Country	Station name
9545	Antigua	250	ATG	DW
(cont)	Sackville	250	CAN	DW
9550	MEYERTON	250	AFS	Channel Africa
	PT.ALEGRE	5	B	R Nova Esperanca
	DHAKA	250	BGD	R Bangladesh
	SANTIAGO	100	CHL	
	JINHUA	500	CHN	China R Intl
	XIAN	120	CHN	China R Intl
	HABANA	250	CUB	R Havana Cuba
	ALLOUIS	500	F	RFI
	PORI	250	FIN	YLE R Finland
	MOYABI	250	GAB/F	RFI
	THESSALONIKI	35	GRC	Vo Greece
	ALIGARH	250	IND	AIR
	BOMBAY	100	IND	AIR
	DELHI	100	IND	AIR
	UJUNGPANDANG	8	INS	RRI
	TOKYO YAMATA	500	J	RCI
	MT.CARLO	100	MCO	TWR
	RANGITAIKI	100	NZL	R New Zealand
	BUCURESTI	250	ROU	R Romania Intl
	KRANJI	250	SNG/G	BBCWS
	DAR ES SALAAM	50	TZA	R Tanzania
	JIGULEVSK	20	RUS	R7
	TACHKENT	20	UZB	Domestic
	OKEECHOBEE	100	USA	WYFR
9555	JEDDAH	50	ARS	BSKSA
	RIYADH	500	ARS	BSKSA
	LA PAZ	10	BOL	
	XIAN	300	CHN	China R Intl
	LAMPERTHEIM	100	D/USA	RFE/RL
	PLAYA DE PALS	250	E	REE
	SKELTON	300	G	RCI
	WOOFFERTON	250	G	BBCWS
	WAMENA	25	INS	RRI
	KIMJAE	250	KOR	R Korea
	MEXICO	1	MEX	La Hora Exacta
	PALAUIG	250	PHL	R Veritas Asia
	MAXOQUEIRA	500	POR	RFE/RL
	S.GABRIEL	100	POR	RFE/RL
	GREENVILLE	250	USA	VoA
	Okeechobee	100	USA	WYFR
9560	ASCENSION	250	ASC	BBCWS
	CARNARVON	100	AUS	R Australia

Freq. [kHz]	Transmitter site	Power [kW]	Country	Station name
9560	DARWIN	250	AUS	R Australia
(cont)	SOFIA	250	BUL	R Sofia
	SANTIAGO	100	CHL	CNR
	URUMQI	50	CHN	Xinjiang
	LIMASSOL	250	CYP/G	BBCWS
	GEDJA	100	ETH	Vo Ethiopia
	PORI	500	FIN	YLE R Finland
	DELHI	100	IND	AIR
	AL KARANAH	500	JOR	R Jordan
	PYONGYANG	400	KRE	R Pyongyang
	FREDRIKSTAD	350	NOR	R Norway Intl
	SVEIO	500	NOR	R Norway Intl
	PALAUIG	250	PHL	R Veritas Asia
	LIMA	20	PRU	
	ANKARA	500	TUR	TRT Vo Turkey
	KHABAROVSK	20	RUS	Domestic
	KINGHISEPP	500	RUS	R Moscow
	Kigali	250	RRW	DW
	Udorn	500	THA	VoA
	Kiev	500	UKR	R Ukraine Intl
9565	CURITIBA	5	B	R Universo
	NANCHANG	50	CHN	China R Intl
	XIAN	150	CHN	China R Intl
	BIBLIS	100	D/USA	RFE/RL
	ATHINAI	100	GRC	Vo Greece
	DIOSD	100	HNG	R Budapest
	ALIGARH	250	IND	AIR
	DELHI	100	IND	AIR
	UJUNGPANDANG	100	INS	RRI
	BRIECH	500	MRC/USA	VoA
	PALAUIG	250	PHL	R Veritas Asia
	MAXOQUEIRA	500	POR	RFE/RL
	SINES	250	POR	DW
	KIGALI	250	RRW	DW
	MAHE	75	SEY	FEBA
	TBILISI	100	GEO	R Moscow
	VLADIVOSTOK	100	RUS	R Moscow
	BETHANY	250	USA	Vo OAS
	Riyadh	500	ARS	BSKSA
9570	DHAKA	250	BGD	R Bangladesh
	MINSK	240	BLR	R Moscow
	XIAN	300	CHN	China R Intl
	HABANA	250	CUB	R Havana Cuba
	BIBLIS	100	D/USA	RFE/RL

Freq. [kHz]	Transmitter site	Power [kW]	Country	Station name
9570	MOYABI	500	GAB	NHK R Japan
(cont)	TOKYO YAMATA	300	J	NHK R Japan
	KIMJAE	250	KOR	R Korea
	S.GABRIEL	100	POR	R Portugal
	BUCURESTI	250	ROU	R Romania Intl
	KRANJI	100	SNG/G	BBCWS
	RIAZAN	100	RUS	R Moscow
	Kaduna	50	NIG	R Nigeria 2
9575	XIAN	150	CHN	China R Intl
	LAMPERTHEIM	100	D/USA	RFE/RL
	ALLOUIS	100	F	RFI
	MOYABI	250	GAB/F	RFI
	MONTSINERY	500	GUF	RFI
	ROMA	100	I	RAI
	MADRAS	10	IND	AIR
	MEDAN	50	INS	RRI
	MEXICO	100	MEX	R Mexico
	PORO	50	PHL	VoA
	MUGE	100	POR	R Renascenca
	IRKUTSK	100	RUS	R Moscow
	SERPUKHOV	240	RUS	R Moscow
	BETHANY	250	USA	VoA
	Nador	250	MRC	R Mediterranee Intl
	Okeechobee	100	USA	WYFR
9580	LUSHNJA	100	ALB	R Tirana
	JEDDAH	50	ARS	BSKSA
	SHEPPARTON	100	AUS	R Australia
	DHAKA	250	BGD	R Bangladesh
	BEIJING	50	CHN	CNR
	NOBLEJAS	350	E	REE
	WOOFFERTON	300	G	VoA
	MOYABI	250	GAB	Africa No 1
	TSANG TSUI	250	HKG/G	BBCWS
	TOKYO YAMATA	300	J	NHK R Japan
	KIMJAE	100	KOR	R Korea
	PYONGYANG	200	KRE	R Pyongyang
	MASIRAH	100	OMA/G	BBCWS
	KARACHI	50	PAK	R Pakistan
	MALOLOS	50	PHL	VoA
	SINES	250	POR	
	KAZAN	250	RUS	R Moscow
	KINGHISEPP	100	RUS	R Moscow
	BELGRADE	500	YUG	R Yugoslavia
	LUSAKA	50	ZMB	Zambia NBC

Freq. [kHz]	Transmitter site	Power [kW]	Country	Station name
9585	S.PAULO	8	B	R CBN Globo
	LIMASSOL	250	CYP/G	BBCWS
	WOOFFERTON	250	G	VoA
	KAVALLA	250	GRC	VoA
	DELHI	100	IND	AIR
	PAKANBARU	50	INS	RRI
	KIMJAE	250	KOR	R Korea
	BRIECH	500	MRC/USA	VoA
	AL KHAISAH	250	QAT	Qatar BS
	ADRA	500	SYR	Syrian Arab R
	Malabo	100	GNE	R East Africa
	Wertachtal	500	D	DW
9590	BONAIRE RNW	250	ATN	R Netherlands
	SACKVILLE	250	CAN/G	BBCWS
	XIAN	150	CHN	China R Intl
	LIMASSOL	100	CYP/G	BBCWS
	AGANA	100	GUM	KTWR
	FLEVO	500	HOL	R Netherlands
	TOKYO YAMATA	300	J	NHK R Japan
	TALATA VOLON	300	MDG	R Netherlands
	FREDRIKSTAD	350	NOR	R Norway Intl
	KVITSOY	500	NOR	R Norway Intl
	SVEIO	500	NOR	R Norway Intl
	MASIRAH	100	OMA/G	BBCWS
	TINANG	250	PHL	VoA
	BUCURESTI	250	ROU	R Romania Intl
	SINGAPORE	250	SNG	Warna R
	ANKARA	250	TUR	TRT Vo Turkey
	MOSKVA	100	RUS	Domestic
	OMSK	100	RUS	R Moscow
	BETHANY	250	USA	R Marti/VoA
	DELANO	250	USA	BBC
	GREENVILLE	250	USA	VoA
	NOBLESVILLE	100	USA	WHRI
9595	SOFIA	500	BUL	R Sofia
	URUMQI	50	CHN	Xinjiang Uighur
	EKALA	300	CLN	SLBC
	BIBLIS	100	D/USA	RFE/Rl
	ALIGARH	250	IND	AIR
	MANOKWARI	25	INS	RRI
	REYKJAVIK	10	ISL	Icelandic BS
	TOKYO NAGARA	50	J	R Tanpa 1
	KIMJAE	250	KOR	R Korea
	MAHE	75	SEY	FEBA

Freq. [kHz]	Transmitter site	Power [kW]	Country	Station name
9595	SONSONATE	25	SLV	
(cont)	DUBAI	300	UAE	UAE R Dubai
	MONTEVIDEO	10	URG	R Monte Carlo
	SERPUKHOV	100	RUS	R Moscow
	BELGRADE	500	YUG	R Yugoslavia
	Maxoquiera	250	POR	RFE/RL
9600	ASCENSION	250	ASC	BBCWS
	RIO DE JANEIRO	8	B	
	KUNMING	50	CHN	China R
	HABANA	100	CUB	R Havana Cuba
	S.M.GALERIA	500	CVA	Vatican R
	NOBLEJAS	350	E/CHN	REE
	QUITO	500	EQA	HCJB
	RAMPISHAM	500	G	BBCWS
	WOOFFERTON	300	G	BBCWS
	FLEVO	500	HOL	R Netherlands
	PYONGYANG	400	KRE	R Pyongyang
	BENGHAZI	100	LBY	Libya Jamahiriyah B
	MEXICO	1	MEX	R Unam
	MASIRAH	100	OMA/G	BBCWS
	MUGE	100	POR	R Renascenca
	S.GABRIEL	100	POR	R Portugal
	KRANJI	250	SNG/G	BBCWS
	MOSKVA	100	RUS	R Moscow
	OKHOTSK	100	RUS	R Moscow
	Kiev	500	UKR	R Ukraine Intl
9605	S.CRUZ	1	BOL	
	SOFIA	100	BUL	R Sofia
	KUNMING	50	CHN	China R
	S.M.GALERIA	500	CVA	Vatican R
	JUELICH	100	D	DW
	WERTACHTAL	500	D/USA	VoA
	ALLOUIS	100	F	RFI
	RAMPISHAM	500	G	BBCWS
	MONTSINERY	500	GUF	RFI
	ALIGARH	250	IND	AIR
	PALU	50	INS	RRI
	TALATA VOLON	300	MDG	R Netherlands
	KRANJI	250	SNG/G	BBCWS
	SERPUKHOV	50	RUS	Domestic
	OKEECHOBEE	100	USA	WYFR
	Trincomalee	250	CLN	DW
9610	ASCENSION	250	ASC	BBCWS
	BEIJING	50	CHN	China R

Freq. [kHz]	Transmitter site	Power [kW]	Country	Station name
9610	BRAZZAVILLE	50	COG	R Natl Congolaise
(cont)	DELHI	250	IND	AIR
	KAMALABAD	500	IRN	IRIB
	TOKYO YAMATA	100	J	NHK R Japan
	MT.CARLO	500	MCO	TWR
	NOUAKCHOTT	100	MTN	R Mauritanie
	IQUITOS	2	PRU	
	MOSKVA	100	RUS	R Moscow
	S.PETERSBURG	500	RUS	R Moscow
	Wanneroo	10	AUS	VLW9
	Kigali	50	RRW	R Rwanda
9615	ANCHOR POINT	100	ALS	KNLS
	S.PAULO	8	B	R Cultura
	PERKARA	250	CLN	DW
	JUELICH	100	D	DW
	WERTACHTAL	500	D	DW
	BOMBAY	100	IND	AIR
	SAMARINDA	50	INS	RRI
	REYKJAVIK	10	ISL	Icelandic BS
	TRIPOLI	500	LBY	Libya Jamahiriyah B
	BRIECH	500	MRC/USA	VoA
	ISLAMABAD	100	PAK	R Pakistan
	MARULAS	3	PHL	
	PALAUIG	250	PHL	R Veritas Asia
	SINES	250	POR	R Portugal/DW
	MAHE	250	SEY/G	BBCWS
	JIGULEVSK	240	RUS	R Moscow
	REDWOOD CITY	50	USA	KGEI
	Pori	500	FNL	YLE R Finland
9620	JEDDAH	50	ARS	BSKSA
	RIYADH	500	ARS	BSKSA
	DHAKA	250	BGD	R Bangladesh
	BEIJING	120	CHN	China R Intl
	ARGANDA	100	E	REE
	NOBLEJAS	350	E	REE
	ABIS	250	EGY	R Cairo
	ABU ZAABAL	100	EGY	R Cairo
	ALIGARH	250	IND	AIR
	MAPUTO	120	MOZ	R Mozambique
	PORO	50	PHL	VoA
	TINANG	250	PHL	VoA
	HOERBY	500	S	R Sweden
	UDORN	500	THA/USA	VoA
	MONTEVIDEO	20	URG	SODRE

Freq. [kHz]	Transmitter site	Power [kW]	Country	Station name
9620	MOSKVA	150	RUS	R Moscow
(cont)	VLADIVOSTOK	100	RUS	R Moscow
	BELGRADE	100	YUG	R Yugoslavia
	Trincomalee	250	CLN	DW
9625	SACKVILLE	100	CAN	CBC Natl Sce
	KUNMING	120	CHN	China R Intl
	BIBLIS	100	D/USA	RFE/Rl
	LAMPERTHEIM	100	D/USA	RFE/RL
	PLAYA DE PALS	500	E	REE
	YOGYAKARTA	100	INS	RRI
	REYKJAVIK	10	ISL	Icelandic BS
	LISBON	250	POR	RFE/RL
	BUCURESTI	250	ROU	R Romania Intl
	OKEECHOBEE	100	USA	WYFR
	Laz Paz	15	BOL	R Fides
9630	LUSHNJA	100	ALB	R Tirana
	BONAIRE RNW	250	ATN	R Netherlands
	APARECIDA	10	B	R Aparecida
	DHAKA	250	BGD	R Bangladesh
	SANTIAGO	10	CHL	
	KUNMING	50	CHN	China R Intl
	CARIARI	100	CTR/E	REE
	HABANA	500	CUB	R Havana Cuba
	NOBLEJAS	350	E	REE
	ALLOUIS	100	F	RFI
	DELHI	50	IND	AIR
	JERUSALEM	300	ISR	Kol Israel
	SINES	250	POR	R Portugal
	MAHE	250	SEY/G	BBCWS
	KAZAN	100	RUS	R Moscow
	SERPUKHOV	100	RUS	R Moscow
	Meyerton	100	AFS	R Oranje
	Taipei	300	TWN	CBS Network 4
9635	KABUL	100	AFG	R Afghanistan
	SACKVILLE	100	CAN	RCI/BBCWS
	BAODING	120	CHN	China R Intl
	LIMASSOL	250	CYP/G	BBCWS
	HOLZKIRCHEN	250	D/USA	RFE
	RAMPISHAM	500	G	BBCWS
	KAVALLA	250	GRC	Vo Greece
	UJUNGPANDANG	50	INS	RRI
	BAMAKO 2	50	MLI	Radiodiffusion Malienne
	BEIRA	100	MOZ	R Mozambique
	BRIECH	500	MRC/USA	VoA

Freq. [kHz]	Transmitter site	Power [kW]	Country	Station name
9635	S.GABRIEL	100	POR	R Portugal
(cont)	CUZCO	1	PRU	
	SINGAPORE	250	SNG	City Sounds
	VLADIVOSTOK	100	RUS	R Moscow
	Greenville	250	USA	VoA
	Flevo	500	HOL	R Netherlands
9640	BOUCHAOUI	50	ALG	RTV Algerienne
	ANTIGUA	125	ATG	BBCWS
	BRASILIA	250	B/D	DW
	PERKARA	250	CLN	DW
	NAUEN	500	D	DW
	WERTACHTAL	500	D	DW
	TOKYO YAMATA	100	J	NHK R Japan
	KIMJAE	250	KOR	R Korea
	PYONGYANG	200	KRE	R Pyongyang
	CYCLOPS	250	MLT	DW
	ULAN BATOR	250	MNG	China R Intl
	ISLAMABAD	10	PAK	R Pakistan
	PALAUIG	250	PHL	VoA
	MONTEVIDEO	10	URG	
	MOSKVA	250	RUS	R Moscow
	PETROPAVLO KAM	100	RUS	R Moscow
	S.PETERSBURG	200	RUS	R Moscow/R Ukraine Intl
9645	CARNARVON	300	AUS	R Australia
	S.PAULO	8	B	R Bandeirantes
	MINSK	50	BLR	Domestic
	BAOJI	50	CHN	China R
	COLOMBO	35	CLN	SLBC
	S.M.GALERIA	500	CVA	Vatican R
	MOYABI	500	GAB	Africa No 1
	KAVALLA	250	GRC	Vo Greece
	PT.AU PRINCE	100	HTI	
	BANDA ACEH	50	INS	RRI
	KUJANG	400	KRE	R Pyongyang
	ULAN BATOR	100	MNG	
	ISLAMABAD	100	PAK	R Pakistan
	IBA	100	PHL	VoA
	PORO	50	PHL	VoA
	KAZAN	100	RUS	R Moscow
9650	DHAKA	250	BGD	R Bangladesh
	SACKVILLE	250	CAN	RCI/R Korea
	S.M.GALERIA	250	CVA	Vatican R
	NAUEN	500	D	DW
	WERTACHTAL	500	D	DW

Freq. [kHz]	Transmitter site	Power [kW]	Country	Station name
9650	NOBLEJAS	350	E	REE
(cont)	WOOFFERTON	300	G	VoA
	CONAKRY	100	GUI	R Conakry
	AGAT	100	GUM	KSDA
	FLEVO	500	HOL	R Netherlands
	GAUHATI	50	IND	AIR
	TOKYO YAMATA	300	J	RFI
	PYONGYANG	200	KRE	R Korea
	CYCLOPS	250	MLT	DW
	THUMRAIT	100	OMA	R Oman
	SINES	250	POR	DW
	MANZINI	25	SWZ	TWR
	MONTEVIDEO	10	URG	
	MOSKVA	100	RUS	R Moscow
9655	WIEN	500	AUT	R Austria Intl
	MINSK	20	BLR	Domestic
	LHASA	50	CHN	China R
	PERKARA	250	CLN	DW
	HABANA	100	CUB	R Havana Cuba
	WERTACHTAL	500	D/USA	RFE/RL
	NABIRE	25	INS	RRI
	TRIPOLI	500	LBY	Libya Jamahiriyah B
	KVITSOY	500	NOR	R Norway Intl
	SVEIO	500	NOR	R Norway Intl
	BOCAUE	100	PHL	VoA
	HOERBY	500	S	R Sweden
	KENGA	100	RUS	R Moscow
	KOMSOMOLSKAMUR	250	RUS	R Moscow
	TCHITA	100	RUS	R Moscow
	VOLGOGRAD	20	URS	Domestic
	Bogota	20	CLM	R Diffusion Nacional
	Wellington	100	NZL	R New Zealand Intl
	Udorn	500	THA	R Thailand
9660	BAODING	120	CHN	China R Intl
	LIMASSOL	100	CYP/G	BBCWS
	HOLZKIRCHEN	250	D/USA	DW
	LAMPERTHEIM	100	D/USA	DW
	TOKYO YAMATA	100	J	NHK R Japan/RCI
	KARACHI	50	PAK	R Pakistan
	IBA	100	PHL	FEBC
	PALAUIG	250	PHL	R Veritas Asia
	IRKUTSK	1000	RUS	R Moscow
	KINSHASA	50	ZAI	Zaire BC
	Brisbane	10	AUS	VLQ9

Freq. [kHz]	Transmitter site	Power [kW]	Country	Station name
9660	Playa de Pals	250	E	REE
(cont)	Briech	500	MRC	VoA
	Mahe	100	SEY	FEBA
9665	JEDDAH	50	ARS	BSKSA
	FLORIANOPOLIS	10	B	R Marumby
	SHIJIAZHUANG	500	CHN	China R Intl
	PORI	250	FIN	YLE R Finland
	KAVALLA	250	GRC	VoA
	ALIGARH	250	IND	AIR
	DELHI	250	IND	AIR
	SEMARANG	50	INS	RRI
	KIMJAE	250	KOR	R Korea
	PYONGYANG	200	KRE	R Pyongyang
	IBA	100	PHL	FEBC
	BUCURESTI	250	ROU	R Romania Intl
	KICHINEV	500	MDA	R Moscow
	KURSK	240	RUS	R Moscow
	BETHANY	250	USA	VoA
	Meyerton	100	AFS	Afrikaans S
	Antigua	250	ATG	DW
	Julich	100	D	DW
	Sines	250	POR	IBRA R
	Qatar	250	QAT	Qatar BS
	Ankara	500	TUR	TRT Vo Turkey
9670	ANTIGUA	250	ATG	DW
	KUNMING	50	CHN	China R Intl
	PERKARA	250	CLN	DW
	NAUEN	500	D	Dw
	WERTACHTAL	500	D/USA	RFE/RL
	ABIS	250	EGY	R Cairo
	QUITO	100	EQA	HCJB
	SKELTON	300	G	RCI/NHK R Japan
	KAVALLA	250	GRC	Voa
	MARPI	100	MRA	KFBS
	BRIECH	500	MRC/USA	VoA
	ISLAMABAD	100	PAK	R Pakistan
	MAXOQUEIRA	500	POR	RFE/RL
	SINES	250	POR	RFE/RL
	HOERBY	500	S	R Sweden
	MONTEVIDEO	10	URG	
	EKATERINBURG	20	RUS	Domestic
	KALININGRAD	100	RUS	R Moscow
	KOMSOMOLSKAMUR	100	RUS	R Moscow
	BETHANY	250	USA	BBC

80

Freq. [kHz]	Transmitter site	Power [kW]	Country	Station name
9670	GREENVILLE	250	USA	VoA
(cont)	Kigali	250	RRW	DW
9675	LUSHNJA	100	ALB	R Tirana
	CACHOEIRA PAUL	10	B	R Cancao Nova
	KUNMING	50	CHN	China R
	XIAN	300	CHN	China R Intl
	NOBLEJAS	350	E	REE
	QUITO	500	EQA	HCJB
	MOYABI	500	GAB/J	NHK R Japan
	MONTSINERY	500	GUF	NHK R Japan
	DELHI	100	IND	AIR
	JAKARTA	100	INS	RRI
	MATARAM	50	INS	RRI
	PADANG CERMIN	250	INS	RRI
	PORO	35	PHL	VoA
	WARSZAWA	100	POL	Polish R Warsaw
	LIMA	8	PRU	R del Pacifico
	ANKARA	250	TUR	TRT Vo Turkey
	EREVAN	100	ARM	R Moscow/R Ukraine Intl
	Meyerton	250	AFS	Channel Africa
	Fredrikstad	350	NOR	R Norway Intl
	Kavalla	250	GRC	VoA
	Tunis	100	TUN	ERTT
9680	LHASA	50	CHN	China R
	JUELICH	100	D	DW
	WERTACHTAL	500	D	DW
	BIBLIS	100	D/USA	RFE/RL
	LAMPERTHEIM	100	D/USA	RFE/RL
	KAVALLA	250	GRC	VoA
	REYKJAVIK	10	ISL	Icelandic BS
	TOKYO YAMATA	300	J	NHK R Japan
	MUGE	100	POR	R Renascenca
	MONTEVIDEO	10	URG	
	DELANO	250	USA	VoA
	OKEECHOBEE	100	USA	WYFR/VoFC
	Playa de Pals	250	E	RFE/RL
	Udorn	500	THA	VoA
9685	OULED FAYET	100	ALG	RTV Algerienne
	S.PAULO	8	B	R Gazeta
	BAODING	120	CHN	China R Intl
	ARGANDA	100	E	REE
	MONTSINERY	500	GUF	NHK R Japan
	KENDARI	50	INS	RRI
	AREQUIPA	1	PRU	R Continental

Freq. [kHz]	Transmitter site	Power [kW]	Country	Station name
9685	UDORN	250	THA/USA	VoA
(cont)	ANKARA	500	TUR	TRT Vo Turkey
	DAR ES SALAAM	50	TZA	R Tanzania
	LVOV	1000	UKR	R Ukraine Intl
	IRKUTSK	250	RUS	R Moscow
	KENGA	500	RUS	R Moscow
	MOSKVA	100	RUS	R Moscow
9690	GRAL PACHECO	100	ARG	R Argentina al Exterior
	ANTIGUA	250	ATG	DW
	KUNMING	120	CHN	China R Intl
	PERKARA	250	CLN	DW
	JUELICH	100	D	DW
	WERTACHTAL	500	D	DW
	NOBLEJAS	350	E/CHN	China R Intl
	PT.AU PRINCE	100	HTI	
	BHOPAL	50	IND	AIR
	FENOARIVO	30	MDG	
	CYCLOPS	250	MLT	DW
	ISLAMABAD	100	PAK	R Pakistan
	BUCURESTI	250	ROU	R Romania Intl
	UDORN	250	THA/USA	VoA
	ALMA ATA	20	KAZ	Kazakh R
	TULA	20	RUS	Kazakh R
	DELANO	250	USA	BBCWS
9695	MEYERTON	500	AFS	Channel Africa
	MANAUS	8	B	R Rio Mar
	S.M.GALERIA	500	CVA	Vatican R
	BIBLIS	100	D/USA	RFE/Rl
	LAMPERTHEIM	100	D/USA	RFE/Rl
	NOBLEJAS	350	E	RFE/RL
	SORONG	50	INS	RRI
	MAXOQUEIRA	500	POR	RFE/RL
	HOERBY	500	S	R Sweden
	MAKTA	120	UAE	UAE R Abu Dhabi
	S.PETERSBURG	200	RUS	R Moscow
9700	ANTIGUA	250	ATG	DW
	DHAKA	250	BGD	R Bangladesh
	SOFIA	150	BUL	R Sofia
	SACKVILLE	250	CAN	RCIA
	XIAN	150	CHN	China R Intl
	WERTACHTAL	500	D	DW
	ABU ZAABAL	100	EGY	R Cairo
	KAVALLA	250	GRC	VoA
	ALIGARH	250	IND	AIR

Freq. [kHz]	Transmitter site	Power [kW]	Country	Station name
9700	KIMJAE	250	KOR	R Korea
(cont)	RANGITAIKI	100	NZL	R New Zealand Intl/ BBCWS
	ISLAMABAD	250	PAK	R Pakistan
	KIGALI	250	RRW	DW
	KAZAN	100	RUS	R Moscow
	TBILISI	100	GEO	R Moscow
9705	JEDDAH	50	ARS	BSKSA
	S.GONCALO	8	B	R Nacional
	BIBLIS	100	D/USA	RFE/RL
	LAMPERTHEIM	100	D/USA	RFE/RL
	PLAYA DE PALS	250	E	REE
	GEDJA	100	ETH	Vo Ethiopia
	ALIGARH	250	IND	AIR
	DELHI	50	IND	AIR
	PONTIANAK	50	INS	RRI
	TRIPOLI	500	LBY	Libya Jamahiriyah B
	MEXICO	10	MEX	R Mexico Intl
	NIAMEY	100	NGR	La Voix du Sahel
	MAXOQUEIRA	500	POR	RFE/RL
	S.GABRIEL	100	POR	VoA
	UDORN	500	THA/USA	VoA
	ARMAVIR	10	RUS	Domestic
	CELINOGRAD	20	RUS	Domestic
	IAKUTSK	20	RUS	Domestic
	TACHKENT	20	UZB	R Tashkent
	OKEECHOBEE	50	USA	WYFR
9710	SHEPPARTON	100	AUS	R Australia
	LANZHOU	15	CHN	China R
	KAVALLA	250	GRC	VoA
	ROMA	100	I	RAI
	TOKYO YAMATA	300	J	NHK R Japan
	SITKUNAI	50	LTU	R Vilnius
	MAURITIUS	10	MAU	Mauritius R
	TARAPOTO	1	PRU	
	ANKARA	250	TUR	TRT Vo Turkey
	KONEVO	50	RUS	Domestic
	SERPUKHOV	100	RUS	R Ukraine Intl
9715	BONAIRE RNW	250	ATN	R Netherlands
	SUCRE	1	BOL	R La Plata
	BRAZZAVILLE	50	COG	R Nacional Congolaise
	JUELICH	100	D	DW
	WERTACHTAL	500	D	DW
	ALLOUIS	500	F	RFI

Freq. [kHz]	Transmitter site	Power [kW]	Country	Station name
9715	KAVALLA	250	GRC	VoA
(cont)	RHODOS	50	GRC	VoA
	MONTSINERY	500	GUF	RFI
	DELHI	50	IND	AIR
	BIAK	100	INS	RRI
	PORO	50	PHL	VoA
	MAXOQUEIRA	500	POR	RFE/RL
	KINGHISEPP	200	RUS	R Moscow
	TACHKENT	50	UZB	R Tashkent
	OKEECHOBEE	50	USA	WYFR
9720	LUANDA	100	AGL	R Nacional
	BONAIRE RNW	250	ATN	R Netherlands
	BEIJING	120	CHN	China R Intl
	EKALA	100	CLN	SLBC/DW
	KAMALABAD	500	IRN	IRIB
	ULAN BATOR	250	MNG	R Moscow
	JIGULEVSK	100	RUS	R Moscow
	RIAZAN	200	RUS	R Moscow
	BELGRADE	500	YUG	R Yugoslavia
9725	LUSHNJA	100	ALB	R Tirana
	CURITIBA	8	B	R Clube Paranaense
	SACKVILLE	250	CAN	NHK R Japan
	HUHHOT	50	CHN	China R Intl
	BIBLIS	100	D/USA	RFE/RL
	ROMA	100	I	RAI
	AMBOINA	100	INS	RRI
	REYKJAVIK	10	ISL	Icelandic BS
	LISBON	250	POR	RFE/RL
	MAXOQUEIRA	500	POR	RFE/RL
	SERPUKHOV	100	RUS	R Moscow
	Baghdad	500	IRQ	R Baghdad
9730	MEYERTON	500	AFS	Channel Africa
	LUSHNJA	100	ALB	R Tirana
	RIYADH	500	ARS	BSKSA
	YANGON	50	BRM	R Myanmar
	BAODING	120	CHN	China R Intl
	NAUEN	500	D	DW
	PORI	500	FIN	YLE R Finland
	DELHI	100	IND	AIR
	JERUSALEM	300	ISR	Kol Israel
	KAZAN	20	RUS	Domestic
	KHABAROVSK	100	RUS	Domestic
	HANOI	15	VTN	Vo Vietnam
	Taipei	250	TWN	VoFC

Freq. [kHz]	Transmitter site	Power [kW]	Country	Station name
9735	DHAKA	250	BGD	R Bangladesh
	WERTACHTAL	500	D	DW
	MERAUKE	100	INS	RRI
	CYCLOPS	250	MLT	DW
	SEEB	100	OMA	R Oman
	THUMRAIT	100	OMA	R Oman
	BOCAUE	50	PHL	VoA
	ASUNCION	100	PRG	R Nacional del Paraguay
	KIGALI	250	RRW	DW
	ARMAVIR	250	RUS	R Moscow
	IRKUTSK	200	RUS	R Moscow
9740	KUNMING	50	CHN	China R Intl
	LIMASSOL	250	CYP/G	BBCWS
	ABIS	250	EGY	R Cairo
	KAVALLA	250	GRC	VoA
	BRIECH	500	MRC/USA	VoA
	KARACHI	50	PAK	R Pakistan
	LISBON	250	POR	RFE/RL
	KRANJI	250	SNG/G	BBCWS
	ANKARA	250	TUR	TRT Vo Turkey
	MOSKVA	250	RUS	R Moscow
	TACHKENT	100	UZB	R Tashkent
	Skelton	300	G	RCI
	Moyabi	500	GAB	RFI
9745	BRASILIA	250	B	R Bras
	ST.MARIA	10	B	
	ABU HAYAN	60	BHR	R Bahrain
	CARIARI	100	CTR/E	REE
	WERTACHTAL	500	D/USA	RFE/Rl
	NOBLEJAS	350	E	REE
	QUITO	100	EQA	HCJB
	ALLOUIS	100	F	RFI
	KAVALLA	250	GRC	VoA
	BANDJARMASIN	50	INS	RRI
	KAMALABAD	500	IRN	IRIB
	ABU GHRAIB	250	IRQ	R Baghdad
	KUJANG	200	KRE	R Pyongyang
	TRIPOLI	500	LBY	Libya Jamahiriyah B
	SINES	250	POR	DW
	Kiev	500	UKR	R Ukraine Intl
9750	SANTIAGO	10	CHL	
	HUHHOT	50	CHN	China R
	LIMASSOL	100	CYP/G	BBCWS
	RAMPISHAM	500	G	BBCWS

Freq. [kHz]	Transmitter site	Power [kW]	Country	Station name
9750	SKELTON	250	G	BBCWS
(cont)	WOOFFERTON	250	G	BBCWS
	ATHINAI	100	GRC	Vo Greece
	TOKYO YAMATA	300	J	NHK R Japan
	KIMJAE	250	KOR	R Korea
	SULAIBIYAH	500	KWT	R Kuwait
	MEXICO	100	MEX	R Mexico
	KAJANG	100	MLA	Vo Malaysia
	PAPEETE	20	OCE	RFO
	MASIRAH	100	OMA/G	BBCWS
	MAXOQUEIRA	500	POR	RFE/RL
	BUCURESTI	250	ROU	R Romania
	DAR ES SALAAM	50	TZA	R Tanzania
	LVOV	1000	UKR	R Ukraine Intl
	ARMAVIR	500	RUS	R Moscow
	TACHKENT	100	UZB	R Tashkent
9755	SACKVILLE	250	CAN	RCI
	BAOJI	50	CHN	CNR 2
	MOKATTAM	100	EGY	R Cairo
	DELHI	100	IND	AIR
	SURAKARTA	50	INS	RRI
	PYONGYANG	200	KRE	R Korea
	TINANG	250	PHL	VoA
	NIKOLAEVSKAMUR	240	RUS	R Moscow
	PETROZAVODSK	100	RUS	R Moscow
	SM Galeria	500	CVA	Vatican R
9760	LUSHNJA	100	ALB	R Tirana
	WAVRE	100	BEL	R Vlaanderen Intl
	LIMASSOL	100	CYP/G	BBCWS
	NOBLEJAS	350	E	REE
	RAMPISHAM	500	G	BBCWS
	SKELTON	300	G	BBCWS
	WOOFFERTON	300	G	VoA
	TOKYO NAGARA	50	J	R Tanpa 2
	TINANG	250	PHL	VoA
	LISBON	250	POR	VoA
	KENGA	100	RUS	R Moscow
	KINGHISEPP	200	RUS	R Moscow
9765	BEIJING	500	CHN	China R Intl
	JUELICH	100	D	DW
	WERTACHTAL	500	D	DW
	NOBLEJAS	350	E	REE
	QUITO	100	EQA	HCJB
	DELHI	100	IND	AIR

Freq. [kHz]	Transmitter site	Power [kW]	Country	Station name
9765	PONTIANAK	100	INS	RRI
(cont)	CYCLOPS	250	MLT	Vo the Mediterranean
	KIGALI	250	RRW	DW
	ARMAVIR	100	RUS	R Moscow
	IRKUTSK	240	RUS	R Moscow
	VOLGOGRAD	1000	RUS	R Moscow
9770	CARNARVON	100	AUS	R Australia
	BAOJI	50	CHN	China R
	LIMASSOL	100	CYP/G	BBCWS/Cyprus BC
	JUELICH	100	D	DW
	WERTACHTAL	500	D	DW
	ABU ZAABAL	100	EGY	R Cairo
	ALLOUIS	500	F	RFI
	RAMPISHAM	500	G	BBCWS
	MOYABI	250	GAB/F	RFI
	MONTSINERY	500	GUF	RFI
	DELHI	100	IND	AIR
	KARACHI	50	PAK	R Pakistan
	TINANG	250	PHL	VoA
	MAHE	75	SEY	FEBA
	ABU DHABI	500	UAE	UAE R Abu Dhabi
	MONTEVIDEO	10	URG	
	KINSHASA	10	ZAI	Zaire R
	Bamako	50	MLI	China R Intl
	Okeechobee	100	USA	WYFR
9775	Urumuqi	50	CHN	CNR 2
	Yekaterinburg	100	RUS	AWR
	Greenville	500	USA	VoA
9780	Poro	50	PHL	FEBC
	San Gabriel	100	POR	R Portugal
	Alma Ata	50	KAZ	R Alma Ata
9785	Guam	100	GUM	KTWR
	Rancho Simi	50	USA	KVOH
9790	Allouis	500	F	RFI
	Moyabi	500	GAB	RFI
	Montsinery	500	GUF	RFI
	Tashkent	50	UZB	R Tashkent
9800	Abu Zaabal	250	EGY	R Cairo
	Allouis	500	F	RFI
	Athens	100	GRC	Vo Greece
	Montsinery	500	GUF	RFI
	Poro	50	PHL	FEBC

Freq. [kHz]	Transmitter site	Power [kW]	Country	Station name
9805	Allouis	500	F	RFI
	Moyabi	500	GAB	RFI
9810	Mahe	100	SEY	FEBA
	Bratislava	100	SVK	Slovak R Intl
	Irkutsk	250	RUS	R Netherlands
	Sottens	500	SUI	Swiss R Intl
	Velke Kostolany	100	TCH	R Prague/Slovak R Intl
9815	Havana	500	CUB	R Havana Cuba
	Jerusalem	500	ISR	Kol Israel
	S Gabriel	100	POR	R Portugal
	Novosibirsk	1000	RUS	DW
	Samara	500	RUS	DW
	Denton	50	USA	KCBI
9820	Bocaue	50	PHL	FEBC
9825	Rampisham	500	G	BBCWS
	Skelton	300	G	BBCWS
	Flevo	500	HOL	R Netherlands
	Birmingham	500	USA	WEWN
9830	Al Karanah	500	JOR	R Jordan
	Bocaue	100	PHL	FEBC
9835	Diosd	250	HNG	R Budapest
	Novosibirsk	100	RUS	AWR
9840	Bonaire	250	ATN	R Netherlands
	Xian	500	CHN	China R Intl
	Kabd	500	KWT	R Kuwait
	Moscow	100	RUS	AWR
	Greenville	250	USA	VoA
	Cypress Creek	500	USA	Monitor R Intl
	Tashkent	100	UZB	Tashkent R
	Vietnam	50	VTN	Vo Vietnam
9845	Kunming	120	CHN	China R Intl
	Diosd	100	HNG	RFI
	Jerusalem	500	ISR	Kol Israel
	Bocaue	100	PHL	FEBC
	Taipei	250	TWN	VoFC
	Alma Ata	500	KAZ	R Netherlands
9850	Sofia	500	BUL	R Sofia
	Abis	250	EGY	R Cairo
	Bocaue	100	PHL	FEBC
	Okeechobee	100	USA	WYFR/VoFC
	Noblesville	100	USA	WHRI

Freq. [kHz]	Transmitter site	Power [kW]	Country	Station name
9855	Xian	120	CHN	China R Intl
	Rome	100	I	RAI
	Vladivostok	200	RUS	R Netherlands
9860	Flevo	500	HOL	R Netherlands
	Talata Volondry	300	MDG	R Netherlands
	Palauig	250	PHL	R Veritas Asia
	Vladivostok	200	RUS	R Netherlands
	Sottens	500	SUI	Swiss R Intl
	Kiev	500	UKR	R Ukraine Intl
9865	Bonaire	250	ATN	R Netherlands
9870	Riyadh	500	ARS	BSKSA
	Moosbrunn	500	AUT	R Austria Intl
	Guam	100	GUM	KTWR
	Kimjae	250	KOR	R Korea
9875	Moosbrunn	500	AUT	R Austria Intl
	Arganda	100	E	REE
	Bocaue	100	PHL	FEBC
9880	Moosbrunn	500	AUT	R Austria Intl
	Kabd	500	KWT	R Kuwait
9885	Riyadh	500	ARS	BSKSA
	Mopeng Hill	100	BOT	VoA
	Sottens	500	SUR	Swiss R Intl
	Tashkent	20	UZB	R Tashkent
9890	Poro	250	PHL	VoA
9895	Flevo	500	HOL	R Netherlands
	Talata Volondry	300	MDG	R Netherlands
9900	Abis	250	EGY	R Cairo
9905	Wavre	250	BEL	R Vlaanderen Intl
	Sofia	100	BUL	R Sofia
9910	Aligarh	250	IND	AIR
	Madras	100	IND	AIR
9915	Rampisham	500	G	BBCWS
	Skelton	300	G	BBCWS
9920	Beijing	500	CHN	China R Intl
9925	Wavre	250	BEL	R Vlaanderen Intl
9930	Wavre	250	BEL	R Vlaanderen Intl
9935	Thessaloniki	35	GRC	ERT
9950	Abis	250	EGY	R Cairo Intl

Freq. [kHz]	Transmitter site	Power [kW]	Country	Station name
9950 (cont)	Aligarh	250	IND	AIR
	Adra	500	SYR	R Damascus
9955	Adra	500	SYR	R Damascus
	Taipei	100	TWN	VoFC/WYFR
	Miami	50	USA	R Miami Intl
9977	Pyongyang	400	KRE	R Pyongyang
9985	Birmingham	500	USA	WEWN
9990	Abis	250	EGY	R Cairo
9995	Adra	500	SYR	R Damascus
11000	Urumqui	50	CHN	CNR Taiwan 2
11335	Pyongyang	400	KRE	R Pyongyang
11375	Beijing	50	CHN	CNR Minorities
11402	Reykjavik	10	ISL	Icelandic BS
11445	Beijing	500	CHN	China R Intl
11500	Xian	500	CHN	China R Intl
11515	Beijing	500	CHN	China R Intl
11520	Karachi	50	PAK	R Pakistan
11550	Reykjavik	10	ISL	Icelandic BS
	Tunis	100	TUN	ERTT
	Taipei	50	TWN	WYFR
11560	Abis	250	EGY	R Cairo
11570	Islamabad	250	PAK	R Pakistan
11575	Beijing	120	CHN	China R Intl
11580	Guam	100	GUM	KTWR
	Greenville	250	USA	VoA
	Okeechobee	100	USA	WYRR
11585	Jerusalem	500	ISR	Kol Israel
11587	Jerusalem	500	ISR	Kol Israel
11590	Jerusalem	500	ISR	Kol Israel
11595	Thessaloniki	35	GRC	ERT
11600	Beijing	120	CHN	China R Intl
11603	Jerusalem	500	ISR	Kol Israel
11620	SM Galeria	500	CVA	Vatican R
	Bangalore	500	IND	AIR
11625	SM Galeria	500	CVA	Vatican R
11630	Sofia	500	BUL	R Sofia

Freq. [kHz]	Transmitter site	Power [kW]	Country	Station name
11640	SM Galeria	500	CVA	Vatican R
	Islamabad	250	PAK	R Pakistan
11645	Wavre	250	BEL	R Vlaanderen Intl
	Plovdiv	250	BUL	R Sofia
	Athens	100	GRC	Vo Greece
11650	Xian	120	CHN	China R Intl
	Guam	100	GUM	KTWR
	Saipan	100	MRA	KFBS
	Bocaue	50	PHL	FEBC
	Hoerby	350	S	R Sweden
	Bethany	250	USA	VoA
11655	Bonaire	250	ATN	R Netherlands
	Talata Volondry	300	MDG	R Netherlands
	Flevo	500	HOL	R Netherlands
11660	Bonaire	250	ATN	R Netherlands
	Carnarvon	300	AUS	R Australia
	Plovdiv	250	BUL	Domestic
	Beijing	120	CHN	China R Intl
	Allouis	500	F	RFI
	Guam	100	GUM	KTWR
11665	Abu Zaabal	250	EGY	R Cairo
	Guam	100	GUM	KTWR
	Mahe	100	SEY	FEBA
11670	Allouis	500	F	RFI
	Montsinery	500	GUF	RFI
11675	Jerusalem	500	ISR	Kol Israel
	Mahe	100	SEY	FEBA
11680	Rampisham	500	G	BBCWS
	Skelton	300	G	BBCWS
	Moyabi	500	GAB	RFI
	Montsinery	500	GUF	RFI
	Flevo	500	HOL	R Netherlands
	Pyongyang	200	KRE	R Pyongyang
	Greenville	250	USA	VoA
11685	Riyadh	500	ARS	BSKSA
	Moyabi	500	GAB	RFI
	Montsinery	500	GUF	RFI
11690	Beijing	120	CHN	Swiss R Intl
	Bocaue	50	PHL	FEBC
11695	Shepparton	100	AUS	R Australia
	Montsinery	500	GUF	China R Intl

Freq. [kHz]	Transmitter site	Power [kW]	Country	Station name
11695	Hoerby	350	S	R Sweden
(cont)	Birmingham	500	USA	WEWN
	Greenville	500	USA	VoA
11705	ST.MARIA	10	B	R TransAmerica
	DHAKA	250	BGD	R Bangladesh
	HUHHOT	50	CHN	China R Intl
	COLOMBO	35	CLN	VoA
	WERTACHTAL	500	D	DW
	ALLOUIS	500	F	RFI
	MOYABI	250	GAB/F	RFI
	MONTSINERY	500	GUF	RFI
	TOKYO YAMATA	300	J	RCI
	KUJANG	200	KRE	R Pyongyang
	SVEIO	500	NOR	R Norway Intl
	HOERBY	500	S	R Sweden
	ANKARA	250	TUR	TRT Vo Turkey
	KINGHISEPP	500	RUS	R Moscow
	SERPUKHOV	240	RUW	R Moscow
	TACHKENT	100	UZB	R Tashkent
	OKEECHOBEE	100	USA	WYFR
	Udorn	500	THA	VoA
11710	GRAL PACHECO	100	ARG	R Argentina al Exterior
	JEDDAH	50	ARS	BSKSA
	LINGSHI	50	CHN	China R Intl
	LIMASSOL	250	CYP/G	BBCWS
	NOBLEJAS	350	E/CHN	China R Intl
	FLEVO	500	HOL	R Netherlands
	REYKJAVIK	10	ISL	Icelandic B S
	BRIECH	500	MRC/USA	VoA
	ISLAMABAD	100	PAK	R Pakistan
	PALAUIG	250	PHL	R Veritas Asia
	MAHE	100	SEY	FEBA
	BICHKEK	100	RUS	R Moscow
	MOSKVA	250	RUS	R Moscow
	Brazzaville	100	COG	R National Congolaise
	Abu Dhabi	500	UAE	UAE R Abu Dhabi
11715	BOUCHAOUI	50	ALG	RTV Algerienne
	SACKVILLE	250	CAN	RCI/R Korea
	PERKARA	250	CLN	DW
	S.M.GALERIA	250	CVA	Vatican R
	WERTACHTAL	500	D/USA	RFE/RL
	NOBLEJAS	350	E	REE
	ABIS	250	EGY	R Cairo
	ATHINAI	100	GRC	Vo Greece

Freq. [kHz]	Transmitter site	Power [kW]	Country	Station name
11715	KAVALLA	250	GRC	VoA
(cont)	THESSALONIKI	35	GRC	ERT
	FLEVO	500	HOL	R Netherlands
	ALIGARH	250	IND	AIR
	DELHI	250	IND	AIR
	MEDAN	100	INS	RRI
	TOKYO YAMATA	300	J	RFI/NHK R Japan
	BAMAKO 1	50	MLI	China R Intl
	CYCLOPS	250	MLT	DW
	PORO	50	PHL	VoA
	LISBON	250	POR	VoA
	TULA	250	RUS	R Moscow
	Moosbrunn	300	AUT	RCI
11720	BRANDON	10	AUS	R Australia
	WAVRE	100	BEL	R Vlaanderen Intl
	SOFIA	500	BUL	R Sofia
	SANTIAGO	25	CHL	
	BEIJING	50	CHN	China R Intl
	PERKARA	250	CLN	DW
	HABANA	100	CUB	R Havana Cuba
	LIMASSOL	250	CYP/G	BBCWS
	MONTSINERY	500	GUF	RFI
	MEXICO	100	MEX	R Mexico
	MASIRAH	100	OMA/G	BBCWS
	PALAUIG	250	PHL	R Veritas Asia
	PORO	50	PHL	VoA
	ARMAVIR	100	RUS	R Moscow
	MOSKVA	240	RUS	R Ukraine Intl
	KINSHASA	10	ZAI	Zaire R
	Kvitsoy	500	NOR	R Norway Intl
11725	LAMPERTHEIM	100	D/USA	RFE/RL
	BIAK	300	INS	RRI
	KIMJAE	250	KOR	R Korea
	LISBON	250	POR	RFE/RL
	MAXOQUEIRA	500	POR	RFE/RL
	LVOV	1000	UKR	R Ukraine Intl
	KAZAN	100	RUS	R Moscow
	OKEECHOBEE	100	USA	WYFR
11730	ORCHA	20	BLR	Belarus R
	SACKVILLE	250	CAN	RCI
	KUNMING	50	CHN	China R Intl
	LIMASSOL	250	CYP/G	BBCWS
	NOBLEJAS	350	E	REE
	FLEVO	500	HOL	R Netherlands

Freq. [kHz]	Transmitter site	Power [kW]	Country	Station name
11730	DELHI	100	IND	AIR
(cont)	KVITSOY	500	NOR	R Norway Intl
	THUMRAIT	100	OMA	R Oman
	TINANG	250	PHL	VoA
	MAHE	250	SEY/G	BBCWS
	SFAX	100	TUN	Tunis R
	KALATCH	500	RUS	R Moscow
	KHABAROVSK	100	RUS	R Moscow
	KICHINEV	500	MDA	R Moscow
	Jeddah	500	ARS	BSKSA
	Tokyo Yamata	300	J	RCI
11735	SACKVILLE	250	CAN	RCI
	PERKARA	250	CLN	DW
	JUELICH	100	D	DW
	QUITO	500	EQA	HCJB
	SKELTON	300	G	VoA
	DELHI	250	IND	AIR
	UJUNGPANDANG	100	INS	RRI
	REYKJAVIK	10	ISL	Icelandic B S
	TOKYO YAMATA	300	J	NHK R Japan
	KUJANG	400	KRE	R Pyongyang
	MT.CARLO	500	MCO	TWR
	FREDRIKSTAD	350	NOR	R Norway Intl
	KVITSOY	500	NOR	R Norway Intl
	RANGITAIKI	100	NZL	R New Zealand Intl
	PORO	100	PHL	VoA
	TINANG	250	PHL	Voa
	ANKARA	250	TUR	TRT Vo Turkey
	MONTEVIDEO	5	URG	R Oriental
	SERPUKHOV	100	RUS	R Moscow
	BIRMINGHAM	500	USA	WEWN
	BELGRADE	100	YUG	R Yugoslavia
	Cylcops	250	MLT	DW
11740	RIYADH	500	ARS	BSKSA
	BEIJING	50	CHN	CNR 2
	S.M.GALERIA	100	CVA	Vatican R
	WERTACHTAL	500	D	DW
	NOBLEJAS	350	E	REE
	SKELTON	300	G	VoA
	KAVALLA	250	GRC	VoA
	ABU GHRAIB	250	IRQ	R Baghdad
	KIMJAE	100	KOR	R Korea
	PYONGYANG	200	KRE	R Pyongyang
	MEXICO	5	MEX	R Mexico

Freq. [kHz]	Transmitter site	Power [kW]	Country	Station name
11740	BUCURESTI	250	ROU	R Romania Intl
(cont)	KIGALI	250	RRW	DW
	KRANJI	250	SNG/G	BBCWS
	MANZINI	25	SWZ	TWR
	IRKUTSK	50	RUS	Domestic
	OKEECHOBEE	100	USA	WYFR
11745	LUSHNJA	100	ALB	R Tirana
	RIYADH	500	ARS	BSKSA
	BEIJING	120	CHN	China R Intl
	BANGALORE	500	IND	AIR
	JAYAPURA	100	INS	RRI
	REYKJAVIK	10	ISL	Icelandic B S
	KVITSOY	500	NOR	R Norway Intl
	ADRA	500	SYR	Damascus R
	VINNITSA	500	UKR	R Ukraine Intl
	MOSKVA	240	RUS	R Moscow
	S.PETERSBURG	200	RUS	R Moscow
	Meyerton	500	AFS	Channel Africa
	Brasilia	250	B	R Bras
	Taipei	100	TWN	VoFC
11750	ASCENSION	250	ASC	BBCWS
	XIAN	150	CHN	China R Intl
	KAVALLA	250	GRC	VoA
	JERUSALEM	300	ISR	Kol Israel
	TOKYO	10	J/USA	R Tanpa
	BRIECH	500	MRC/USA	VoA
	MASIRAH	100	OMA/G	BBCWS
	TINANG	250	PHL	VoA
	KRANJI	250	SNG/G	BBCWS
	ARMAVIR	240	RUS	R Moscow
	KAZAN	100	RUS	R Moscow
	TBILISI	100	GEO	R Moscow
	Ankara	250	TUR	TRT Vo Turkey
11755	BEIJING	240	CHN	China R Intl
	PORI	500	FIN	YLE R Finland
	WOOFFERTON	300	G	VoA
	JAKARTA	100	INS	RRI
	TRIPOLI	500	LBY	Libya Jamahiriyah B
	JIGULEVSK	100	RUS	R Moscow
	NOVOSIBIRSK	240	RUS	R Moscow
	S.PETERSBURG	240	RUS	R Moscow
	TCHITA	100	RUS	R Moscow
	BELGRADE	500	YUG	R Yugoslavia

Freq. [kHz]	Transmitter site	Power [kW]	Country	Station name
11760	HABANA	100	CUB	R Havana Cuba
	LIMASSOL	250	CYP/G	BBCWS
	RAMPISHAM	500	G	BBCWS
	WOOFFERTON	250	G	BBCWS
	DELHI	250	IND	AIR
	JAKARTA	100	INS	RRI
	TOKYO YAMATA	300	J	NHK R Japan
	MT.CARLO	500	MCO	TWR
	MASIRAH	100	OMA/G	BBCWS
	ISLAMABAD	250	PAK	R Pakistan
	TINANG	250	PHL	VoA
	ARMAVIR	1000	RUS	R Moscow
	KRASNOIARSK	20	RUS	Domestic
	SAMARA	150	RUS	R Moscow
	TBILISI	240	GEO	R Moscow
	VOLGOGRAD	20	RUS	R Vedo
11765	ASCENSION	250	ASC	BBCWS
	CURITIBA	10	B	
	SOFIA	250	BUL	R Sofia
	SHIJIAZHUANG	500	CHN	China R Intl
	JUELICH	100	D	DW
	WERTACHTAL	500	D	DW
	REYKJAVIK	10	ISL	Icelandic B S
	TOKYO YAMATA	300	J	NHK R Japan
	DUCHANBE	240	TAD	R Moscow
	KAZAN	100	RUS	R Moscow
	KENGA	240	RUS	R Moscow
11770	MEYERTON	500	AFS	Channel Africa
	DHAKA	250	BGD	R Bangladesh
	SANTIAGO	25	CHL	
	BEIJING	50	CHN	China R
	ALLOUIS	100	F	RFI
	KAVALLA	250	GRC	VoA
	ALIGARH	250	IND	AIR
	DELHI	100	IND	AIR
	MEXICO	10	MEX	R Mexico
	IKORODU	500	NIG	R Nigeria
	LISBON	250	POR	RFE/RL
	ARMAVIR	1000	RUS	R Moscow
	EKATERINBURG	20	RUS	Kudymkar
	KHABAROVSK	200	RUS	R Moscow
	OKEECHOBEE	100	USA	WYFR
	ADEN	100	YEM	Yemen Arab R

Freq. [kHz]	Transmitter site	Power [kW]	Country	Station name
11775	BEIJING	120	CHN	China R Intl
	LIMASSOL	100	CYP/G	BBCWS
	NOBLEJAS	350	E	REE
	BUCURESTI	250	ROU	R Romania Intl/ R Moldova
	DELANO	250	USA	VoA
	Ankara	250	TUR	TRT Vo Turkey
	Taipei	300	TWN	CBS 2
11780	RIYADH	500	ARS	BSKSA
	WIEN	500	AUT	R Austria Intl
	BRASILIA	250	B	R Nacional da Amazonia
	KUNMING	50	CHN	China R Intl
	RAMPISHAM	500	G	BBCWS
	KAVALLA	250	GRC	VoA
	REYKJAVIK	10	ISL	Icelandic B S
	KUJANG	200	KRE	R Pyongyang
	FREDRIKSTAD	350	NOR	R Norway Intl
	KAZAN	100	RUS	R Moscow
	TBILISI	240	GEO	R Ukraine Intl
	Kamalabad	500	IRN	IRIB
11785	ASCENSION	250	ASC	BBCWS
	BRASILIA	250	B	R Bras
	PT.ALEGRE	8	B	R Guaiba
	PERKARA	250	CLN	DW
	JUELICH	100	D	DW
	NAUEN	500	D	DW
	ABU ZAABAL	100	EGY	R Cairo
	MOYABI	500	GAB	RFI
	ALIGARH	250	IND	AIR
	JAKARTA	100	INS	RRI
	REYKJAVIK	10	ISL	Icelandic B S
	CYCLOPS	250	MLT	DW
	AL KHAISAH	250	QAT	Qatar B S
	KIGALI	250	RRW	DW
	ALMA ATA	100	KAZ	R Alma Ata
	JIGULEVSK	100	RUS	R Moscow
	MOSKVA	250	RUS	R Moscow
	Udorn	500	THA	VoA
11790	SANTIAGO	25	CHL	
	BEIJING	50	CHN	China R Intl
	ARGANDA	100	E	REE
	ALLOUIS	100	F	RFI
	SKELTON	300	G	BBCWS

Freq. [kHz]	Transmitter site	Power [kW]	Country	Station name
11790	MONTSINERY	500	GUF	RFI
(cont)	ALIGARH	250	IND	AIR
	PADANG CERMIN	250	INS	RRI
	KAMALABAD	500	IRN	IRIB
	TRIPOLI	500	LBY	Libya Jamahiriyah B
	BAMAKO 1	50	MLI	China R Intl
	ULAN BATOR	50	MNG	R Ulan Bator
	ISLAMABAD	250	PAK	R Pakistan
	PALAUIG	250	PHL	R Veritas Asia
	BUCURESTI	250	ROU	R Romania Intl
	MAHE	75	SEY	FEBA
	BLAGOVECHTCHEN	100	RUS	R Moscow
	KICHINEV	1000	MDA	R Moscow
	NOBLESVILLE	100	USA	WHRI
11795	ANTIGUA	250	ATG	DW
	XIAN	150	CHN	China R Intl
	JUELICH	100	D	DW
	NAUEN	500	D	DW
	WERTACHTAL	500	D	DW
	REYKJAVIK	10	ISL	Icelandic B S
	TRIPOLI	500	LBY	Libya Jamahiriyah B
	SINES	250	POR	RFE/RL
	KIGALI	250	RRW	DW
	UDORN	250	THA/USA	VoA
	DUBAI	300	UAE	UAE R Dubai
	KENGA	1000	RUS	R Moscow
	TBILISI	100	GEO	R Moscow
	KINSHASA	10	ZAI	Zaire BC
11800	SHEPPARTON	100	AUS	R Australia
	EKALA	100	CLN	SLBC
	HABANA	500	CUB	R Havana Cuba
	GEDJA	100	ETH	Vo Ethiopia
	MOYABI	250	GAB/F	RFI
	EJURA	250	GHA	Ghana BC
	ROMA	100	I	RAI
	JIGULEVSK	240	RUS	R Moscow
	KHABAROVSK	240	RUS	R Moscow
	MOSKVA	100	RUS	R Moscow
11805	RIO DE JANEIRO	10	B	R Globo
	BAOJI	50	CHN	China R Intl
	ALLOUIS	100	F	RFI
	WOOFFERTON	300	G	VoA
	KAVALLA	250	GRC	VoA
	AGANA	100	GUM	KTWR

Freq. [kHz]	Transmitter site	Power [kW]	Country	Station name
11805	PT.AU PRINCE	100	HTI	
(cont)	BANGALORE	500	IND	AIR
	SURABAJA	50	INS	RRI
	REYKJAVIK	10	ISL	Icelandic B S
	KIMJAE	100	KOR	R Korea
	KUJANG	200	KRE	R Pyongyang
	BRIECH	500	MRC/USA	VoA
	TINANG	250	PHL	VoA
	LISBON	250	POR	VoA
	UDORN	250	THA/USA	VoA
	BICHKEK	100	RUS	R Moscow
	KALATCH	1000	RUS	R Moscow
	BELGRADE	500	YUG	R Yugoslavia
	Mahe	100	SEY	FEBA
	Salah el Deen	500	IRQ	R Baghdad
11810	ANTIGUA	250	ATG	DW
	BRASILIA	250	B/D	DW
	NAUEN	500	D	DW
	ATHINAI	100	GRC	Vo Greece
	DELHI	100	IND	AIR
	AL KARANAH	500	JOR	R Jordan
	KIMJAE	250	KOR	R Korea
	ISLAMABAD	250	PAK	R Pakistan
	BUCURESTI	250	ROU	R Romania Intl
	KIGALI	250	RRW	DW
	MAHE	75	SEY	FEBA
	ARMAVIR	240	RUS	R Moscow
	TACHKENT	240	UZB	R Moscow
	Salah el Deen	500	IRQ	R Baghdad
11815	BONAIRE TWR	100	ATN	R Netherlands
	GOIANIA	8	B	R Brasil Central
	CARIARI	100	CTR/E	REE
	HOLZKIRCHEN	250	D/USA	RFE/RL
	LAMPERTHEIM	100	D/USA	RFE/RL
	NOBLEJAS	350	E	REE
	RAMPISHAM	500	G	BBCWS
	DELHI	100	IND	AIR
	PALEMBANG	100	IND	AIR
	SALAH EL DEEN	500	IRQ	R Baghdad
	TOKYO YAMATA	300	J	NHK R Japan
	TRIPOLI	500	LBY	Libya Jamahiriyah B
	WARSZAWA	100	POL	Polish R Warsaw
	LISBON	250	POR	RFE/RL
	MAXOQUEIRA	500	POR	RFE/RL

Freq. [kHz]	Transmitter site	Power [kW]	Country	Station name
11815	DUCHANBE	100	TAD	R Dushanbe
(cont)	KHABAROVSK	100	RUS	R Moscow
	TBILISI	100	GEO	R Moscow
	Xian	120	CHN	China R Intl
11820	JEDDAH	50	ARS	BSKSA
	ASCENSION	250	ASC	BBCWS
	DHAKA	100	BGD	R Bangladesh
	LHASA	50	CHN	China R Intl
	NOBLEJAS	350	E	REE
	ATHINAI	100	GRC	Vo Greece
	KAVALLA	250	GRC	VoA
	TSANG TSUI	250	HKG/G	BBCWS
	AL KARANAH	500	JOR	R Jordan
	MAPUTO	120	MOZ	Em Nacional
	PALAUIG	250	PHL	R Veritas Asia
	PORO	50	PHL	VoA
	TINANG	250	PHL	VoA
	AL KHAISAH	250	QAT	Qatar B S
	HOERBY	500	S	R Sweden
	BICHKEK	240	RUS	R Moscow
	MOSKVA	500	RUS	R Moscow
	BIRMINGHAM	500	USA	WEWN
11825	LUSHNJA	100	ALB	R Tirana
	ORCHA	20	BLR	Belarus R
	JUELICH	100	D	DW
	WERTACHTAL	500	D	DW
	PLAYA DE PALS	250	E	REE
	WOOFFERTON	300	G	VoA
	BIAK	300	INS	RRI
	REYKJAVIK	10	ISL	Icelandic B S
	PAPEETE	20	OCE	RFO
	LISBON	250	POR	RFE/RL
	ALMA ATA	20	KAZ	R Alma Ata
	KENGA	100	RUS	R Moscow
	Playa de Pals	300	E	REE
	Taipei	100	TWN	VoFC
11830	GOIANIA	10	B	R Anhanguera
	BEIJING	50	CHN	China R Intl
	S.M.GALERIA	500	CVA	Vatican R
	LIMASSOL	250	CYP/G	BBCWS
	ALIGARH	250	IND	AIR
	BOMBAY	100	IND	AIR
	DELHI	100	IND	AIR
	KUJANG	200	KRE	R Pyongyang

Freq. [kHz]	Transmitter site	Power [kW]	Country	Station name
11830	BUCURESTI	250	ROU	R Romania Intl
(cont)	SFAX	100	TUN	ERTT
	EKATERINBURG	240	RUS	R Moscow
	MOSKVA	250	RUS	R Moscow
	OKEECHOBEE	100	USA	WYFR/VoFC
	Bethany	250	USA	Vo OAS
11835	LUSHNJA	100	ALB	R Tirana
	JEDDAH	50	ARS	BSKSA
	BONAIRE RNW	250	ATN	R Netherlands
	EKALA	35	CLN	SLBC
	WERTACHTAL	500	D/USA	RFE/RL
	QUITO	500	EQA	HCJB
	ALLOUIS	100	F	RFI
	MOYABI	500	GAB/J	NHK R Japan
	KAVALLA	250	GRC	VoA
	MAPUTO	25	MOZ	Em Nacional
	TINANG	250	PHL	VoA
	KIGALI	250	RRW	DW
	MONTEVIDEO	5	URG	R El Espectador
	JIGULEVSK	250	RUS	R Moscow
	BETHANY	250	USA	VoA
	GREENVILLE	500	USA	VoA
	BELGRADE	500	YUG	R Yugoslavia
11840	LUSHNJA	100	ALB	R Tirana
	ORCHA	20	BLR	Belarus R
	SACKVILLE	250	CAN	China R Intl
	KUNMING	120	CHN	China R Intl
	EKALA	300	CLN	NHK R Japan
	LIMASSOL	250	CYP/G	BBCWS
	WERTACHTAL	500	D/USA	RFE/RL
	NOBLEJAS	350	E	REE
	TOKYO YAMATA	300	J	NHK R Japan
	TINANG	250	PHL	VoA
	WARSZAWA	100	POL	Polish R Warsaw
	S.GABRIEL	100	POR	R Portugal
	BUCURESTI	250	ROU	R Romania Intl
	IUJNSAKHALINSK	50	RUS	Domestic
	KENGA	100	RUS	Domestic
	KICHINEV	500	MDA	R Ukraine Intl
	Mahe	50	SEY	FEBA
11845	SACKVILLE	100	CAN	RCI
	KUNMING	120	CHN	China R Intl
	LIMASSOL	250	CYP/G	BBCWS
	QUITO	500	EQA	HCJB

Freq. [kHz]	Transmitter site	Power [kW]	Country	Station name
11845	ALLOUIS	100	F	RFI
(cont)	RAMPISHAM	500	G	BBCWS
	WOOFFERTON	300	G	VoA
	BANDUNG	50	INS	RRI
	KUJANG	200	KRE	R Pyongyang
	BOCAUE	100	PHL	FEBC
	MONTEVIDEO	10	URG	
	ARMAVIR	240	RUS	R Moscow
	SERPUKHOV	100	RUS	R Moscow
11850	DHAKA	250	BGD	R Bangladesh
	NOBLEJAS	350	E	REE
	RAMPISHAM	500	G	BBCWS
	EJURA	250	GHA	Ghana B S
	DELHI	100	IND	AIR
	KIMJAE	250	KOR	R Korea
	ULAN BATOR	250	MNG	R Ulan Bator
	MASIRAH	100	OMA/G	BBCWS
	ISLAMABAD	100	PAK	R Pakistan
	BOCAUE	100	PHL	FEBC
	ASUNCION	5	PRG	
	KRANJI	250	SNG/G	BBCWS
	KALATCH	240	RUS	R Moscow
	KENGA	240	RUS	R Moscow
	KHABAROVSK	100	RUS	R Moscow
	RIAZAN	1000	RUS	R Moscow
	VOLGOGRAD	240	RUS	R Moscow
	Sveio	500	NOR	R Norway Intl
11855	CARNARVON	250	AUS	R Australia
	APARECIDA	1	B	R Aparecida
	SACKVILLE	250	CAN	RCI
	JINHUA	500	CHN	China R Intl
	WOOFFERTON	300	G	VoA
	DELHI	100	IND	AIR
	UJUNGPANDANG	50	IND	AIR
	JERUSALEM	300	ISR	Kol Israel
	KUJANG	200	KRE	R Pyongyang
	BRIECH	500	MRC/USA	VoA
	LISBON	250	POR	VoA
	NOVOSIBIRSK	240	RUS	R Moscow
	SAMARA	20	RUS	R Moscow
	OKEECHOBEE	100	USA	WYFR
	Udorn	500	THA	VoA
11860	ASCENSION	250	ASC	BBCWS
	SOFIA	500	BUL	R Sofia

Freq. [kHz]	Transmitter site	Power [kW]	Country	Station name
11860	HABANA	100	CUB	R Havana Cuba
(cont)	ALIGARH	250	IND	AIR
	DELHI	100	IND	AIR
	AHWAZ	500	IRN	IRIB
	REYKJAVIK	10	ISL	Icelandic B S
	TOKYO YAMATA	300	J	NHK R Japan
	KIMJAE	250	KOR	R Korea
	SVEIO	500	NOR	R Norway Intl
	MAHE	250	SEY/G	BBCWS
	KRANJI	250	SNG/G	NHK R Japan
	MONTEVIDEO	10	URG	
	KRASNOIARSK	100	RUS	R Moscow
	NIJNIINOVGOROD	1000	RUS	R Moscow
	Salah el Deen	500	IRQ	R Baghdad
	Taipei	250	TWN	VoFC
11865	ANTIGUA	250	ATG	DW
	BONAIRE TWR	50	ATN	R Netherlands
	HUHHOT	50	CHN	China R Intl
	PERKARA	250	CLN	DW
	JUELICH	100	D	DW
	NAUEN	500	D	DW
	WERTACHTAL	500	D	DW
	HOLZKIRCHEN	250	D/USA	RFE/RL
	LAMPERTHEIM	100	D/USA	RFE/RL
	RAMPISHAM	500	G	BBCWS
	WOOFFERTON	250	G	VoA
	FLEVO	500	HOL	R Netherlands
	TRIPOLI	500	LBY	Libya Jamahiriyah B
	CYCLOPS	250	MLT	DW
	FREDRIKSTAD	350	NOR	R Norway Intl
	BOCAUE	50	PHL	FEBC
	TINANG	250	PHL	VoA
	LISBON	250	POR	RFE/RL
	SINES	250	POR	RFE/RL
	DAKAR	100	SEN	Senegal R
	KRANJI	250	SNG/G	BBCWS
	LUBUMBASHI	100	ZAI	Zaire BS
11870	SOFIA	500	BUL	R Sofia
	KUNMING	50	CHN	China R Intl
	NOBLEJAS	350	E	REE
	DELHI	100	IND	AIR
	IBA	100	PHL	VoA
	TINANG	250	PHL	VoA
	IRKUTSK	1000	RUS	R Moscow

Freq. [kHz]	Transmitter site	Power [kW]	Country	Station name
11870	KHABAROVSK	240	RUS	R Moscow
(cont)	SERPUKHOV	250	RUS	R Moscow
	TACHKENT	50	UZB	R Tashkent
	BELGRADE	500	YUG	R Yugoslavia
11875	SACKVILLE	100	CAN	RCI
	HABANA	250	CUB	R Havana Cuba
	BIBLIS	100	D/USA	RFE/RL
	LAMPERTHEIM	100	D/USA	RFE/RL
	ABIS	250	EGY	R Cairo
	WOOFFERTON	300	G	VoA
	KAVALLA	250	GRC	VoA
	DELHI	100	IND	AIR
	SALAH EL DEEN	500	IRQ	R Baghdad
	TOKYO YAMATA	300	J	NHK R Japan
	BAMAKO 1	50	MLI	China R Intl
	BRIECH	500	MRC/USA	VoA
	KIGALI	250	RRW	DW
	KALATCH	1000	RUS	R Moscow
	KHABAROVSK	100	RUS	R Moscow
	Ankara	250	TUR	TRT Vo Turkey
11880	ASCENSION	250	ASC	BBCWS
	BRANDON	10	AUS	R Australia
	SHEPPARTON	100	AUS	R Australia
	XIAN	150	CHN	China R Intl
	CARIARI	100	CTR/E	REE
	NOBLEJAS	350	E	REE
	ALLOUIS	100	F	RFI
	MONTSINERY	500	GUF	RFI
	ROMA	100	I	RAI
	DELHI	250	IND	AIR
	TOKYO YAMATA	100	J	NHK R Japan
	MEXICO	5	MEX	R Mexico
	FREDRIKSTAD	350	NOR	R Norway Intl
	ARMAVIR	240	RUS	R Moscow
	DUCHANBE	250	TJK	R Moscow
	EKATERINBURG	240	RUS	R Moscow
	MOSKVA	250	RUS	R Moscow
	LUSAKA	50	ZMB	Zambia R
11885	BONAIRE TWR	100	ATN	R Netherlands
	HOLZKIRCHEN	250	D/USA	RFE/RL
	PLAYA DE PALS	500	E	RFE/RL
	UJUNGPANDANG	250	INS	RRI
	TOKYO YAMATA	300	J	NHK R Japan
	KAJANG	100	MLA	Vo Malaysia

Freq. [kHz]	Transmitter site	Power [kW]	Country	Station name
11885	BUCURESTI	250	ROU	R Romania Intl
(cont)	ABU DHABI	500	UAE	UAE R Abu Dhabi
	MONTEVIDEO	10	URG	
	DUCHANBE	240	TJK	R Moscow
	Taipei	100	TWN	CBS 1
	Sackville	250	CAN	RCI
	Okeechobee	100	USA	WYFR
11890	DHAKA	100	BGD	R Bangladesh
	SANTIAGO	100	CHL	
	BAODING	120	CHN	China R Intl
	BEIJING	120	CHN	China R Intl
	NOBLEJAS	350	E	REE
	SEEB	100	OMA	R Oman
	THUMRAIT	100	OMA	R Oman
	S.GABRIEL	100	POR	R Portugal
	ARMAVIR	100	RUS	R Moscow
	BICHKEK	240	RUS	R Moscow
	RIAZAN	240	RUS	R Moscow
	SAMARA	100	RUS	R Moscow
	GREENVILLE	250	USA	VoA
11895	PT.ALEGRE	1	B	
	HOLZKIRCHEN	250	D/USA	RFE/RL
	DELHI	100	IND	AIR
	YOGYAKARTA	100	INS	RRI
	TINANG	250	PHL	VoA
	MAXOQUEIRA	500	POR	RFE/RL
	ANKARA	250	TUR	TRT VoTurkey
	EKATERINBURG	240	RUS	R Moscow
	GREENVILLE	500	USA	VoA
	Flevo	500	HOL	R Netherlands
	Tehran	500	IRN	IRIB
11900	MEYERTON	250	AFS	Channel Africa
	PORI	500	FIN	YLE R Finland
	REYKJAVIK	10	ISL	Icelandic B S
	KUJANG	200	KRE	R Pyongyang
	RANGITAIKI	100	NZL	R New Zealand Intl
	MONTEVIDEO	20	URG	
	ARMAVIR	240	RUS	R Moscow
	DUCHANBE	500	TJK	R Dushanbe
	KAZAN	100	RUS	R Moscow
	KOMSOMOLSKAMUR	100	RUS	R Moscow
	PETROPAVLO KAM	100	RUS	R Moscow
	Flevo	500	HOL	R Netherlands

Freq. [kHz]	Transmitter site	Power [kW]	Country	Station name
11905	SACKVILLE	100	CAN	RCI
	BAODING	120	CHN	China R Intl
	BEIJING	120	CHN	China R Intl
	JUELICH	100	D	DW
	NAUEN	500	D	DW
	BIBLIS	100	D/USA	RFE/RL
	LAMPERTHEIM	100	D/USA	RFE/RL
	RAMPISHAM	500	G	BBCWS
	ROMA	100	I	RAI
	KUJANG	200	KRE	R Pyongyang
	LISBON	250	POR	RFE/RL
	SINES	250	POR	RFE/RL
	BANGKOK	50	THA	R Thailand
	BICHKEK	240	RUS	R Moscow
	OMSK	240	RUS	R Moscow
	Curitiba	10	B	R Universo
	Udorn	500	THA	VoA
11910	DHAKA	250	BGD	R Bangladesh
	XIAN	120	CHN	REE/RFI
	HABANA	50	CUB	R Havana Cuba
	QUITO	250	EQA	HCJB
	DIOSD	100	HNG	R Budapest
	JASZBERENY	250	HNG	R Budapest
	ROMA	100	I	RAI
	BANGALORE	500	IND	AIR
	KAMALABAD	500	IRN	IRIB
	TOKYO YAMATA	300	J	NHK R Japan
	HOERBY	500	S	R Sweden
	ADRA	500	SYR	R Damascus
	MOSKVA	100	RUS	R Moscow
	TBILISI	100	GEO	R Moscow
	Shepparton	100	AUS	R Australia
11915	PT.ALEGRE	8	B	R Gaucha
	XIAN	150	CHN	China R Intl
	JUELICH	100	D	DW
	WERTACHTAL	500	D	DW
	WOOFFERTON	300	G	VoA
	TOKYO YAMATA	100	J	NHK R Japan
	KIMJAE	250	KOR	R Korea
	BRIECH	500	MRC/USA	VoA
	MAXOQUEIRA	500	POR	RFE/RL
	SINES	250	POR	RFE/RL
	CONCEPCION	100	PRG	
	LIMA	40	PRU	

Freq. [kHz]	Transmitter site	Power [kW]	Country	Station name
11915	BLAGOVECHTCHEN	240	RUS	R Moscow
(cont)	PETROPAVLO KAM	100	RUS	R Moscow
	GREENVILLE	250	USA	VoA
	Okeechobee	100	USA	WYFR/VoFC
11920	ABIDJAN	500	CTI	Radiodiff Ivorienne
	ARGANDA	100	E	REE
	NOBLEJAS	350	E	REE
	DELHI	50	IND	AIR
	TANGER	50	MRC	RTV Marocaine
	KVITSOY	500	NOR	R Norway Intl
	TINANG	250	PHL	VoA
	KRANJI	100	SNG/G	BBCWS
	ARMAVIR	500	RUS	R Moscow
	KAZAN	240	RUS	R Moscow
	NOVOSIBIRSK	240	RUS	R Moscow
11925	WIEN	300	AUT	R Austria Intl
	S.PAULO	10	B	R Bandeirantes
	BEIJING	50	CHN	China R intl
	BIBLIS	100	D/USA	RFE/RL
	QUITO	500	EQA	HCJB
	SKELTON	300	G	BBCWS
	WOOFFERTON	300	G	VoA
	MOYABI	500	GAB/J	NHK R Japan
	ALIGARH	250	IND	AIR
	CYCLOPS	250	MLT	Vo Mediterranean
	BRIECH	500	MRC/USA	VoA
	FREDRIKSTAD	350	NOR	R Norway Intl
	SVEIO	500	NOR	R Norway Intl
	TINANG	250	PHL	Voa
	MAXOQUEIRA	500	POR	RFE/RL
	MAHE	100	SEY	FEBA
	ADRA	500	SYR	R Damascus
	ANKARA	250	TUR	TRT Vo Turkey
	KALININGRAD	150	RUS	R Moscow
	MOSKVA	100	RUS	R Moscow
	BETHANY	250	USA	VoA
11930	BONAIRE TWR	100	ATN	R Netherlands
	ALLOUIS	500	F	RFI
	MOYABI	250	GAB/F	RFI
	ZAHEDAN	500	IRN	IRIB
	KUJANG	200	KRE	R Pyongyang
	PORO	50	PHL	VoA
	TINANG	250	PHL	VoA
	IAKUTSK	20	RUS	Domestic

Freq. [kHz]	Transmitter site	Power [kW]	Country	Station name
11930	KAZAN	240	RUS	R Moscow
(cont)	KINGHISEPP	200	RUS	R Moscow
	GREENVILLE	250	USA	VoA/R Marti
	Mahe	100	SEY	FEBA
	Sveio	500	NOR	R Norway Intl
11935	RIYADH	500	ARS	BSKSA
	CURITIBA	8	B	
	S.M.GALERIA	250	CVA	Vatican R
	PLAYA DE PALS	250	E	REE
	SKELTON	300	G	RCI
	FLEVO	500	HOL	R Netherlands
	DELHI	250	IND	AIR
	BANDJARMASIN	100	INS	RRI
	KIMJAE	250	KOR	R Korea
	LISBON	250	POR	RFE/RL
	GREENVILLE	250	USA	VoA
11940	SACKVILLE	250	CAN	RCI
	ALIGARH	250	IND	AIR
	AL KARANAH	500	JOR	R Jordan
	LANCERS	100	LSO/G	BBCWS
	KARACHI	50	PAK	R Pakistan
	ENCARNACION	5	PRG	
	BUCURESTI	250	ROU	R Romania Intl
	TCHITA	1000	RUS	R Moscow
	Singapore	50	SNH	Radio 1
	Meyerton	500	AFS	BBCWS
11945	BAODING	240	CHN	China R Intl
	XIAN	150	CHN	China R Intl
	JUELICH	100	D	DW
	WERTACHTAL	500	D	DW
	NOBLEJAS	350	E	REE
	TSANG TSUI	250	HKG/G	BBCWS
	FLEVO	500	HOL	R Netherlands
	KIMJAE	100	KOR	R Korea
	KUJANG	400	KRE	R Pyongyang
	MALOLOS	50	PHL	VoA
	LISBON	250	POR	RFE/RL
	ENCARNACION	5	PRG	
	ANKARA	250	TUR	TRT Vo Turkey
	DUBAI	300	UAE	UAE R Dubai
	EREVAN	1000	ARM	R Moscow
	KHABAROVSK	20	RUS	Tatar R
	DELANO	250	USA	VoA
	Antigua	250	ATG	DW

Freq. [kHz]	Transmitter site	Power [kW]	Country	Station name
11950	JEDDAH	50	ARS	BSKSA
	RIO DE JANEIRO	8	B	R Mec
	LHASA	15	CHN	Xizang Tibetan
	HABANA	250	CUB	R Havana Cuba
	FLEVO	500	HOL	R Netherlands
	MALOLOS	50	PHL	VoA
	ALMA ATA	100	KAZ	Kazakh R
	ARMAVIR	100	RUS	R Moscow
11955	LUANDA	100	AGL	R Nacional
	SACKVILLE	100	CAN	RCI
	XIAN	150	CHN	China R Intl
	LIMASSOL	250	CYP/G	BBCWS
	ALLOUIS	500	F	RFI
	RAMPISHAM	500	G	BBCWS
	MOYABI	250	GAB/F	RFI
	KAVALLA	250	GRC	VoA
	MONTSINERY	500	GUF	RFI
	TOKYO YAMATA	300	J	RCI
	AL KARANAH	500	JOR	R Jordan
	MASIRAH	100	OMA/G	BBCWS
	KRANJI	250	SNG/G	BBCWS
	ANKARA	250	TUR	TRT Vo Turkey
	DUBAI	300	UAE	UAE R Dubai
	MONTEVIDEO	10	URG	
11960	WAVRE	100	BEL	R Vlaanderen Intl
	ORCHA	200	BLR	Belarus R
	BEIJING	50	CHN	China R Intl
	QUITO	100	EQA	HCJB
	BANGALORE	500	IND	AIR
	JERUSALEM	300	ISR	Kol Israel
	BAMAKO 1	50	MLI	Radiodiff Malienne
	ARMAVIR	100	RUS	R Moscow
	EREVAN	100	ARM	R Moscow
	KRASNOIARSK	100	RUS	R Moscow
	SERPUKHOV	240	RUS	R Moscow
11965	RIYADH	500	ARS	BSKSA
	S.PAULO	8	B	R Record
	PERKARA	250	CLN	DW
	WERTACHTAL	500	D	RCI
	ALLOUIS	500	F	RFI
	MONTSINERY	500	GUF	RFI
	CONAKRY	100	GUI	Radiodiff Guineenne
	JAYAPURA	100	INS	RRI
	CYCLOPS	250	MLT	DW

Freq. [kHz]	Transmitter site	Power [kW]	Country	Station name
11965 (cont)	KARACHI	50	PAK	R Pakistan
	TINANG	250	PHL	VoA
	KIGALI	250	RRW	DW
	ARMAVIR	100	RUS	R Moscow
	KALININGRAD	100	RUS	R Moscow
	KAZAN	100	RUS	R Moscow
	TACHKENT	100	UZB	R Tashkent
	DELANO	250	USA	VoA
	Moepeng Hill	100	BOT	VoA
11970	BEIJING	50	CHN	China R Intl
	HABANA	100	CUB	R Havana Cuba
	LAMPERTHEIM	100	D/USA	RFE/RL
	PLAYA DE PALS	250	E	RFE/RL
	ALLOUIS	500	F	RFI
	MONTSINERY	500	GUF	RFI
	DELHI	100	IND	AIR
	KATHMANDU	100	NPL	R Nepal
	MAXOQUEIRA	500	POR	RFE/RL
	BUCURESTI	250	ROU	R Romania Intl
	ABU DHABI	500	UAE	UAE R Abu Dhabi
	KENGA	240	RUS	R Moscow
	RIAZAN	150	RUS	KNLS
	OKEECHOBEE	100	USA	WYFR
11975	Abis	250	EGY	R Cairo
	Allouis	500	F	RFI
	Tashkent	250	UZB	R Tashkent
11980	Xian	240	CHN	China R Intl
	Kabd	500	KWT	R Kuwait
11990	Abis	250	EGY	R Cairo
	Kabd	500	KWT	R Kuwait
	Litomysl	100	SVK	Slovak R Intl/R Prague
11995	Allouis	500	F	RFI
	Moyabi	500	GAB	RFI
	Montsinery	500	GUF	RFI
	Bocaue	100	PHL	FEBC
	Tinang	250	PHL	VoA
12000	Ekaterinburg	200	RUS	Domestic/external
12005	Tunis	100	TUN	ERTT
12010	Yerevan	250	ARM	R Moscow
12015	Moyabi	500	GAB	RFI
	Ulan Bator	250	MNG	R Ulan Bator

Freq. [kHz]	Transmitter site	Power [kW]	Country	Station name
12020	Moscow	250	RUS	R Moscow
	Bocaue	100	PHL	FEBC
	Hanoi	50	VTN	Vo Vietnam
12025	Allouis	500	F	RFI
	Moyabi	500	GAB	RFI
	Agana	100	GUM	KTWR
12030	Dhaka	250	BGD	R Bangladesh
	Moscow	250	RUS	R Moscow
12035	Noblejas	300	E	REE
	Allouis	500	F	RFI
	Moyabi	500	GAB	Swiss R Intl
	Moscow	250	RUS	R Moscow/China R Intl
	Hanoi	50	VTN	Vo Vietnam
12040	Woofferton	250	G	BBCWS
	Tinang	250	PHL	VoA
	Moscow	250	RUS	R Moscow
12045	Novosibirsk	1000	RUS	DW
	Samara	250	RUS	DW
12050	Abis	250	EGY	R Cairo
	Moscow	250	RUS	R Moscow
12055	Xian	500	CHN	China R Intl
	Vladivostok	500	RUS	China R Intl
	Litomysl	100	TCH	R Prague
12060	Samara	100	RUS	AWR/R Moscow
12070	Moscow	250	RUS	R Moscow
12080	Moepeng Hill	100	BOT	VoA
12085	Sofia	500	BUL	R Sofia
	Damascus	500	SYR	R Damascus
12095	Rampisham	500	G	BBCWS
	Skelton	300	G	BBCWS
12105	Athens	100	GRC	Vo Greece
12110	Beijing	120	CHN	China R Intl
12120	Beijing	120	CHN	CNR 1
13580	Litomysl	100	TCH	R Prague
13590	Islamabad	50	PAK	R Pakistan
	Litomysl	100	TCH	R Prague
13595	Millerstown	100	USA	WCJR
13605	Carnarvon	300	AUS	R Australia

Freq. [kHz]	Transmitter site	Power [kW]	Country	Station name
13605	Darwin	250	AUS	R Australia
(cont)	Abu Dhabi	500	UAE	UAE R Abu Dhabi
13610	Sackville	250	CAN	RCI
	Julich	100	D	DW
13615	Saipan	100	MRA	KHBI
	Birmingham	500	USA	WEWN
13620	Dhaka	250	BGD	R Bangladesh
	Kabd	500	KWT	R Kuwait
13625	Saipan	100	MRA	KHBI
13635	Sottens	500	SUI	Swiss R Intl
13645	Sofia	500	BUL	R Sofia
	Minsk	20	BLR	Belarus R
13650	Sackville	250	CAN	RCI
	Salah el Deen	500	IRQ	R Baghdad
	Pyongyang	400	KRE	R Pyongyang
13660	Havana	500	CUB	R Havana Cuba
	Rampisham	500	G	BBCWS
13665	Islamabad	100	PAK	R Pakistan
13670	Sofia	500	BUL	R Sofia
	Sackville	250	CAN	RCI
	Kimjae	100	KOR	R Korea
13675	Wavre	250	BEL	R Vlaanderen Intl
	Plovdiv	500	BUL	VoA
	Dubai	500	UAE	UAE R Dubai
13680	Salah el Deen	500	IRQ	R Baghdad
13685	Wavre	250	BEL	R Vlaanderen Intl
	Montsinery	500	GUF	China R Intl
	Islamabad	100	PAK	R Pakistan
	Sottens	500	SUI	Swiss R Intl
13690	Sackville	250	CAN	RCI
	Wertachtal	500	D	DW
13695	Budapest	250	HNG	R Budapest
	Okeechobee	100	USA	WYFR
	Rancho Simi	50	USA	KVOH
13700	Flevo	500	HOL	R Netherlands
	Talata Volondry	300	MDG	R Netherlands
	Moscow	250	RUS	R Netherlands
	Samara	250	RUS	R Netherlands
13710	Moepeng Hill	100	BOT	VoA

Freq. [kHz]	Transmitter site	Power [kW]	Country	Station name
13710	Volgograd	20	RUS	R Vedo
(cont)	Birmingham	500	USA	WEWN
	Cypress Creek	500	USA	Monitor R Intl
13715	Havana	500	CUB	R Havana Cuba
	Litomysl	100	TCH	R Prague
13720	Sackville	250	CAN	RCI
	Agana	100	GUM	KTWR
13730	Moosbrunn	500	AUT	R Austria Intl
13740	Wavre	250	BEL	R Vlaanderen Intl
	Bethany	250	USA	VoA
	Birmingham	500	USA	WEWN
	Denton	50	USA	KCBI
13745	Rampisham	500	G	BBCWS
13750	Costa Rica	20	CTR	AWR
	Jerusalem	500	ISR	Kol Israel
13755	Carnarvon	300	AUS	R Australia
13760	Julich	100	D	DW
	Pyongyang	400	KRE	R Pyongyang
	Cypress Creek	500	USA	Monitor R Intl
	Noblesville	100	USA	WHRI
13770	Pori	1000	FNL	YLE R Finland
	Flevo	500	HOL	R Netherlands
	Birmingham	500	USA	WEWN
	Scotts Corners	500	USA	WCSN
13775	Greenville	250	USA	WCSN
13780	Wertachtal	500	D	DW
	Ulan Bator	250	MNG	R Ulan Bator
	Sines	250	POR	DW
13785	Pyongyang	400	KRE	R Pyongyang
13790	Sackville	250	CAN	DW
	Wertachtal	500	D	DW
13835	Reykjavik	10	ISL	Icelandic B S
13845	Nashville	100	USA	WWCR
13855	Reykjavik	10	ISL	Icelandic B S
15010	Hanoi	50	VTN	Vo Vietnam
15020	Aligarh	250	IND	AIR
15050	Aligarh	250	IND	AIR
15060	Riyadh	500	ARS	BSKSA

Freq. [kHz]	Transmitter site	Power [kW]	Country	Station name
15070	Rampisham	500	G	BBCWS
	Skelton	300	G	BBCWS
15075	Delhi	50	IND	AIR
	Khampur	250	IND	AIR
15080	Plovdiv	500	BUL	R Bulgaria/VoA
15084	Tehran	500	IRN	IRIB
15090	SM Galeria	500	CVA	Vatican R
15095	Jerusalem	500	ISR	Kol Israel
	Bocaue	100	PHL	FEBC
	Damascus	500	SYR	R Damascus
15100	Xian	150	CHN	China R Intl
	Bocaue	100	PHL	FEBC
15105	MEYERTON	500	AFS/G	BBCWS
	ASCENSION	250	ASC	BBCWS
	ANTIGUA	250	ATG	DW
	DHAKA	250	BGD	R Bangladesh
	BAODING	240	CHN	China R Intl
	XIAN	150	CHN	China R Intl
	PERKARA	250	CLN	DW
	JUELICH	100	D	DW
	NAUEN	500	D	DW
	WERTACHTAL	500	D	DW
	KAVALLA	250	GRC	VoA
	TEGUCIGALPA	1	HND	
	DELHI	100	IND	AIR
	JERUSALEM	300	ISR	Kol Israel
	TANGER	50	MRC	RTV Marocaine
	BUCURESTI	250	ROU	R Moldova/ R Romania Intl
	NOBLESVILLE	100	USA	WHRI
15110	SANTIAGO	100	CHL	
	BEIJING	120	CHN	China R Intl
	NOBLEJAS	350	E	REE
	BANGALORE	500	IND	AIR
	MEXICO	100	MEX	R Mexico
	BAMAKO 1	50	MLI	China R Intl
	EKATERINBURG	240	RUS	R Moscow
	KAZAN	240	RUS	R Moscow
	MOSKVA	500	RUS	R Moscow
	SERPUKHOV	1000	RUS	R Moscow
15115	SANTIAGO	100	CHL	
	ABU ZAABAL	100	EGY	R Cairo

Freq. [kHz]	Transmitter site	Power [kW]	Country	Station name
15115	QUITO	100	EQA	HCJB
(cont)	RAMPISHAM	500	G	BBCWS
	SKELTON	250	G	BBCWS
	RANGITAIKI	100	NZL	R New Zealand Intl
	KARACHI	50	PAK	R Pakistan
	LISBON	250	POR	RFE/RL
15120	BONAIRE RNW	250	ATN	R Netherlands
	EKALA	35	CLN	SLBC
	HABANA	100	CUB	R Havana Cuba
	S.M.GALERIA	100	CVA	Vatican R
	PORI	500	FIN	YLE R Finland
	ALIGARH	250	IND	AIR
	MEXICO	100	MEX	R Mexico
	BAMAKO 1	50	MLI	China R Intl
	IKORODU	500	NIG	R Nigeria
	RANGITAIKI	100	NZL	R New Zealand Intl
	NOVOSIBIRSK	100	RUS	R Moscow
	DELANO	250	USA	VoA
	GREENVILLE	250	USA	VoA
15125	BEIJING	120	CHN	China R Intl
	XIAN	300	CHN	China R Intl
	CARIARI	100	CTR/E	REE
	NOBLEJAS	350	E	REE
	KAVALLA	250	GRC	VoA
	MADRAS	100	IND	AIR
	REYKJAVIK	10	ISL	Icelandic B S
	MEXICO	10	MEX	R Mexico
	TINANG	250	PHL	VoA
	JIGULEVSK	250	RUS	AWR/China R Intl
15130	MEYERTON	250	AFS	Channel Africa
	KAVALLA	250	GRC	VoA
	KUJANG	400	KRE	R Pyongyang
	BAMAKO 1	50	MLI	China R Intl
	BRIECH	500	MRC/USA	VoA
	PALAUIG	250	PHL	R Veritas Asia
	LISBON	250	POR	RFE/RL
	MAXOQUEIRA	500	POR	RFE/RL
	SERPUKHOV	240	RUS	R Moscow
	VLADIVOSTOK	240	RUS	R Moscow
	OKEECHOBEE	100	USA	WYFR/VoFC
15135	S.PAULO	8	B	R Record
	SANTIAGO	100	CHL	
	KUNMING	120	CHN	China R Intle

Freq. [kHz]	Transmitter site	Power [kW]	Country	Station name
15135	ALLOUIS	500	F	RFI
(cont)	WOOFFERTON	300	G	VoA
	ATHINAI	100	GRC	Vo Greece
	KAVALLA	250	GRC	VoA
	DIOSD	100	HNG	R Budapest
	DELHI	250	IND	AIR
	CYCLOPS	250	MLT	DW
	KIGALI	250	RRW	DW
	Kiev	250	UKR	R Ukraine Intl
15140	SANTIAGO	25	CHL	R Nacional de Chile
	HABANA	100	CUB	R Havana Cuba
	QUITO	100	EQA	HCJB
	BANGALORE	500	IND	AIR
	DELHI	100	IND	AIR
	PALAUIG	250	PHL	R Veritas Asia
	BICHKEK	250	RUS	R Moscow
	S.PETERSBURG	500	RUS	R Moscow
	BELGRADE	500	YUG	R Yugoslavia
	Sackville	250	CAN	RCI
15145	DHAKA	100	BGD	R Bangladesh
	JUELICH	100	D	DW
	KAVALLA	250	GRC	VoA
	DELHI	250	IND	AIR
	REYKJAVIK	10	ISL	Icelandic B S
	KIMJAE	100	KOR	R Korea
	HOERBY	500	S	R Sweden
	MURMANSK	20	RUS	Domestic
	OKEECHOBEE	100	USA	WYFR
	RED LION	50	USA	WINB
	Mahe	100	SEY	FEBA
15150	MEYERTON	250	AFS	Channel Africa
	SANTIAGO	25	CHL	
	JAKARTA	250	INS	RRI
	PYONGYANG	400	KRE	R Pyongyang
	TALATA VOLON	300	MDG	R Netherlands
	TINANG	250	PHL	VoA
	LIMA	15	PRU	
	ARMAVIR	240	RUS	R Moscow
	KICHINEV	500	MDA	R Moscow
15155	BONAIRE RNW	250	ATN	R Netherlands
	ABU ZAABAL	100	EGY	R Cairo
	QUITO	100	EQA	HCJB
	ALLOUIS	100	F	RFI

Freq. [kHz]	Transmitter site	Power [kW]	Country	Station name
15155	MOYABI	250	GAB/F	RFI
(cont)	ALIGARH	250	IND	AIR
	DELHI	100	IND	AIR
	KIMJAE	100	KOR	R Korea
	BRIECH	500	MRC/USA	VoA
	LISBON	250	POR	RFE/RL
	SINES	250	POR	RFE/RL
	KAZAN	250	RUS	R Moscow
	VOLGOGRAD	20	RUS	R Vedo
15160	BOUCHAOUI	100	ALG	RTV Algerienne
	ASCENSION	250	ASC	BBCWS
	SOFIA	250	BUL	R Sofia
	KAVALLA	250	GRC	VoA
	DIOSD	100	HNG	R Budapest
	JASZBERENY	250	HNG	R Budapest
	KUJANG	200	KRE	R Pyongyang
	MEXICO	10	MEX	La Voz de America Latina
	BRIECH	500	MRC/USA	VoA
	TINANG	250	PHL	VoA
	GREENVILLE	250	USA	VoA
15165	JEDDAH	50	ARS	BSKSA
	JINHUA	500	CHN	China R Intl
	XIAN	150	CHN	China R Intl
	HABANA	100	CUB	R Havana Cuba
	RAMPISHAM	500	G	BBCWS
	ALIGARH	250	IND	AIR
	BANGALORE	500	IND	AIR
	DELHI	50	IND	AIR
	SIRJAN	500	IRN	IRIB
	FREDRIKSTAD	350	NOR	R Norway Intl
	SVEIO	500	NOR	R Norway Intl
	KALATCH	500	RUS	R Moscow
	TACHKENT	100	UZB	Tashkent R
15170	CARNARVON	300	AUS	R Australia
	WERTACHTAL	500	D	DW
	REYKJAVIK	10	ISL	Icelandic B S
	KIMJAE	250	KOR	R Korea
	BRIECH	500	MRC/USA	VoA
	PAPEETE	20	OCE	RFO
	TINANG	250	PHL	VoA
	LISBON	250	POR	RFE/RL
	ADRA	500	SYR	R Damascus
	ARMAVIR	1000	RUS	R Moscow
	IRKUTSK	100	RUS	R Moscow

Freq. [kHz]	Transmitter site	Power [kW]	Country	Station name
15170	OKEECHOBEE	100	USA	WYFR
(cont)	Bamako	50	MLI	China R Intl
15175	RIYADH	500	ARS	BSKSA
	DHAKA	250	BGD	R Bangladesh
	SANTIAGO	100	CHL	
	ALIGARH	250	IND	AIR
	FREDRIKSTAD	350	NOR	R Norway Intl
	MAHE	100	SEY	FEBA
	BICHKEK	500	RUS	R Moscow
	ORENBURG	240	RUS	R Moscow
	BELGRADE	500	YUG	R Yugoslavia
15180	SANTIAGO	100	CHL	
	XIAN	150	CHN	China R Intl
	NOBLEJAS	350	E	REE
	ALLOUIS	500	F	RFI
	SKELTON	300	G	BBCWS
	SALAH EL DEEN	500	IRQ	R Baghdad
	KUJANG	400	KRE	R Pyongyang
	KVITSOY	500	NOR	R Norway Intl
	TINANG	50	PHL	VoA
	BUCURESTI	120	ROU	R Romania Intl
	ARMAVIR	240	RUS	R Moscow
	KOMSOMOLSKAMUR	100	RUS	R Moscow
	S.PETERSBURG	240	RUS	R Moscow
15185	JUELICH	100	D	DW
	NAUEN	500	D	DW
	WERTACHTAL	500	D	DW
	SKELTON	250	G	BBCWS
	KAVALLA	250	GRC	VoA
	BANGALORE	500	IND	AIR
	REYKJAVIK	10	ISL	Icelandic B S
	IKORODU	500	NIG	R Nigeria
	TINANG	250	PHL	VoA
	LISBON	250	POR	RFE/RL
	KIGALI	250	RRW	DW
	JIGULEVSK	240	RUS	R Moscow
	SERPUKHOV	100	RUS	R Moscow
	GREENVILLE	500	USA	VoA
	RED LION	50	USA	WINB
15190	ASCENSION	250	ASC	BBCWS
	BELO HORIZONTE	5	B	R Inconfidencia
	WAVRE	100	BEL	R Vlaanderen Intl
	BRAZZAVILLE	50	COG	R National Congolaise

Freq. [kHz]	Transmitter site	Power [kW]	Country	Station name
15190	HABANA	500	CUB	R Havana Cuba
(cont)	ALLOUIS	100	F	RFI
	TOKYO YAMATA	100	J	NHK R Japan
	ISLAMABAD	10	PAK	R Pakistan
	TINANG	250	PHL	R Philipinas
	HOERBY	500	S	R Sweden
	ADRA	500	SYR	R Damascus
	ALMA ATA	240	KAZ	R Alma Ata
15195	DHAKA	250	BGD	R Bangladesh
	BAODING	240	CHN	China R Intl
	HABANA	100	CUB	R Havana Cuba
	ISMANING	100	D/USA	RFE/RL
	ALLOUIS	100	F	RFI
	MOYABI	500	GAB/J	NHK R Japan
	DELHI	100	IND	AIR
	TOKYO YAMATA	300	J	NHK R Japan
	KUJANG	200	KRE	R Pyongyang
	BRIECH	500	MRC/USA	VoA
	KVITSOY	500	NOR	R Norway Intl
	TINANG	250	PHL	VoA
	SONSONATE	50	SLV	
15200	BREST	20	BLR	Belarus R
	ALLOUIS	500	F	RFI
	MONTSINERY	500	GUF	RFI
	AGANA	100	GUM	KTWR
	ABU GHRAIB	250	IRQ	R Baghdad
	JERUSALEM	100	ISR	Kol Israel
	KATHMANDU	100	NPL	R Nepal
	S.GABRIEL	100	POR	R Portugal
	EKATERINBURG	20	RUS	Tatar R
	TACHKENT	100	UZB	R Tashkent 2
15205	BOUCHAOUI	50	ALG	RTV Algerienne
	ANTIGUA	250	ATG	DW
	WOOFFERTON	300	G	VoA
	KAVALLA	250	GRC	VoA
	ABU GHRAIB	250	IRQ	R Baghdad
	KIMJAE	250	KOR	R Korea
	BRIECH	500	MRC/USA	VoA
	TINANG	250	PHL	VoA
	SINES	250	POR	DW
	GREENVILLE	250	USA	VoA
15210	XIAN	120	CHN	China R Intl
	S.M.GALERIA	250	CVA	Vatican R

Freq. [kHz]	Transmitter site	Power [kW]	Country	Station name
15210	NOBLEJAS	350	E	REE
(cont)	ABIS	250	EGY	R Cairo
	SALAH EL DEEN	500	IRQ	R Baghdad
	TOKYO YAMATA	100	J	NHK R Japan
	KIMJAE	250	KOR	R Korea
	TINANG	250	PHL	VoA
	ASUNCION	100	PRG	
	MOSKVA	250	RUS	R Moscow
15215	BOUCHAOUI	100	ALG	RTV Algerienne
	S.LUIZ	3	B	
	KUJANG	200	KRE	R Pyongyang
	BRIECH	500	MRC/USA	VoA
	TINANG	250	PHL	VoA
	LISBON	250	POR	RFE/RL
	ALMA ATA	20	KAZ	R Alma Ata
	ARMAVIR	20	RUS	Domestic
	OMSK	20	RUS	Domestic
	PETROZAVODSK	20	RUS	Domestic
	OKEECHOBEE	100	USA	WYFR
15220	MEYERTON	500	AFS	Channel Africa
	ANTIGUA	125	ATG	BBCWS
	WAVRE	100	BEL	R Vlaanderen Intl
	HABANA	100	CUB	R Havana Cuba
	ABIS	250	EGY	R Cairo
	ABU ZAABAL	100	EGY	R Cairo
	DIOSD	100	HNG	R Budapest
	ROMA	100	I	RAI
	DELHI	100	IND	AIR
	FREDRIKSTAD	350	NOR	R Norway Intl
	KVITSOY	500	NOR	R Norway Intl
	DUCHANBE	150	TJK	R Dushanbe
	MOSKVA	240	RUS	R Moscow
	Bucharest	150	ROU	R Moldova Intl
15225	ASCENSION	250	ASC	BBCWS
	JUELICH	100	D	DW
	RAMPISHAM	500	G	BBCWS
	AGAT	100	GUM	KSDA
	ROMA	100	I	RAI
	KIMJAE	250	KOR	R Korea
	BRIECH	500	MRC/USA	VoA
	ARMAVIR	1000	RUS	R Moscow
15230	HABANA	250	CUB	R Havana Cuba
	ROMA	100	I	RAI

Freq. [kHz]	Transmitter site	Power [kW]	Country	Station name
15230	DELHI	100	IND	AIR
(cont)	TOKYO YAMATA	100	J	NHK R Japan
	KUJANG	200	KRE	R Pyongyang
	HOERBY	500	S	R Sweden
	MELO	5	URG	
	ALMA ATA	1000	KAZ	R Alma Ata
	MOSKVA	250	RUS	R Moscow
15235	SACKVILLE	250	CAN	RCI
	BEIJING	120	CHN	China R Intl
	WERTACHTAL	500	D/USA	VoA
	RAMPISHAM	500	G	BBCWS
	WOOFFERTON	300	G	VoA
	DELHI	100	IND	AIR
	TRIPOLI	500	LBY	Libya Jamahiriyah B
	BRIECH	500	MRC/USA	VoA
	MASIRAH	100	OMA/G	BBCWS
	TINANG	50	PHL	VoA
	SFAX	100	TUN	ERTT
15240	CARNARVON	250	AUS	R Australia
	SHEPPARTON	100	AUS	R Australia
	SANTIAGO	100	CHL	
	NOBLEJAS	350	E	REE
	PORI	500	FIN	YLE R Finland
	REYKJAVIK	10	ISL	Icelandic B S
	TOKYO YAMATA	300	J	NHK RJapan
	HOERBY	500	S	R Sweden
	EKATERINBURG	240	RUS	R Moscow
	MOSKVA	20	RUS	Azerbaijani R
15243	PORI	1000	FIN	YLE R Finland [ssb]
15245	BEIJING	50	CHN	China R Intl
	LIMASSOL	250	CYP/G	BBCWS
	JUELICH	100	D	DW
	NAUEN	500	D	DW
	ROMA	100	I	RAI
	KUJANG	400	KRE	R Pyongyang
	BRIECH	500	MRC/USA	VoA
	MASIRAH	100	OMA/G	BBCWS
	SINES	250	POR	DW
	KOMSOMOLSKAMUR	200	RUS	R Moscow
	PETROPAVLO KAM	240	RUS	R Moscow
	GREENVILLE	500	USA	VoA
	KINSHASA	100	ZAI	Zaire BC
15250	COLOMBO	35	CLN	VoA

Freq. [kHz]	Transmitter site	Power [kW]	Country	Station name
15250	QUITO	250	EQA	HCJB
(cont)	DELHI	100	IND	AIR
	ISLAMABAD	100	PAK	R Pakistan
	TINANG	50	PHL	VoA
	BUCURESTI	250	ROU	R Romania Intl/ R Moldova
	Salah el Deen	500	IRQ	R Baghdad
	Alma Ata	20	KAZ	R Alma Ata
15255	DHAKA	100	BGD	R Bangladesh
	ABU ZAABAL	100	EGY	R Cairo
	KAVALLA	250	GRC	VoA
	LISBON	250	POR	VoA
	BUCURESTI	250	ROU	R Romania Intl
	ARMAVIR	20	RUS	Domestic
	EKATERINBURG	240	RUS	R Moscow
	RIAZAN	100	RUS	R Moscow
15260	ASCENSION	250	ASC	BBCWS
	SACKVILLE	250	CAN/G	BBCWS
	XIAN	150	CHN	China R Intl
	HABANA	500	CUB	R Havana Cuba
	LIMASSOL	250	CYP/G	BBCWS
	ROMA	100	I	RAI
	KAMALABAD	500	IRN	IRIB
	TOKYO	10	J /USA	R Tanpa
	BRIECH	500	MRC/USA	VoA
	KAZAN	240	RUS	R Moscow
15265	BRASILIA	250	B	R Bras
	KAVALLA	250	GRC	VoA
	BANGALORE	500	IND	AIR
	UDORN	500	THA/USA	VoA
	ABU DHABI	500	UAE	UAE R Abu Dhabi
	EKATERINBURG	240	RUS	R Moscow
	KAZAN	150	RUS	R Moscow
	KICHINEV	1000	MDA	R Moscow
	Greenville	500	USA	VoA
15270	BEIJING	50	CHN	China R Intl
	QUITO	500	EQA	HCJB
	WOOFFERTON	300	G	VoA
	ALIGARH	250	IND	AIR
	DELHI	100	IND	AIR
	TOKYO YAMATA	100	J	NHK R Japan
	PALAUIG	250	PHL	R Veritas Asia
	BUCURESTI	250	ROU	R Romania Intl

Freq. [kHz]	Transmitter site	Power [kW]	Country	Station name
15270	KIGALI	250	RRW	DW
(cont)	HOERBY	500	S	R Sweden
	ALMA ATA	20	KAZ	R Alma Ata
	CELINOGRAD	20	RUS	Domestic
	EKATERINBURG	20	RUS	Domestic
	Taipei	250	TWN	VoFC
15275	RIYADH	500	ARS	BSKSA
	WIEN	300	AUT	R Austria Intl
	BEIJING	120	CHN	China R Intl
	JUELICH	100	D	DW
	WERTACHTAL	500	D	DW
	ALIGARH	250	IND	AIR
	MONTEVIDEO	10	URG	
15280	JEDDAH	50	ARS	BSKSA
	NOBLEJAS	350	E	REE
	RAMPISHAM	500	G	BBCWS
	MONTSINERY	500	GUF	RFI
	TSANG TSUI	250	HKG/G	BBCWS
	BOMBAY	100	IND	AIR
	BRIECH	500	MRC/USA	VoA
	MASIRAH	100	OMA/G	BBCWS
	KRANJI	100	SNG/G	BBCWS
	JIGULEVSK	240	RUS	R Moscow
	SERPUKHOV	240	RUS	R Moscow
	REDWOOD CITY	50	USA	KGEI
15285	BEIJING	120	CHN	China R Intl
	ABU ZAABAL	100	EGY	R Cairo
	EJURA	250	GHA	Ghana B C
	TEMA	100	GHA	Ghana B C
	KIMJAE	100	KOR	R Korea
	TINANG	250	PHL	VoA
	VOLGOGRAD	20	RUS	Domestic
	Kiev	500	UKR	R Ukraine Intl
15290	XIAN	300	CHN	China R Intl
	HABANA	100	CUB	R Havana Cuba
	HOLZKIRCHEN	250	D/USA	RFE/RL
	PLAYA DE PALS	250	E	RFE/RL
	REYKJAVIK	10	ISL	Icelandic B S
	TINANG	250	PHL	VoA
	ALMA ATA	100	KAZ	R Alma Ata
	ARMAVIR	1000	RUS	R Moscow
	KICHINEV	1000	MDA	R Moscow
15295	QUITO	100	EQA	HCJB

Freq. [kHz]	Transmitter site	Power [kW]	Country	Station name
15295 *(cont)*	REYKJAVIK	10	ISL	Icelandic B S
	KAJANG	100	MLA	Vo Malaysia
	MAPUTO	120	MOZ	Em Nacional
	ISLAMABAD	100	PAK	R Pakistan
	KAZAN	250	RUS	R Moscow
	KHABAROVSK	240	RUS	R Moscow
	TACHKENT	100	UZB	R Tashkent
	RED LION	50	USA	WINB
15300	ALLOUIS	500	F	RFI
	MOYABI	250	GAB/F	RFI
	MONTSINERY	500	GUF	RFI
	JERUSALEM	300	ISR	Kol Israel
	TINANG	250	PHL	VoA
	DUBAI	500	UAE	UAE R Dubai
15305	SACKVILLE	250	CAN	RCI
	WERTACHTAL	500	D/USA	VoA
	DELHI	100	IND	AIR
	ISLAMABAD	100	PAK	R Pakistan
	PORO	35	PHL	VoA
	KAZAN	100	RUS	R Moscow
	KRUSK	250	RUS	R Moscow
15310	DHAKA	250	BGD	R Bangladesh
	SOFIA	500	BUL	R Bulgaria
	CONAKRY	100	GUI	Radiodiff Guineenne
	KUJANG	200	KRE	R Pyongyang
	MASIRAH	100	OMA/G	BBCWS
	Agana	100	GUM	AWR
15315	BONAIRE RNW	250	ATN	R Netherlands
	DHAKA	250	BGD	R Bangladesh
	MINSK	20	BLR	Belarus R
	SACKVILLE	100	CAN	RCI
	HABANA	250	CUB	R Havana Cuba
	LAMPERTHEIM	100	D/USA	RFE/RL
	ALLOUIS	100	F	RFI
	ABU DHABI	500	UAE	UAE R Abu Dhabi
	ALMA ATA	240	KAZ	R Moscow
	ARMAVIR	500	RUS	R Moscow
	CELINOGRAD	20	RUS	Domestic
	IRKUTSK	250	RUS	R Moscow
	BETHANY	250	USA	BBCWS
15320	SHEPPARTON	100	AUS	R Australia
	DHAKA	100	BGD	R Bangladesh
	ORCHA	100	BLR	Belarus R

Freq. [kHz]	Transmitter site	Power [kW]	Country	Station name
15320	SANTIAGO	100	CHL	
(cont)	XIAN	150	CHN	China R Intl
	DELHI	100	IND	AIR
	REYKJAVIK	10	ISL	Icelandic B S
	DUBAI	300	UAE	UAE R Dubai
	SERPUKHOV	240	RUS	R Moscow
15325	S.PAULO	1	B	
	SACKVILLE	250	CAN	RCI
	LIMASSOL	250	CYP/G	BBCWS
	NOBLEJAS	350	E	REE
	RAMPISHAM	500	G	BBCWS
	SKELTON	300	G	BBCWS
	ALIGARH	250	IND	AIR
	ISLAMABAD	250	PAK	R Pakistan
	LISBON	250	POR	RCI
	MAHE	100	SEY	FEBA
	TULA	100	RUS	R Moscow
	Ankara	500	TUR	TRT Vo Turkey
	Montsinery	500	GUF	NHK R Japan
15330	SOFIA	250	BUL	R Bulgaria
	BEIJING	120	CHN	China R Intl
	ROMA	100	I	RAI
	TANGER	50	MRC	RTV Marocaine
	MAHE	100	SEY	FEBA
	ADRA	500	SYR	R Damascus
	KENGA	250	RUS	R Moscow
	KRUSK	500	RUS	R Moscow
	GREENVILLE	250	USA	VoA
	Pori	1000	FNL	YLE R Finland
15335	ABIS	250	EGY	R Cairo
	ALIGARH	250	IND	AIR
	BANGALORE	500	IND	AIR
	MADRAS	100	IND	AIR
	KIMJAE	250	KOR	R Korea
	TANGER	100	MRC	RTV Marocaine
	SVEIO	500	NOR	R Norway Intl
	KARACHI	50	PAK	R Pakistan
	BUCURESTI	250	ROU	R Romania/R Moldova
15340	DHAKA	100	BGD	R Bangladesh
	HABANA	500	CUB	R Havana Cuba
	LIMASSOL	250	CYP/G	BBCWS
	LAMPERTHEIM	100	D/USA	RFE/RL
	RAMPISHAM	500	G	BBCWS

Freq. [kHz]	Transmitter site	Power [kW]	Country	Station name
15340	SKELTON	250	G	BBCWS
(cont)	ROMA	100	I	RAI
	KUJANG	200	KRE	R Pyongyang
	LISBON	250	POR	RFE/RL
	BUCURESTI	250	ROU	R Romania Intl
	KRANJI	100	SNG/G	BBCWS
	KICHINEV	500	MDA	R Moscow
	NOVOSIBIRSK	150	RUS	R Moscow
15345	GRAL PACHECO	100	ARG	R Argentina al Exterior
	RIYADH	500	ARS	BSKSA
	BONAIRE TWR	50	ATN	TWR
	SIRJAN	500	IRN	IRIB
	SULAIBIYAH	500	KWT	R Kuwait
	BOCAUE	100	PHL	FEBC
	AL KHAISAH	250	QAT	Qatar B S
	MOSKVA	240	RUS	R Moscow
15350	BEIJING	50	CHN	China R Intl
	JUELICH	100	D	DW
	NAUEN	500	D	DW
	WERTACHTAL	500	D	DW
	QUITO	50	EQA	HCJB
	MONTSINERY	500	GUF	NHK R Japan
	JUNGLINSTER	10	LUX	R Luxembourg
	BOCAUE	50	PHL	FEBC
	PALAUIG	250	PHL	R Veritas Asia
	ANKARA	500	TUR	TRT Vo Turkey
	DUCHANBE	1000	TJK	R Moscow
	IRKUTSK	250	RUS	R Moscow
	SERPUKHOV	250	RUS	R Moscow
	KINSHASA	100	ZAI	Zaire R
15355	BONAIRE TWR	100	ATN	TWR
	MOYABI	500	GAB/J	NHK R Japan
	MAXOQUEIRA	500	POR	RFE/RL
	LITOMYSL	100	TCH	R Prague
	MONTEVIDEO	10	URG	
	VOLGOGRAD	1000	RUS	R Moscow
	OKEECHOBEE	100	USA	WYFR
15360	MOEPENG HILL	100	BOT/USA	VoA
	LIMASSOL	250	CYP/G	BBCWS
	ALLOUIS	500	F	RFI
	ALIGARH	250	IND	AIR
	BOMBAY	100	IND	AIR
	KIMJAE	250	KOR	R Korea

Freq. [kHz]	Transmitter site	Power [kW]	Country	Station name
15360	TANGER	50	MRC	RTV Marocaine
(cont)	KRANJI	100	SNG/G	BBCWS
	ALMA ATA	20	KAZ	R Alma Ata
	CELINOGRAD	20	RUS	Domestic
	KENGA	100	RUS	R Moscow
15365	SHEPPARTON	100	AUS	R Australia
	NOBLEJAS	350	E	REE
	ALLOUIS	500	F	RFI
	MONTSINERY	500	GUF	RFI
	ALIGARH	250	IND	AIR
	DELHI	100	IND	AIR
	ZAHEDAN	500	IRN	IRIB
	BUCURESTI	250	ROU	R Romania Intl
	MOSKVA	200	RUS	R Moscow
	GREENVILLE	250	USA	VoA
15370	NAUEN	500	D	DW
	PLAYA DE PALS	250	E	RFE/RL
	TOKYO YAMATA	300	J	BBCWS
	LISBON	250	POR	RFE/RL
	MAXOQUEIRA	500	POR	RFE/RL
	BUCURESTI	250	ROU	R Romania
	KIGALI	250	RRW	DW
	NOVOSIBIRSK	240	RUS	R Moscow
	Taipei	250	TWN	VoFC
15375	BONAIRE TWR	50	ATN	TWR
	MOEPENG HILL	100	BOT/USA	VoA
	NOBLEJAS	350	E	REE
	ABU ZAABAL	100	EGY	R Cairo
	REYKJAVIK	10	ISL	Icelandic B S
	THUMRAIT	100	OMA	R Oman
	PALAUIG	50	PHL	R Veritas Asia
	MANZINI	100	SWZ	TWR
	KENGA	240	RUS	R Moscow
15380	JEDDAH	50	ARS	BSKSA
	DARWIN	250	AUS	R Australia
	BEIJING	50	CHN	China R Intl
	BIBLIS	100	D/USA	RFE/RL
	NOBLEJAS	350	E	REE
	MOYABI	500	GAB/J	NHK R Japan
	MARPI	100	MRA	KFBS
	ISLAMABAD	100	PAK	R Pakistan
	LISBON	250	POR	RFE/RL
	BUCURESTI	250	ROU	R Romania Intl

Freq. [kHz]	Transmitter site	Power [kW]	Country	Station name
15380	KRANJI	250	SNG/G	BBCWS
(cont)	SIMFEROPOL	1000	UKR	R Ukraine Intl
	Cariari de Pococi	100	CTR	REE
15385	SOFIA	500	BUL	R Sofia
	ANKARA	500	TUR	TRT Vo Turkey
	ALMA ATA	20	KAZ	R Alma Ata
	EREVAN	1000	ARM	R Moscow
	NIJNIINOVGOROD	240	RUS	R Moscow
	NOVOSIBIRSK	240	RUS	R Moscow
15390	ASCENSION	250	ASC	BBCWS
	SACKVILLE	250	CAN	RCI
	BEIJING	50	CHN	China Natl R 1
	LIMASSOL	250	CYP/G	BBCWS
	JUELICH	100	D	DW
	WOOFFERTON	250	G	BBCWS
	BRIECH	500	MRC/USA	VoA
	BUCURESTI	250	ROU	R Moldova Intl
	HOERBY	500	S	R Sweden
15395	COLOMBO	35	CLN	VoA
	LIMASSOL	250	CYP/G	BBCWS
	ARGANDA	100	E	REE
	RAMPISHAM	500	G	BBCWS
	TINANG	250	PHL	VoA
	DUBAI	500	UAE	UAE R Dubai
	ARMAVIR	100	RUS	R Moscow
15400	ASCENSION	250	ASC	BBCWS
	BAODING	120	CHN	China R Intl
	PORI	500	FIN	YLE R Finland
	SKELTON	300	G	BBCWS
	ABU DHABI	500	UAE	UAE R Abu Dhabi
	DUBAI	300	UAE	UAE R Dubai
	GREENVILLE	250	USA	VoA
	Okeechobee	100	USA	WYFR
15405	ALLOUIS	500	F	RFI
	MARPI	100	MRA	KHBI
	BUCURESTI	250	ROU	R Romania Intl
	ANKARA	250	TUR	TRT Vo Turkey
	BICHKEK	1000	RUS	R Moscow
	MOSKVA	100	RUS	R Moscow
15410	ANTIGUA	250	ATG	DW
	WIEN	100	AUT	R Austria Intl
	ATHINAI	100	GRC	Vo Greece
	KAVALLA	250	GRC	VoA

Freq. [kHz]	Transmitter site	Power [kW]	Country	Station name
15410	TOKYO YAMATA	300	J	NHK R Japan
(cont)	KUJANG	200	KRE	R Pyongyang
	BRIECH	500	MRC/USA	VoA
	KARACHI	50	PAK	R Pakistan
	BOCAUE	50	PHL	FEBC
	PALAUIG	250	PHL	R Veritas Asia
	TINANG	250	PHL	VoA
	KIGALI	250	RRW	DW
	PETROPAVLO KAM	100	RUS	R Moscow
15415	RIYADH	500	ARS	BSKSA
	RIBEIRAO PRETO	1	B	
	JERUSALEM	300	ISR	Kol Israel
	KUJANG	200	KRE	R Pyongyang
	TRIPOLI	500	LBY	Libya Jamahiriyah B
	LISBON	250	POR	RFE/RL
	MAXOQUEIRA	500	POR	RFE/RL
	ALMA ATA	500	KAZ	R Moscow
	KENGA	500	RUS	R Moscow
	KICHINEV	1000	MDA	R Moscow
15420	MEYERTON	250	AFS/G	BBCWS
	MINSK	20	BLR	Belarus R
	BAODING	120	CHN	China R Intl
	XIAN	300	CHN	China R Intl
	LIMASSOL	100	CYP/G	BBCWS
	ABU ZAABAL	100	EGY	R Cairo
	DELHI	100	IND	AIR
	MAHE	250	SEY/G	BBCWS
	SERPUKHOV	250	RUS	R Moscow
	NEW ORLEANS	100	USA	WRNO
15425	SACKVILLE	250	CAN	RCI
	EKALA	35	CLN	SLBC
	WERTACHTAL	500	D	DW
	ALLOUIS	100	F	RFI
	JERUSALEM	300	ISR	Kol Israel
	TINANG	50	PHL	VoA
	SINES	250	POR	DW
	KENGA	1000	RUS	R Moscow
	PETROPAVLO KAM	240	RUS	R Moscow
	Wanneroo	50	AUS	VLW15
15430	RIYADH	500	ARS	BSKSA
	HABANA	100	CUB	R Havana Cuba
	RAMPISHAM	500	G	BBCWS
	WOOFFERTON	250	G	BBCWS

Freq. [kHz]	Transmitter site	Power [kW]	Country	Station name
15430 (cont)	REYKJAVIK	10	ISL	Icelandic B S
	KIMJAE	250	KOR	R Korea
	MEXICO	50	MEX	R Mexico Intl
	MAHE	75	SEY	FEBA
	SCHWARZENBURG	150	SUI	Swiss R Intl
	ANKARA	250	TUR	TRT Vo Turkey
15435	JEDDAH	50	ARS	BSKSA
	BEIJING	120	CHN	China R Intl
	JUELICH	100	D	DW
	WERTACHTAL	500	D	DW
	ALLOUIS	500	F	RFI
	KAVALLA	250	GRC	VoA
	MONTSINERY	500	GUF	RFI
	AL KARANAH	500	JOR	R Jordan
	TRIPOLI	500	LBY	Libya Jamahiriyah B
	DAR ES SALAAM	100	TZA	R Tanzania
	TULA	240	RUS	R Moscow
	Dubai	500	UAE	UAE R Dubai
	VLADIVOSTOK	1000	RUS	R Moscow
15440	KUNMING	120	CHN	China R Intl
	PORI	500	FIN	YLE R Finland
	DUCHANBE	1000	TAD	R Moscow
	RIAZAN	240	RUS	R Moscow
	OKEECHOBEE	100	USA	WYFR/VoFC
15445	BONAIRE TWR	100	ATN	TWR
	BRASILIA	250	B	China R Intl
	MOEPENG HILL	100	BOT/USA	VoA
	BIBLIS	100	D/USA	RFE/RL
	LAMPERTHEIM	100	D/USA	RFE/RL
	PORI	500	FIN	YLE R Finland
	WOOFFERTON	300	G	VoA
	TOKYO YAMATA	100	J	NHK R Japan
	ISLAMABAD	250	PAK	R Pakistan
	BUCURESTI	250	ROU	R Romania Intl
	MAHE	100	SEY	FEBA
	UDORN	500	THA/USA	VoA
	Beijing	120	CHN	RFI
15450	Moosbrunn	500	AUT	R Austria Intl
	Beijing	120	CHN	China R Intl
	Tunis	100	TUN	ERTT
15455	Erevan	500	ARM	R Yerevan
	Lvov	500	UKR	R Ukraine Intl
15465	Bocaue	100	PHL	FEBC

Freq. [kHz]	Transmitter site	Power [kW]	Country	Station name
15470	Sines	250	POR	DW
	Tashkent	500	UZB	R Tashkent
15475	Moyabi	500	GAB	Africa No 1
15480	Jerusalem	500	ISR	Kol Israel
15485	Erevan	500	ARM	R Yerevan
15495	Kabd	500	KWT	R Kuwait
15500	Beijing	50	CHN	China Natl R 2
15505	Kabd	500	KWT	R Kuwait
	Sottens	500	SUI	Swiss R Intl
	Litomysl	100	TCH	R Prague Intl
15510	Erevan	500	ARM	R Yerevan
	Darwin	250	AUS	R Australia
	Shepparton	100	AUS	R Australia
	Moscow	100	RUS	AWR
15515	Allouis	100	F	RFI
	Islamabad	100	PAK	R Pakistan
	Bocaue	100	PHL	FEBC
	S Gabriel	100	POR	R Portugal
15520	Dhaka	100	BGD	R Bangladesh
15525	Samara	500	RUS	DW
15530	Darwin	250	AUS	R Australia
	Allouis	500	F	RFI
	Diosd	250	HNG	RFI
	Flevo	500	HOL	R Netherlands
	Talata Volondry	300	MDG	R Netherlands
	Palauig	100	PHL	R Veritas Asia
15540	Samara	500	RUS	China R Intl
15545	Wertachtal	500	D	DW
15550	Beijing	120	CHN	China Natl R 1
	Athens	100	GRC	Vo Greece
	Islamabad	100	PAK	R Pakistan
15555	Islamabad	100	PAK	R Pakistan
15560	Bonaire	250	ATN	R Netherlands
15566	Okeechobee	100	USA	WYFR
15575	Carnarvon	300	AUS	R Australia
	Darwin	250	AUS	R Australia
	Limassol	300	CYP	BBCWS
	Kimjae	250	KOR	R Korea
15580	Greenville	250	USA	VoA

Freq. [kHz]	Transmitter site	Power [kW]	Country	Station name
15590	Limassol	300	CYP	BBCWS
	Salt Lake City	100	USA	KTBN
15595	Cyclops	250	MLT	DW
15600	Moepeng Hill	100	BOT	VoA
	Kuming	500	CHN	China R Intl
15605	Bratislava	100	SVK	Slovak R
	Velke Kostolany	250	TCH	R Prague
15610	Agana	100	GUM	KSDA/KTWR
	Nashville	100	USA	WWCR
15615	Jerusalem	500	ISR	Kol Israel
15630	Darwin	250	AUS	R Australia
15640	Jerusalem	500	ISR	Kol Israel
15645	Lvov	500	UKR	R Ukraine Intl
15650	Athens	100	GRC	Vo Greece
	Jerusalem	500	ISR	Kol Israel
15665	Cypress Creek	500	USA	Monitor R Intl
	Scotts Corners	500	USA	WCSN
15675	Karachi	50	PAK	R Pakistan
15685	Nashville	100	USA	WWCR
15690	Birmingham	500	USA	WEWN
15725	Denton	50	USA	KCBI
15770	Reykjavik	10	ISL	Icelandic B S
17387	Bangalore	250	IND	AIR
17490	Quito	30	EQA	HCJB [ssb]
17500	Tunis	100	TUN	ERTT
17510	Birmingham	500	USA	WEWN
17515	Wavre	250	BEL	R Vlaanderen Intl
17525	S M Galeria	500	CVA	Vatican R
	Athens	100	GRC	Vo Greece
17530	Karachi	100	PAK	R Pakistan
17535	Rimavska Sobota	250	SVK	Slovak R Intl/R Prague
17540	Islamabad	100	PAK	R Pakistan
17545	Jerusalem	500	ISR	Kol Israel
17555	Wavre	250	BEL	R Vlaanderen Intl
	Saipan	100	MRA	KHBI

Freq. [kHz]	Transmitter site	Power [kW]	Country	Station name
17555	Islamabad	250	PAK	R Pakistan
(cont)	Cypress Creek	500	USA	Monitor R Intl
17560	Julich	100	D	DW
	Montsinery	500	GUF	RFI
17575	Jerusalem	500	ISR	Kol Israel
17580	Flevo	500	HOL	R Netherlands
	Talata Volondry	300	MDG	R Netherlands
	Komsomolsk	200	RUS	R Netherlands
17595	Abis	250	EGY	R Cairo
	Tangier	50	MRC	RTV Marocaine
	S Gabriel	100	POR	R Portugal
17605	Erevan	500	ARM	R Yerevan
	Bonaire	250	ATN	R Netherlands
	Alma Ata	20	KAZ	R Alma Ata
17610	Flevo	500	HOL	R Netherlands
	Talata Volondry	300	MDG	R Netherlands
17620	Allouis	500	F	RFI
	Moyabi	500	GAB	RFI
	Montsinery	500	GUF	RFI
17625	Lvov	100	UKR	R Yerevan
17630	Xian	500	CHN	China R Intl
	Moyabi	500	GAB	Africa No 1
17635	Sottens	500	SUI	Swiss R Intl
17640	Rampisham	500	G	BBCWS
	Skelton	250	G	BBCWS
	Greenville	250	USA	VoA
17645	Abu Dhabi	500	UAE	UAE R Abu Dhabi
17650	Moepeng Hill	100	BOT	VoA
	Kuming	500	CHN	China R Intl
	Allouis	500	F	RFI
17655	Tashkent	200	UZB	R Netherland
17670	Carnarvon	300	AUS	R Australia
	Abu Zaabal	250	EGY	R Cairo
17675	Samara	250	RUS	DW
17680	Lvov	250	UKR	R Yerevan
17690	Erevan	200	ARM	R Yerevan
	Abis	250	EGY	R Cairo
17695	Darwin	250	AUS	R Australia

Freq. [kHz]	Transmitter site	Power [kW]	Country	Station name
17695	Rampisham	500	G	BBCWS
(cont)	Skelton	250	G	BBCWS
17700	Beijing	50	CHN	China R 2
17705	MINSK	20	BLR	Belarus R
	MOEPENG HILL	100	BOT/USA	VoA
	HABANA	100	CUB	R Havana Cuba
	SKELTON	250	G	BBCWS
	KAVALLA	250	GRC	VoA
	DELHI	250	IND	AIR
	BRIECH	500	MRC/USA	VoA
	ISLAMABAD	250	PAK	R Pakistan
	TINANG	250	PHL	VoA
	MOSKVA	20	RUS	Domestic
17710	BEIJING	120	CHN	China R Intl
	XIAN	150	CHN	China R Intl
	ABIS	250	EGY	R Cairo
	RAMPISHAM	500	G	BBCWS
	JERUSALEM	300	ISR	Kol Israel
	DUCHANBE	240	TAD	R Moscow
	KAZAN	240	RUS	R Moscow
	TCHITA	100	RUS	R Moscow
	GREENVILLE	500	USA	VoA
	Meyerton	500	AFS	Channel Africa
17715	ANTIGUA	250	ATG	DW
	CARNARVON	250	AUS	R Australia
	ORCHA	20	BLR	Armenian R
	SANTIAGO	100	CHL	
	PERKARA	250	CLN	DW
	JUELICH	100	D	DW
	WERTACHTAL	500	D	Dw
	NOBLEJAS	350	E	REE
	SKELTON	300	G	BBCWS
	GREENVILLE	250	USA	VoA
17720	ALLOUIS	100	F	RFI
	MONTSINERY	500	GUF	RFI
	KARACHI	50	PAK	R Pakistan
	PORO	100	PHL	VoA
	BUCURESTI	250	ROU	R Romania Intl
	IRKUTSK	250	RUS	R Moscow
	KHABAROVSK	100	RUS	R Moscow
	PETROPAVLO KAM	100	RUS	R Moscow
	VOLGOGRAD	20	RUS	Domestic
	Taipei	100	TWN	VoFC

Freq. [kHz]	Transmitter site	Power [kW]	Country	Station name
17725	LIMASSOL	250	CYP/G	BBCWS
	ISMANING	100	D/USA	RFE/RL
	DELHI	100	IND	AIR
	REYKJAVIK	10	ISL	Icelandic B S
	BRIECH	500	MRC/USA	VoA
	KARACHI	50	PAK	R Pakistan
	LISBON	250	POR	RFE/RL
	LITOMYSL	100	TCH	R Prague
	MOSKVA	120	RUS	R Moscow
	OKEECHOBEE	100	USA	WYFR
17730	DHAKA	100	BGD	R Bangladesh
	HABANA	250	CUB	R Havana Cuba
	NOBLEJAS	350	E	REE
	ALMA ATA	20	RUS	R Alma Ata
	DUCHANBE	240	TAD	R Moscow
	SERPUKHOV	250	RUS	R Moscow
	BETHANY	250	USA	VoA
	SM Galeria	500	CVA	Vatican R
17735	MINSK	20	BLR	Belarus R
	ALIGARH	250	IND	AIR
	BRIECH	500	MRC/USA	VoA
	TINANG	250	PHL	VoA
	LISBON	250	POR	RFE/RL
	KAZAN	240	RUS	R Moscow
	KICHINEV	500	MDA	R Moscow
17740	LIMASSOL	250	CYP/G	BBCWS
	WOOFFERTON	250	G	VoA
	ALIGARH	250	IND	AIR
	ABU GHRAIB	250	IRQ	R Baghdad
	SALAH EL DEEN	250	IRQ	R Baghdad
	REYKJAVIK	10	ISL	Icelandic B S
	KUJANG	200	KRE	R Pyongyang
	KVITSOY	500	NOR	R Norway Intl
	TINANG	250	PHL	VoA
	HOERBY	500	S	R Sweden
	ABU DHABI	500	UAE	UAE R Abu Dhabi
	BICHKEK	240	RUS	R Moscow
	GREENVILLE	500	USA	VoA
	Pori	1000	FNL	YLE R Finland [ssb]
	Riyadh	500	ARS	BSKSA
17745	BOUCHAOUI	100	ALG	RTV Algerienne
	SANTIAGO	100	CHL	
	ABIS	250	EGY	R Cairo

Freq. [kHz]	Transmitter site	Power [kW]	Country	Station name
17745	S.GABRIEL	100	POR	R Portugal
(cont)	BUCURESTI	250	ROU	R Romania Intl
	KRUSK	500	RUS	R Moscow
17750	CARNARVON	300	AUS	R Australia
	BRASILIA	250	B	China R Intl/R Bras
	DHAKA	250	BGD	R Bangladesh
	LIMASSOL	250	CYP/G	BBCWS
	RAMPISHAM	500	G	BBCWS
	KIMJAE	250	KOR	R Korea
	ISLAMABAD	250	PAK	R Pakistan
	LISBON	250	POR	RFE/RL
	MAXOQUEIRA	500	POR	RFE/RL
	MAHE	100	SEY	FEBA
	ANKARA	250	TUR	TRT Vo Turkey
	ABU DHABI	500	UAE	UAE R Abu Dhabi
	OKEECHOBEE	100	USA	WYFR/VoFC
17755	RIYADH	500	ARS	BSKSA
	ASCENSION	250	ASC	BBCWS
	NOBLEJAS	350	E	REE
	REYKJAVIK	10	ISL	Icelandic B S
	KIMJAE	100	KOR	R Korea
	PYONGYANG	200	KRE	R Pyongyang
	TACHKENT	100	UZB	R Tashkent
17760	WAVRE	100	BEL	R Vlanderen Intl
	HABANA	100	CUB	R Havana Cuba
	LIMASSOL	250	CYP/G	BBCWS
	LAMPERTHEIM	100	D/USA	DW
	DELHI	250	IND	AIR
	TINANG	250	PHL	R Philipinas
	ACHKHABAD	1000	TKM	R Moscow
	KICHINEV	500	MDA	R Moscow
	MOSKVA	240	RUS	R Moscow
	BIRMINGHAM	500	USA	WEWN
	Riyadh	500	ARS	BSKSA
17765	MINSK	20	BLR	Belarus R/R Alma Ata
	JUELICH	100	D	DW
	WERTACHTAL	500	D	DW
	SIRJAN	500	IRN	IRIB
	KUJANG	200	KRE	R Pyongyang
	MEXICO	10	MEX	R Mexico Intl
	TINANG	250	PHL	VoA
	TULA	500	RUS	R Moscow
	VOLGOGRAD	20	RUS	R Alma Ata

Freq. [kHz]	Transmitter site	Power [kW]	Country	Station name
17770	WERTACHTAL	500	D/USA	VoA
	NOBLEJAS	350	E	REE
	ABIS	250	EGY	R Cairo
	AL KHAISAH	250	QAT	Qatar B S
	EREVAN	500	ARM	R Moscow
17775	RIYADH	500	ARS	BSKSA
	EKALA	300	CLN	DW
	ALLOUIS	100	F	RFI
	PORI	500	FIN	YLE R Finland
	KUJANG	200	KRE	R Pyongyang
	BICHKEK	1000	RUS	R Moscow
	TACHKENT	240	UZB	R Tashkent
	RANCHO SIMI	50	USA	KVOH
	Yamata	300	J	NHK R Japan
17780	SOFIA	250	BUL	R Bulgaria
	PERKARA	250	CLN	NHK R Japan
	JUELICH	100	D	DW
	RAMPISHAM	500	G	BBCWS
	ROMA	100	I	RAI
	REYKJAVIK	10	ISL	Icelandic B S
	KIMJAE	250	KOR	R Korea
	CYCLOPS	250	MLT	DW
	MARPI	100	MRA	FEBC
	MASIRAH	100	OMA/G	BBCWS
	TINANG	250	PHL	VoA
	LVOV	1000	UKR	R Ukraine Intl
	KICHINEV	500	RUS	R Moscow
17785	ALLOUIS	500	F	RFI
	BANGALORE	500	IND	AIR
	REYKJAVIK	10	ISL	Icelandic B S
	BRIECH	500	MRC/USA	VoA
	KARACHI	50	PAK	R Pakistan
	ALMA ATA	240	KAZ	R Alma Ata
	KRUSK	240	RUS	R Moscow
	NIJNIINOVGOROD	240	RUS	R Moscow
17790	MEYERTON	500	AFS/G	BBCWS
	ASCENSION	250	ASC	BBCWS
	SANTIAGO	100	CHL	
	QUITO	500	EQA	HCJB
	SIRJAN	500	IRN	IRIB
	MASIRAH	100	OMA/G	BBCWS
	PORO	100	PHL	VoA
	TINANG	250	PHL	VoA

Freq. [kHz]	Transmitter site	Power [kW]	Country	Station name
17790	BUCURESTI	250	ROU	R Romania Intl
(cont)	KRANJI	100	SNG/G	BBCWS
	ARMAVIR	1000	RUS	R Ukraine Intl
17795	SHEPPARTON	100	AUS	R Australia
	ALLOUIS	100	F	RFI
	WOOFFERTON	300	G	VoA
	ROMA	100	I	RAI
	DELHI	50	IND	AIR
	SINES	250	POR	DW
	EREVAN	1000	ARM	R Yerevan
	VLADIVOSTOK	250	RUS	R Moscow
	Sveio	500	NOR	R Norway Intl
17800	DHAKA	250	BGD	R Bangladesh
	WERTACHTAL	500	D	DW
	ABIS	250	EGY	R Cairo
	ALLOUIS	100	F	RFI
	IKORODU	500	NIG	R Nigeria
	KATHMANDU	100	NPL	R Nepal
	ISLAMABAD	100	PAK	R Pakistan
	KIGALI	250	RRW	DW
	BETHANY	250	USA	VoA
	GREENVILLE	500	USA	VoA
	Bucharest	250	ROU	R Moldova Intl
	Qatar	250	QAT	Qatar B S
17805	MINSK	20	BLR	Belarus R
	HOLZKIRCHEN	250	D/USA	RFE/RL
	WERTACHTAL	500	D/USA	RFE/RL
	NOBLEJAS	350	E	REE
	ALIGARH	250	IND	AIR
	DELHI	100	IND	AIR
	LISBON	250	POR	RFE/RL
	BUCURESTI	250	ROU	R Romania Intl
	ALMA ATA	240	KAZ	R Alma Ata
	GREENVILLE	500	USA	VoA
	OKEECHOBEE	100	USA	WYFR/VoFC
17810	MEYERTON	500	AFS	Channel Africa
	ASCENSION	250	ASC	BBCWS
	ANTIGUA	250	ATG	DW
	TOKYO YAMATA	300	J	NHK R Japan
	KIMJAE	250	KOR	R Korea
	CYCLOPS	250	MLT	DW
	ISLAMABAD	100	PAK	R Pakistan
	MOSKVA	250	RUS	Tatar R

Freq. [kHz]	Transmitter site	Power [kW]	Country	Station name
17815	S.PAULO	1	B	R Cultura
	NOBLEJAS	350	E	REE
	DELHI	50	IND	AIR
	TANGER	50	MRC	RTV Marocaine
	FREDRIKSTAD	350	NOR	R Norway Intl
	BUCURESTI	250	ROU	R Romania Intl
	BICHKEK	240	RUS	R Moscow
	KICHINEV	1000	MDA	R Moscow
	SERPUKHOV	250	RUS	R Moscow
17820	SACKVILLE	250	CAN	RCI
	EKALA	300	CLN	DW
	HABANA	50	CUB	R Havana Cuba
	PORO	100	PHL	VoA
	SFAX	100	TUN	ERTT
	KAZAN	240	RUS	R Moscow
	Abu Dhabi	500	UAE	UAE R Abu Dhabi
17825	SOFIA	250	BUL	R Bulgaria
	PERKARA	250	CLN	DW
	WERTACHTAL	500	D	DW
	CYCLOPS	250	MLT	DW
	AL KHAISAH	250	QAT	Qatar B S
	DUBAI	300	UAE	UAE R Dubai
	Pori	1000	FNL	YLE R Finland [ssb]
17830	ASCENSION	250	ASC	BBCWS/VoA
	SACKVILLE	250	CAN	RCI
	KAVALLA	250	GRC	VoA
	TSANG TSUI	250	HKG/G	BBCWS
	DELHI	250	IND	AIR
	KRANJI	125	SNG/G	BBCWS
	DUBAI	300	UAE	UAE R Dubai
	ARMAVIR	240	RUS	R Moscow
	GREENVILLE	500	USA	VoA
	NOBLESVILLE	100	USA	WHRI
17835	DHAKA	100	BGD	R Bangladesh
	SANTIAGO	100	CHL	
	KUJANG	200	KRE	R Pyongyang
	LISBON	250	POR	RFE/RL
	BICHKEK	240	RUS	R Moscow
	DUCHANBE	1000	TAD	R Moscow
	Havana	100	CUB	R Havana Cuba
17840	ANTIGUA	125	ATG	BBCWS
	WOOFFERTON	250	G	BBCWS
	KIMJAE	250	KOR	R Korea

Freq. [kHz]	Transmitter site	Power [kW]	Country	Station name
17840	FREDRIKSTAD	350	NOR	R Norway Intl
(cont)	KVITSOY	350	NOR	R Norway Intl
	SVEIO	500	NOR	R Norway Intl
	TINANG	250	PHL	R Philipinas
	BICHKEK	1000	RUS	R Moscow
	MOSKVA	20	RUS	R Moscow
	BIRMINGHAM	500	USA	WEWN
17845	JUELICH	100	D	DW
	WERTACHTAL	500	D	DW
	NOBLEJAS	350	E	REE
	ALLOUIS	500	F	RFI
	KAVALLA	250	GRC	VoA
	TOKYO YAMATA	300	J	NHK R Japan
	OKEECHOBEE	100	USA	WYFR/VoFC
	Riyadh	500	ARS	BSKSA
17850	SACKVILLE	100	CAN	RCI
	EKALA	35	CLN	SLBC
	ALLOUIS	500	F	RFI
	DELHI	50	IND	AIR
	SULAIBIYAH	500	KWT	R Kuwait
	BUCURESTI	250	ROU	R Romania Intl
	ALMA ATA	100	KAZ	R Alma Ata
	EKATERINBURG	240	RUS	R Moscow
	KHABAROVSK	240	RUS	R Moscow
17855	SHIJIAZHUANG	500	CHN	China R Intl
	BRIECH	500	MRC/USA	VoA
	ABU DHABI	500	UAE	UAE R Abu Dhabi
	KICHINEV	1000	MDA	R Moscow
17860	ASCENSION	250	ASC	BBCWS
	ANTIGUA	250	ATG	BBCWS
	MONTSINERY	500	GUF	RFI
	KIMJAE	100	KOR	R Korea
	KVITSOY	500	NOR	R Norway Intl
	SINES	250	POR	DW
	KIGALI	250	RRW	DW
	ALMA ATA	1000	KAZ	R Moscow
	KHABAROVSK	240	RUS	R Moscow
	KRUSK	100	RUS	R Moscow
	NOVOSIBIRSK	250	RUS	R Moscow
	TCHITA	1000	RUS	R Moscow
17865	WERTACHTAL	500	D/USA	VoA
	KAVALLA	250	GRC	VoA
	MARPI	100	MRA	Monitor R Intl

Freq. [kHz]	Transmitter site	Power [kW]	Country	Station name
17865	BRIECH	500	MRC/USA	VoA
(cont)	KVITSOY	500	NOR	R Norway Intl
	TINANG	250	PHL	VoA
	Hoerby	350	S	R Sweden
	S M Galeria	500	CVA	Vatican R
17870	WIEN	100	AUT	R Austria Intl
	CARIARI	100	CTR/E	REE
	NOBLEJAS	350	E	REE
	ATHINAI	100	GRC	Vo Greece
	ROMA	100	I	RAI
	KIMJAE	250	KOR	R Korea
	BRIECH	500	MRC/USA	VoA
	BUCURESTI	250	ROU	R Romania Intl
	HOERBY	500	S	R Sweden
	MONTEVIDEO	25	URG	
	TCHITA	1000	RUS	R Moscow
17875	RIO DE JANEIRO	8	B	
	SACKVILLE	250	CAN	RCI
	PERKARA	250	CLN	DW
	JUELICH	100	D	DW
	WERTACHTAL	500	D	DW
	ALLOUIS	500	F	RFI
	MONTSINERY	500	GUF	RFI
	ALIGARH	250	IND	AIR
	DELHI	100	IND	AIR
	BRIECH	500	MRC/USA	VoA
	TINANG	250	PHL	VoA
	LISBON	250	POR	RFE/RL
	ARMAVIR	250	RUS	R Moscow
	EREVAN	100	ARM	Armenian R
	SERPUKHOV	240	RUS	R Moscow
17880	RIYADH	500	ARS	BSKSA
	ASCENSION	250	ASC	BBCWS/VoA
	DARWIN	250	AUS	R Australia
	KUJANG	200	KRE	R Pyongyang
	ISLAMABAD	250	PAK	R Pakistan
	ALMA ATA	240	KAZ	R Moscow
	TULA	240	RUS	R Moscow
17885	LIMASSOL	250	CYP/G	BBCWS
	SULAIBIYAH	500	KWT	R Kuwait
	MAHE	250	SEY/G	BBCWS
	SERPUKHOV	500	RUS	R Moscow
	Munich	100	D	VoA

Freq. [kHz]	Transmitter site	Power [kW]	Country	Station name
17890	CARIARI	100	CTR/E	REE
	NOBLEJAS	350	E	REE
	QUITO	100	EQA	HCJB
	DUBAI	300	UAE	UAE R Dubai
	IRKUTSK	1000	RUS	R Moscow
	MOSKVA	20	RUS	R Moscow
17895	RIYADH	500	ARS	BSKSA
	SACKVILLE	100	CAN	RCI
	WOOFFERTON	300	G	VoA
	DELHI	250	IND	AIR
	SULAIBIYAH	500	KWT	R Kuwait
	TRIPOLI	500	LBY	Libya Jamahiriyah B
	BRIECH	500	MRC/USA	VoA
	KVITSOY	500	NOR	R Norway Intl
	ISLAMABAD	250	PAK	R Pakistan
	LUSAKA	50	ZMB	Zambia R
17900	Islamabad	250	PAK	R Pakistan
17940	Salah el Deen	500	IRQ	R Baghdad
18930	Birmingham	500	USA	WEWN
21455	QUITO	30	EQA	HCJB [ssb]
	ISLAMABAD	250	PAK	R Pakistan
	TINANG	250	PHL	R Philipinas
21460	NOBLEJAS	350	E	REE
	Bangalore	500	I	AIR
21465	KAVALLA	250	GRC	VoA
	ISLAMABAD	250	PAK	R Pakistan
	VOLGOGRAD	500	RUS	R Moscow
21470	LIMASSOL	250	CYP/G	BBCWS
21475	NOBLEJAS	350	E	REE
	KARACHI	50	PAK	R Pakistan
	TINANG	250	PHL	VoA
21480	TALATA VOLON	300	MDG	R Netherlands
	BUCURESTI	250	ROU	R Romania Intl
	S.PETERSBURG	500	RUS	R Moscow
	Flevo	500	HOL	R Netherlands
21485	DUBAI	300	UAE	UAE R Dubai
	GREENVILLE	250	USA	VoA
21490	ASCENSION	250	ASC	BBCWS
	DHAKA	250	BGD	R Bangladesh
	LIMASSOL	250	CYP/G	BBCWS

Freq. [kHz]	Transmitter site	Power [kW]	Country	Station name
21490	ALMA ATA	240	KAZ	R Alma Ata
(cont)	TCHITA	500	RUS	R Moscow
21495	RIYADH	500	ARS	BSKSA
	NOBLEJAS	350	E	REE
21500	SIRJAN	500	IRN	IRIB
	ABU DHABI	500	UAE	UAE R Abu Dhabi
	S.PETERSBURG	240	RUS	R Moscow
	OKEECHOBEE	100	USA	WYFR
	Flevo	500	HOL	R Netherlands
21505	TCHITA	1000	RUS	R Moscow
21510	ARMAVIR	240	RUS	R Moscow
	Lisbon	250	POR	RFE/RL
21515	S.M.GALERIA	500	CVA	Vatican R
	S.GABRIEL	100	POR	R Portugal
	BICHKEK	240	RUS	R Moscow
	Talata Volon	250	MDG	R Netherlands
21520	MOYABI	250	GAB/F	RFI
	KAVALLA	250	GRC	VoA
	ROMA	100	I	RAI
	ISLAMABAD	250	PAK	R Pakistan
21525	CARNARVON	250	AUS	R Australia
	VLADIVOSTOK	150	RUS	R Moscow
	OKEECHOBEE	100	USA	WYFR
21530	FLEVO	500	HOL	R Netherlands
	ARMAVIR	100	RUS	R Moscow
	KRUSK	250	RUS	R Moscow
	Allouis	500	F	RFI
21535	ROMA	100	I	RAI
	Tunis	100	TUN	ERTT
21540	NAUEN	500	D	DW
	NOBLEJAS	350	E	REE
	SIMFEROPOL	500	UKR	R Ukraine Intl
21545	SACKVILLE	250	CAN	RCI
	TEMA	100	GHA	Ghana B C
	DELHI	250	IND	AIR
	KARACHI	50	PAK	R Pakistan
	KINGHISEPP	240	RUS	R Moscow
	MOSKVA	200	RUS	R Moscow
21550	PORO	50	PHL	VoA
	Diosd	100	HNG	R Budapest

Freq. [kHz]	Transmitter site	Power [kW]	Country	Station name
21555	NOBLEJAS	350	E	REE
	KINGHISEPP	240	RUS	R Moscow
	Doha	250	QAT	Qatar B S
21560	JUELICH	100	D	DW
	ROMA	100	I	RAI
	KIGALI	250	RRW	DW
21565	DUCHANBE	240	TAD	R Dushanbe
	IRKUTSK	250	RUS	R Moscow
	S.PETERSBURG	240	RUS	R Moscow
21570	NOBLEJAS	350	E	REE
	TRIPOLI	500	LBY	Libya Jamahiriyah B
	Kavalla	250	GRC	VoA
21575	NOBLEJAS	350	E	REE
	MOYABI	500	GAB	NHK R Japan
	MOSKVA	500	RUS	R Moscow
21580	ALLOUIS	500	F	RFI
	ISLAMABAD	250	PAK	R Pakistan
	TINANG	250	PHL	R Philipinas
	GREENVILLE	250	USA	VoA
21585	ARMAVIR	500	RUS	R Moscow
	Tinang	250	PHL	VoA
21590	BONAIRE RNW	250	ATN	R Netherlands
	WOOFFERTON	250	G	VoA
	S.PETERSBURG	100	RUS	R Moscow
21595	DARWIN	250	AUS	R Australia
	NOBLEJAS	350	E	REE
	SVEIO	500	NOR	R Norway Intl
21600	JUELICH	100	D	DW
	WERTACHTAL	500	D	DW
	LIMA	50	PRU	
	MOSKVA	100	RUS	R Moscow
21605	DUBAI	300	UAE	UAE R Dubai
21610	TOKYO YAMATA	300	J	NHK R Japan
	Greenville	250	USA	VoA
21615	TINANG	250	PHL	VoA
	TACHKENT	100	UZB	R Tashkent
	OKEECHOBEE	100	USA	WYFR
21620	ALLOUIS	100	F	RFI

Freq. [kHz]	Transmitter site	Power [kW]	Country	Station name
21625	IRKUTSK	1000	RUS	R Moscow
	MOSKVA	240	RUS	R Moscow
21630	ABU DHABI	500	UAE	UAE R Abu Dhabi
	ARMAVIR	200	RUS	R Moscow
	Perkara	250	CLN	DW
21635	ALLOUIS	500	F	RFI
	MOYABI	250	GAB/F	RFI
	MONTSINERY	500	GUF	RFI
	TVER	240	RUS	R Moscow
21640	ASCENSION	250	ASC	BBCWS
	PERKARA	250	CLN	DW
	RAMPISHAM	500	G	BBCWS
	MOYABI	500	GAB	NHK R Japan
	SCOTTS CORNERS	500	USA	WCSN
21645	ALLOUIS	500	F	RFI
	MONTSINERY	500	GUF	RFI
	RIAZAN	240	RUS	R Moscow
21650	JUELICH	100	D	DW
	CYCLOPS	250	MLT	DW
21655	S.GABRIEL	100	POR	R Portugal
	IRKUTSK	250	RUS	R Moscow
	MOSKVA	500	RUS	R Moscow
21660	ASCENSION	250	ASC	BBCWS
	ALIGARH	250	IND	AIR
21665	S.M.GALERIA	100	CVA	Vatican R
	BUCURESTI	250	ROU	R Romania Intl
21670	S.M.GALERIA	100	CVA	Vatican R
	DELHI	250	IND	AIR
	ARMAVIR	810	RUS	R Moscow
	Riyadh	500	ARS	BSKSA
21675	SACKVILLE	250	CAN	RCI
	SULAIBIYAH	500	KWT	R Kuwait
	Dubai	500	UAE	UAE R Dubai
21680	PERKARA	250	CLN	DW
	WERTACHTAL	500	D	DW
	CYCLOPS	250	MLT	DW
	ARMAVIR	100	RUS	R Moscow
21685	ALLOUIS	500	F	RFI
	MONTSINERY	500	GUF	RFI

Freq. [kHz]	Transmitter site	Power [kW]	Country	Station name
21690	VLADIVOSTOK	1000	RUS	R Moscow
21695	PERKARA	250	CLN	DW
	KIGALI	250	RRW	DW
21700	NOBLEJAS	350	E	REE
	MOYABI	500	GAB/J	NHK R Japan
	SVEIO	500	NOR	R Norway Intl
	DUBAI	300	UAE	UAE R Dubai
21705	RIYADH	500	ARS	BSKSA
	KVITSOY	500	NOR	R Norway Intl
	SVEIO	500	NOR	R Norway Intl
	RIMAVSKA	250	SVK	Slovak R/R Prague
21710	SACKVILLE	250	CAN	RCI
	S.M.GALERIA	250	CVA	Vatican R
	ROMA	100	I	RAI
	BIRMINGHAM	500	USA	WEWN
21715	TSANG TSUI	250	HKG/G	BBCWS
	KRANJI	100	SNG/G	BBCWS
	TBILISI	100	GEO	R Moscow
21720	EJURA	250	GHA	Ghana BC
	ARMAVIR	100	RUS	R Moscow
	OKEECHOBEE	100	USA	WYFR/VoFC
21725	DARWIN	250	AUS	R Australia
	ARMAVIR	1000	RUS	R Moscow
	VOLGOGRAD	100	RUS	R Moscow
21730	ALLOUIS	100	F	RFI
	ISLAMABAD	250	PAK	R Pakistan
	ARMAVIR	500	RUS	R Moscow
21735	DELHI	250	IND	AIR
	ABU DHABI	500	UAE	UAE R Abu Dhabi
21740	SHEPPARTON	100	AUS	R Australia
	EREVAN	100	ARM	Armenian R
21745	Rampisham	500	G	BBCWS
	Bethany	250	USA	VoA
21760	S Gabriel	100	POR	R Portugal
21765	Montsinery	500	GUF	RFI
21810	Wavre	250	BEL	R Vlaanderen Intl
21815	Wavre	250	BEL	R Vlaanderen Intl
21820	Sottens	250	SUI	Swiss R Intl

Freq. [kHz]	Transmitter site	Power [kW]	Country	Station name
21850	SM Galeria	500	CVA	Vatican R
25690	Abu Dhabi	500	UAE	UAE R Abu Dhabi
25730	Kvitsoy	500	NOR	R Norway Intl
25820	ALLOUIS	100	F	RFI
25970	Flevo	500	HOL	R Netherlands

Section 7

EUROPEAN, MIDDLE EASTERN AND NORTH AFRICAN LONG WAVE STATIONS

Frequency [kHz]	Country	Station Site	Power [kW]	Programme/ Network
153	ROU	Brasov	1200	R Romania 1
	ALG	Bechar	1000	Arabic Network
	D	Donebach	500	DLF
	NOR	Tromsoe	10	P1
	RUS	Ufa	300	Ostankino 4
162	F	Allouis	2000	France Inter
	TUR	Agri	1000	TRT 1
171	MRC	Nador	1200	Medi 1
	RUS	Tbilisskaya	1200	Ostankino 1
	UKR	Lviv	1000	Ostankino 1
180	D	Oranienburg	250	DS Kultur
	D	Saarlouis-Felsburg	2000	Europe No 1
	TUR	Ankara	1200	TRT 2
	KAZ	Alma Ata	250	Kazakh R
189	S	Motala	300	P1
	I	Caltaniessetta	10	Radio Due
	GEO	Tbilisi	500	Georgian R 1
198	G	Droitwich	500	R4 UK
	G	Burghead	50	R4
	G	Westerglen	50	R4
	ALG	Ouargla	1000	Arabic Network
	RUS	St Petersburg	150	Ostankino 3
	TUR	Etimesgut	120	TRT 1
	POL	Warsaw	200	Warsaw 3
207	MRC	Azilal	800	Arabic Network
	D	Aholming	500/250	DLF
	UKR	Kiev	500	Ukrainian R 1
	ISL	Vatnsendi	100	First
216	MCO	Roumoules	1400	R Monte Carlo
	NOR	Oslo	200	P1
225	POL	Warsaw	2000	Warsaw 1
234	LUX	Junglinster	2000	RTL
	RUS	St Petersburg	2000	Ostankino 1
243	DNK	Kalundborg	300	P1
	TUR	Erzurum	200	TRT 1

Frequency [kHz]	Country	Station Site	Power [kW]	Programme/ Network
252	ALG	Tipazi	1500/750	French Network
	FNL	Lahti	200	First Programme
	IRL	Kilmessan	500	Atlantic 252
261	BUL	Plovdiv	500	Programme 1
	D	Burg	200	R Ropa
270	TCH	Uherske Hradiste	1500	Radiozurnal
279	BLR	Minsk	100	Belarus R

Section 8

EUROPEAN, NEAR AND MIDDLE EASTERN AND NORTH AFRICAN MEDIUM WAVE STATIONS

Freq. [kHz]	Country	Station Site	Power [kW]	Programme/ Network
522	D	Hof Saale	0.2	Bayern 1
	CVA	Citta del Vaticano	5	Vatican R
531	ALG	Ain Beida	600/300	Arabic Network
	SUI	Beromunster	500	DRS-1
	D	Leipzig	100	MDR-Info
	E	Oviedo	10	RNE5
	RUS	Cheboksary	30	Ostankino 3
540	HNG	Solt	2000	Kossuth
	MRC	Sidi Bennour	600	Arabic
	BEL	Waver-Overijse	150/50	BRT 2
	IRL	Conamara	2	R Na Gaeltachta
	KWT	Sulaibiyah	1500	R Kuwait Main Prog
549	ALG	Les Trembles	600/300	Arabic Network
	D	Bayreuth	200	DLF
	D	Nordkirchen	100	DLF
	RUS	St Petersburg	100	Ostankino 3
	SLO	Pristina	100	R Slovenia 1
	ARS	Duba	2000	Arabic 1/2
558	TUR	Denizli	600	TRT 1
	SUI	Monte Ceneri-Cima	300	Italian First Prog
	ROU	Targu Jiu	200	2nd Prog/Regional
	FNL	Helsinki	100	First Programme
	E	Valencia	20	RNE5
	D	Neubrandenburg	20	NDR2
	POR	Faro	10	Antena 1
	G	Lots Road	0.3	Spectrum R
	CYP	Paphos	10	CBC1
567	SYR	Samas-Adra	1000	Arabic Network
	IRL	Tullamore	500	RTE R1
	D	Berlin	1	SFB
	I	Bologna	20	R Uno
	POR	Valenca do Minho	10	Antena 1
	E	Marbella	5	RNE5
	RUS	Volgograd	250	R Rossii
	SVK	Rimavska Sobota	20	Slovak R 3

Freq. [kHz]	Country	Station Site	Power [kW]	Programme/ Network
576	LVA	Riga	500	Latvian R 1
	D	Stuttgart	300	SDR 1
	D	Schwerin	250	NDR
	ISR	Tel Aviv	200	Network A
	BUL	Vidin	100	Programme 2
	POR	Braga	10	R Renascenca
585	AUT	Vienna	600/240	ORF1
	TUN	Gafsa	350	Arabic Network
	E	Madrid	200	RNE1
	F	Paris	10	France Inter
	G	Dumfries	2	BBC R Scotland
	ARS	Riyadh	1200	Arabic Programme
594	D	Frankfurt	400	Hessischer RF
	BUL	Pleven	250	Programme 1
	MRC	Oujda	100	Arabic/Regional
	POR	Muge	100	R Renascenca
	ARS	Duba	2000	Arabic Programme
	RUS	Ijevsk	150	R Rossii
	HRV	Osijek	10	Hrvatski R 1
603	F	Lyon-Tramoyes	300	R France Lyon
	ROU	Botosani	50	R Romania 1
	D	Koenigswusterhausen	30	RA
	CYP	Nicosia	20	CBC2
	E	Seville	20	RNE5
	TUN	Sousse	10	Regional
	G	Newcastle	2	BBC R4
	G	Maidstone	0.5	Invicta Super Gold
	G	Cheltenham	0.1	603 R
	TCH	Brno	25	Brno Regional prog
612	BOS	Sarajevo	600	R Bosnia-Hercegovina
	MRC	Sebaa-Aiou	300	R Medi 1
	IRL	Athlone	100	RTE 2FM
	RUS	Petrozavodsk	100	Ostankino 3
	D	Kiel	10	NDR
	E	Lerida	10	RNE1
621	EGY	Batra	1000	Nile Valley R
	BEL	Wavre	300	RTBF 1
	E	Santa Cruz Tenerife	100	RNE1
	RUS	Syktyvkar	50	R Rossii
630	TUN	Djedeida	600	Arabic Network
	ROU	Timisoara	400	R Romania 1
	TUR	Cukurova	300	TRT 1
	NOR	Vigra	100	P1

Freq. [kHz]	Country	Station Site	Power [kW]	Programme/ Network
630	D	Dannenberg	80	SFB
(cont)	POR	Montemorvelho	50	Antena 1
	G	Redruth	2	BBC R Cornwall
	G	Luton	0.3	BBC 3 Counties R
	RUS	Saratov	50	Ostankino 1
639	TCH	Prague	1500	Prague Programme
	CYP	Zakaki	500	BBC World Service
	E	La Coruna	100	RNE1
	IRN	Bonab	400	VoIRI
648	G	Orfordness	500	BBC World Service
	UKR	Simferopol	150	Moscow 1/First
	ALB	Rrogozhina	15	Regional Prog
	E	Palma de Mallorca	10	RNE1
	SLO	Murska Sobota	10	R Slovenia 1
	LBY	Tobruk	300	Tripoli R
657	D	Burg	500	Jugendradio DT64
	D	Neubrandenburg	20	NDR
	I	Naples	120	R Uno
	E	Madrid	20	RNE5
	G	Wrexham	2	BBC R Wales
	G	Bodmin	0.5	BBC R Cornwall
666	SYR	Damas-Sabboura	600	Arabic Network
	LTU	Vilnius	500	R Vilnius
	D	Bodeseesender	300/180	SWF
	POR	Lisbon	135	Antena 1
	E	Barcelona	20	R Miramar
	G	Fulford	0.8	BBC R York
	G	Exeter	0.5	Devonair
675	F	Marseille	600	France Inter
	HOL	Lopik	120	Hilversum 3
	LBY	Benghazi	100	Tripoli R
	UKR	Ujgorod	50	Ukrainian R 3
684	YUG	Belgrade	2000	Serbian R
	E	Seville	250	RNE1
	D	Hof-Saale	40	RIAS
693	CYP	Nicosia	20	CBC 1
	D	Berlin	250	BR
	G	Droitwich	150	BBC R 5 [+ 10 stns]
	I	Potenza	20	R Due
	ALB	Pogradec	10	
	POR	Viseu	10	Antena 1
	YUG	Negotin	10/5	Serbian R
	ALG	Ain-el-Hamam	5	

Freq. [kHz]	Country	Station Site	Power [kW]	Programme/ Network
702	SVK	Banska Bystrica	400	Slovak R 1
	MCO	Monte Carlo	300	R Monte Carlo 2
	MRC	Sebaa-Aioun	140	Network C
	NOR	Finnmark	20	P1
	D	Flensburg	5	NDR
	E	Zamora	5	RNE1
711	F	Rennes	300	R Bleue
	EGY	Abu Zaabal	100	People's Comm Prog
	LBY	Ghadames	50	
	ROU	Sighet	30	R Romania 2
	YUG	Nis	20	Serbian R
	D	Heidelberg	5	SDR
	MRC	Laayoune	600	Arabic/Regional
720	CYP	Zakaki	500	BBC World Serivce
	D	Langenberg	200	WDR
	D	Munich	150	RFE
	POR	Azurara	100	Antena 1
	G	Lisnagarvey	10	BBC R 4
	G	London	0.5	BBC R 4
	G	Londonderry	0.25	BBC R 4
	ROU	Predeal	2	R Romania 2
	TUN	Sfax	200	Sfax Regional Prog
	IRN	Taybad	400	VoIRI
	E	Santa Cruz Tenerife	20	RNE5
729	GRC	Athens	150	ERT 1
	E	Oviedo	50	RNE1
	IRL	Cork	10	RTE R1
	D	Leipzig	5	S1
	D	Putbus	5	NDR2
	G	Manningtree	0.2	BBC Essex
738	ISR	Tel Aviv	1200	Network D
	POL	Poznan	300	Warsaw 4
	E	Barcelona	250	RNE1
	F	Paris	5	RFI
	G	Worcester	0.04	BBC Hereford & Worcester
	RUS	Moscow	5	Ostankino 4
747	BUL	Petrich	500	Programme 1
	HOL	Flevoland	400	Hilversum 1
	SYR	Sarakeb	100	Arabic Network
	E	Cadiz	10	RNE5
756	D	Braunschweig	800/200	DLF
	ROU	Lugoj	400	R Romania 2

Freq. [kHz]	Country	Station Site	Power [kW]	Programme/ Network
756	POR	Lisbon	5	R Comercial
(cont)	G	Redruth	2	BBC R 4
	G	Carlisle	1	BBC R Cumbria
	G	Newtown	1	R Maldwyn
765	SUI	Sottens	600	R Suisse Romande 1
	TUR	Gaziantep	600	TRT 1
	RUS	Medvejiegorsk	150	R Rossii
	GRC	Ioannina	20	ERT 4
	G	Chelmsford	0.5	BBC Essex
	ARS	Damman	1000	
774	BUL	Sofia Stolnik	60	Programme 1
	E	Caceres	60	RNE1
	BOS	Bihac	2	R Bosnia-Hercegovina
	D	Bonn	5	WDR
	G	Enniskillen	1	BBC R 4
	G	Plymouth	1	BBC R 4
	G	Leeds	0.5	BBC R Leeds
	G	Canterbury	0.7	BBC R Kent
	G	Gloucester	0.2	Severn Sound Super Gold
	HRV	Hvar	50	Hrvatski R 1
783	D	Burg	1000	MDR-Info
	SYR	Tartus	600	Arabic Network
	POR	Porto Miramar	50	R Porto
	HRV	Buje	10	Hrvatski R 1
	ARS	Damman	100	
792	GRC	Kavalla	500	VoA
	F	Limoges	300	France Culture
	TCH	Prague	30	Regional Prague Prog
	E	Seville	20	R Sevilla
	G	Londonderry	1	BBC R Ulster
	G	Bedford	0.2	Chiltern Supergold
	RUS	Astrakhan	50	Ostankino 1
801	JOR	Ajlun	2000	Arabic Network
	RUS	Leningrad	1000/500	Moscow 1
	D	Munich	450/420	Bayern 1
	E	Castellon	5	RNE1
	G	Barnstaple	2	BBC R Devon
810	MDN	Skopje	1000	RTV Macedonia
	G	Burghead	100	BBC R Scotland
	G	Westerglen	100	BBC R Scotland
	G	Redmoss	5	BBC R Scotland
	E	Madrid	20	R Madrid

Freq. [kHz]	Country	Station Site	Power [kW]	Programme/ Network
810	D	Berlin	5	DLF
(cont)	RUS	Volgograd	150	Ostankino 3
819	AND	Andorra	900	Sud R
	EGY	Batra	450	Arabic Programme
	POL	Warsaw	300	Warsaw 4
	I	Trieste	25	R Uno
	MRC	Rabat	25	Arabic Network
828	BUL	Shumen	500	Programme 2
	MRC	Oujda	100	French Network
	D	Hannover	100/5	NDR
	D	Freiburg	1	SWF
	E	Barcelona	20	R Barcelona
	G	Bournemouth	0.3	2CR Classic Gold
	G	Sedgley	0.2	BBC R WM
	G	Luton	0.18	Chiltern Supergold
	G	Leeds	0.18	Magic 828
	RUS	Kyzyi	150	Ostankino 3
837	F	Nancy	200	R France Nancy
	UKR	Kharkov	150	Ukrainian R 2
	E	Seville	10	R Popular Seville
	G	Leicester	0.45	BBC R Leicester
	G	Barrow	1	BBC R Furness
	E	Las Palmas	10	R Popular de Ibiza
	HRV	Gospic	1	Hrvatski R 1
846	I	Rome	540	R Due
855	ROU	R Romania	1500	R Romania 2
	E	Murcia	125	RNE1
	D	Berlin	100	RIAS
	G	Plymouth	1	BBC R Devon
	G	Norwich	1	BBC R Norfolk
	G	Preston	0.5	BBC R Lancashire
864	EGY	Santah	500	Holy Koran R
	F	Paris	300	R France Paris
	BUL	Blagoevgrad	30	Programme 2
	TCH	Olomouc	20	Regional Ostrava prog
	ALB	Kelcyra	1	Regional Prog
	ARS	Damman	500	
873	D	Frankfurt	150	AFN
	RUS	St Petersburg	150	R Rossii
	E	Zaragoza	20	R Zaragoza
	HNG	Budapest	20	2nd Programme
	G	Enniskillen	1	BBC R Ulster
	G	King's Lynn	0.25	BBC R Norfolk

Freq. [kHz]	Country	Station Site	Power [kW]	Programme/ Network
882	YUG	Podgorica	600	R Podgorica
	D	Wachenbrunn	250	MDR-Info
	G	Washford	100	BBC R Wales [+3 stns]
	E	Alicante	2	R Popular de Alicante
	ARS	Damman	100	
	RUS	Stavropol	500	Ostankino 3
891	ALG	Algiers	600/300	Arabic Network
	TUR	Antalya	600	TRT 1
	UKR	Ujgorod	150	Ukrainian R 1
	HOL	Hulsberg	20	Hilversum 5
	D	Berlin	5	DS Kultur
900	ARS	Guriat	1000	
	I	Milan	600	R Uno
	TCH	Karlovy Vary	30	Regional Prog
909	G	Moorside Edge	200	BBC 5 Live [+ 10 stns]
	ROU	Cluj	50	R Romania 2
	E	Palma de Mallorca	10	R Cadena Espana
	ALB	Korce	15	
918	SLO	Ljubljana	600/100	R Slovenia 1
	E	Madrid	20	R Intercontinental
927	BEL	Wolvertem	300	BRT1
	TUR	Izmir	200	TRT1
	POR	Evora	1	Regional Programme
	ALG	Timimoun	5	Arabic Programme
936	UKR	Lviv	500	Ukrainian R 1/ R Ukraine Intl
	D	Bremen	100	R Bremen
	I	Venice	20	R Due
	E	Lerida	1	
	G	Chippenham	0.2	Brunel Classic Gold
945	F	Toulouse	300	R France Toulouse
	RUS	Rostov	300	R Rossii
	BOS	Sarajevo	100	R Bosnia-Hercegovina
	BUL	Pleven	30	Programme 2
	GRC	Larissa	5	ERT 4
	G	Derby	0.2	Gem-AM
	TCH	Liberac	6	Regional Programme
954	TUR	Trabzon	300	TRT1
	TCH	Brno	200	Prague Programme
	BUL	Shumen	30	Programme 1
	E	Madrid	20	R Espana
	GRC	Iraklion	20	Regional Programme

Freq. [kHz]	Country	Station Site	Power [kW]	Programme/ Network
954	G	Torbay	0.4	Devonair
(cont)	G	Hereford	0.4	R Wyvern
963	FNL	Pori	600	First Prog/ YLE R Finland
	TUN	Djedeida	200	Intl Network
	BUL	Sofia	150	Programme 1
	POR	Seixal	10	R Renascenca
972	UKR	Kopani	500	Ukrainian R 2
	D	Hamburg	300	NDR
	E	Monforte de Lemos	2	RNE1
981	ALG	Algiers	600/300	French Network
	GRC	Megara	200	ERT 4
	I	Trieste	10	Slovene
	TCH	Ceske Budejovice	7	Prague Programme
	POR	Coimbra	10	R Renascenca
990	D	Berlin	300	RIAS
	ALB	Kukes	15	Regional Programme
	E	Bilbao	10	R Bilbao
	I	Potenza	10	R Uno
	G	Exeter	1	BBC R Devon
	G	Aberdeen	1	BBC R Aberdeen
	G	Tywyn	1	BBC 5 Live
	G	Wolverhampton	0.1	WABC
	G	Doncaster	0.3	Great Yorkshire
	G	London	1	Spectrum R
	G	Redmoss	1	BBC R Scotland
999	I	Turin	50	R Due
	E	Madrid	20	R Popular Madrid
	D	Hoyerswerda	20	Sorbischer Rundfunk
	D	Schwerin	20	RIAS
	MLT	Delimara	5	R Malta 1
	G	Fareham	1	BBC R Solent
	G	Nottingham	0.2	GEM-AM
	G	Preston	0.8	Red Rose Gold
1008	HOL	Flevoland	400	Radio 5
	YUG	Aleksinac	400/120	Serbian R
	BLR	Mozyr	50	Belarus R 2
	GRC	Kerkyra	50	ERT 1/2/Regional
	E	Las Palmas	10	R Cadena Espana
1017	TUR	Istanbul	1200	TRT 1
	D	Wolfsheim	600	SWF
	BUL	Kardjali	30	Programme 1
	D	Seelow	5	RA

Freq. [kHz]	Country	Station Site	Power [kW]	Programme/ Network
1017	G	Telford		WABC
(cont)	SVK	Nitra	50	Hungarian prog [+3 stns]
1026	AUT	Linz Kronstorf	100	ORF 1/3
	BLR	Brest	5	Belarus R 2
	G	Belfast	1	Downtown R
	G	St Helier	1	BBC R Jersey
	G	Cambridge	0.5	BBC R Cambridgeshire
	E	Reus	2	R Reus
	E	Gijon	2	
1035	IRQ	Babel	1000	Arabic Prog
	EST	Tallin	500	Estonian R 2/Ext
	POR	Lisbon	135	R Comercial
	I	Milan	50	R Due
	G	Sheffield	1	BBC R Sheffield
	G	Gillingham	0.5	BBC R Kent
	G	Aberdeen	0.78	NorthSound
	G	Ayr	0.32	West Sound
	G	Crystal Palace	1	Country 1035
1044	MRC	Sebaa Aioun	300	Arabic/REgional
	D	Burg	250	MDR-Info
	GRC	Macedonia	150	ERT 1/2/Regional
	CYP	Limassol	10	CBC 1
	E	San Sebastian	10	R San Sebastian
1053	ROU	Iasi	1000	R Romania 2
	MRC	Tangier	600	Arabic/Regional
	LBY	Tripoli	50	Tripoli R
1062	DNK	Kalundborg	250	P3
	POR	Azurara	100	R Comercial
	I	Cagliari	25	R Uno
	YUG	Svetozarevo	10	R Beograd 1
	TUR	Diyabakir	300	TRT1
1071	SYR	Tartus	60	French Network
	TCH	Prague	60/30	Radiozurnal [+5 stns]
	LAT	Riga	60	Latvian R
	F	Lille	40	France Inter
	BOS	Banja Luka	20	Banja Luka R
1080	POL	Katowice	1500	Warsaw 4
	GRC	Orestias	20	ERT 4/Regional
	E	La Coruna	3	
	E	Granada	5	R Granada
	E	Mallorca	2	R Mallorca

Freq. [kHz]	Country	Station Site	Power [kW]	Programme/ Network
1089	RUS	Krasnodar	300	R Rossii/ R Moscow Intl
	ALB	Durres	150	National/Foreign
	D	Dresden	20	T1
	ALG	Adrar	5	Arabic Network
1098	SVK	Bratislava	750	Slovak R 1
	CYP	Yeni Iskele	100	R Bayrak
	E	Lugo	5	RNE5
	KAZ	Alma Ata	150	Kazakh R
	E	Santa Cruz de Palma	2	R Cadena Espana
1107	EGY	Batra	600	Nile Valley
	LIT	Kaunas	150	R Vilnius
	YUG	Novi Sad	150	R Novi Sad 1
	D	Berlin	10	AFN
	I	Rome	6	R Tre
	G	Northampton	0.5	BBC R Northampton
	G	Wallasey	0.5	BBC R 1
	G	Inverness	1	Moray Firth R
1116	IRQ	Rutba	300	Arabic Programme
	I	Bari	150	R Due
	RUS	Kaliningrad	30	Ostankino 2
	HNG	Miskolc	120	Kossuth R
	D	Karl Marx Stadt	5	S1
	G	Derby	1.2	BBC R Derby
	G	St Peter Port	0.5	BBC R Guernsey
1125	HRV	Zagreb	300/100	Hrvatski R 1
	BEL	La Louviere	20	RTBF 2
	RUS	St Petersburg	20	Ostankino 4
	G	Llandrindod Wells	1	BBC R Wales
	E	Castellon	10	RNE5
	HRV	Deanovec	100	Hrvatski R 1
1134	HRV	Zadar	1200	Hrvatski R 1
	E	Bilbao	10	R Popular de Bilbao
	E	Figueras	2	R P Figueras
	KWT	Sulaibiyah	750	
1143	RUS	Samara	150	Ostankino 3
	HRV	Tovarnik	300	Hrvatski R 1
	D	Stuttgart	10	AFN
	I	Sassari	10	R Due
1152	ROU	Cluj	950	R Romania 2
	G	London	5.5	London News Radio
	G	Glasgow	2	Clyde 2

Freq. [kHz]	Country	Station Site	Power [kW]	Programme/ Network
1152	G	Birmingham	0.8	Xtra-AM
(cont)	G	Manchester	0.35	Piccadilly Gold
	G	Plymouth	0.5	Plymouth Sound
	G	Newcastle-on-Tyne	1	Great North R
1161	BUL	Stara Zagora	500	Programme 1
	F	Strasbourg	200	France Inter
	EGY	Tanta	60	Regional Programme
	G	Bexhill	1	BBC 2 Counties R
	G	Bedford	0.8	BBC 3 Counties R
	G	Swindon	0.2	Brunel Classic Gold
	G	Dundee	0.5	R Tay
	G	Hull	0.35	Great Yorkshire
1170	BLR	Moghilev	1000	R Belarus
	SLO	Beli Kriz	300/100	R Slovenia
	D	Brenburg	20	Sachsenradio
	POR	Vila Read	10	R Comercial
	G	Swansea	0.8	Swansea Sound
	G	Stockton-on-Tees	0.5	Gt North R
	G	Stoke-on-Trent	0.2	Signal Gold
	G	Ipswich	0.28	SGR FM
	G	Portsmouth	0.12	South Coast
	G	High Wycombe		Eleven Seventy
	RUS	Tbilisskaya	1200	Ostankino 3/ R Moscow
1179	S	Soelvesborg	600	R Sweden
	ROU	Bacau	200	R Romania 1
	GRC	Thessaloniki	50	Regional Programme
	E	Murcia	5	R Murcia
1188	HNG	Szolnok	135	Programme 2
	I	San Remo	6	R Due
	BEL	Kuurne	5	BRT 2
	D	Wachenbrunn	20	MDR-Info
	MRC	Casablanca	1	French Network
1197	D	Munich	300	VoA
	BLR	Minsk	50	Belarus R 2
	MRC	Agadir	20	French Network
	G	Enniskillen	1	Virgin R [+8 stns]
1206	POL	Wroclaw	200	Warsaw 4
	F	Bordeaux	100	R France Bordeaux
	ISR	Haifa	50	Network B
1215	ALB	Lushnje	500	Foreign Services

Freq. [kHz]	Country	Station Site	Power [kW]	Programme/ Network
1215	G	Moorside Edge	100	Virgin R [+16 stns]
(cont)	RUS	Bolshakova	1200	Ostankino 3/ R Moscow
1224	BUL	Vidin	500	Programme 1
	IRQ	Nasiriya	300	
	E	Santander	2	R Pop de Santander
	G	Lydd		Virgin R
1233	CYP	Cape Greco	600	R Monte Carlo
	TCH	Prague	400	Radiozurnal
	MRC	Tangier	200	Medi 1
	BEL	Liege	5	RTBF 2
	G	Crawley		Virgin R [+5 stns]
1242	F	Marseille	150	R France Marseille
	UKR	Kiev	150	Ukrainian R 2
	G	Gillingham	0.32	Invicta Super Gold
	G	Isle of Wight	0.5	Isle of Wight R
	G	Dundee		Virgin R [+3 stns]
1251	HNG	Siofok	500	Programme 2
	LBY	Tripoli	500	Tripoli R
	HOL	Hulsberg	10	Hilversum 1
	POR	Porto	10	R Renascenca
	G	Bury St Edmunds	0.5	SGR FM
1260	GRC	Rhodes	500	VoA
	E	Valencia	20	R Valencia
	POL	Szczecin	10	Warsaw 4
	ALB	Fier	1	Regional Programme
	G	Bristol	0.8	Brunel Classic Gold
	G	Wrexham	0.32	Marcher Gold
	G	Leicester	0.2	Sunrise East Midlands
	G	Scarborough	0.5	BBC R York
1269	D	Neumuenster	600	DLF
	YUG	Novi Sad	600	R Novi Sad 2
	E	Leon	2	R Popular de Leon
1278	F	Strasbourg	300	R France Strasbourg
	UKR	Odessa	150	R Liberty
	IRL	Cork	10	RTE 2
	GRC	Florina	20	ERT
	G	Bradford	0.43	Great Yorkshire
1287	SVK	Velke Kostolany	300	R Prague/ R Free Europe
	ISR	Tel Aviv	100	Israel Defence R
	POR	Portalegre	1	Antena 1
	ALG	El Golea	5	Arabic Network

Freq. [kHz]	Country	Station Site	Power [kW]	Programme/ Network
1296	G	Orfordness	500	BBC World Service
	BUL	Kardjali	150	Programme 2
1305	POL	Rzeszow	100	Warsaw 4
	ISR	Haifa	20	Israel Defence R
	ALB	Gjirokaster	15	Regional Programme
	BEL	Marche	10	RTBF 2
	I	Pisa	2	R Tre
	G	Barnsley	0.3	Great Yorkshire
	G	Newport	0.2	Touch AM
1314	NOR	Kvitsoy	1200	P1
	ROU	Timisoara	30	R Romania 1/2
	GRC	Tripolis	20	ERT 4/Regional
	I	Ancona	6	R Due
	UAE	Abu Dhabi	1000	
1323	D	Wachenbrunn	1000/150	RMR
	CYP	Zyyi	200	BBC World Service
	G	Taunton	1	BBC R Bristol
	G	Brighton	0.5	Southern Sound
1332	I	Rome	300	R Uno
	TCH	Moravske	50	Prague/Regional
	ROU	Galatzi	15	Programme 1
	G	Peterborough	0.5	WGMS
	G	Lacock	0.4	BBC Wiltshire Sound
	G	Taunton	0.6	BBC Somerset Sound
	IRN	Teheran	100	VoIRI
1341	HNG	Budapest	300	Programme 2
	G	Lisnagarvey	100	BBC R Ulster
	D	Marneukirchen	1	S1
	E	Tarrasa	2	R Popular de Tarrasa
1350	F	Nancy	100	France Inter
	HNG	Pecs	10	Programme 2
	YUG	Studio B 1	10	Regional Programme
	GRC	Pyrgos	4	ERT 4/Regional Prog
	MTN	Nouakchott	50	ORTM
1359	D	Berlin	250/100	Antenne Brandenburg
	ALB	Tirana	50	R Tirana
	E	Melilla	5	RNE 1
	G	Chelmsford	0.3	Breeze AM
	G	Coventry	0.1	Xtra-AM
	G	Cardiff	0.25	Touch AM
	G	Bournemouth	0.25	BBC R Solent
	IRQ	Kirkuk	120	Kurdish Programme

Freq. [kHz]	Country	Station Site	Power [kW]	Programme/ Network
1368	POL	Krakow	60	Warsaw 4
	I	Venice	20	R Tre
	G	Isle of Man	10	Manx R
	G	Lincoln	2	BBC R Lincolnshire
	G	Crawley	0.5	BBC 2 Counties R
	G	Swindon	0.1	BBC Wiltshire Sound
	ISR	Shivta	20	Israel Defence R
1377	F	Lille	300	R France Lille
	UKR	Lutsk	50	Ukrainian R 2
	POR	Canidelo	10	Antena 1
	YUG	Prizren	10	Regional Programme
	D	Klingenthal	1	Sachsenradio
1386	RUS	Kaliningrad	150	R Moscow
	GRC	Athens	50	ERT 2 .
	IRN	Ahwaz	400	First Programme
1395	ALB	Lusnje	1000	R Tirana
	E	Leon	5	RNE 5
1404	GRC	Komotini	50	Regional
	UKR	Dniepropetrovsk	30	Ukrainian R 2
	F	Ajaccio	20	R France Ajaccio
	LBY	Tripoli	20	Holy Koran Prog
	ROU	Baia Mare	15	R Romania 1
1413	YUG	Pristina	1000	R Pristina 1
	D	Heidenheim	0.2	SDR
	G	Hounslow	0.13	Sunrise R
	OMA	Masirah	750	BBC World Service
1422	D	Saarbrucken	1200/600	SR1
	RUS	Valmeira	50	R Rossii
	ALG	Algiers	50/25	Kabyl & French
1431	UKR	Kopani	500	Ukrainian R 3/ R Ukraine Intl
	D	Dresden	250	S1
	I	Foggia	2	R Due
	G	Southend	0.4	Breeze AM
	G	Reading	0.2	210 Classic Gold
1440	LUX	Marnach	1200	R Luxembourg
	YUG	Svetozarevo	20/10	R Beograd 2/3
	ARS	Damman	1600	
1449	I	Squinzano	50	R Due
	LBY	Miurata	20	Tripoli R
	D	Berlin	5	SFB
	G	Redmoss	2	BBC R 4

Freq. [kHz]	Country	Station Site	Power [kW]	Programme/ Network
1449 (cont)	G	Peterborough	0.1	BBC R Cambridgeshire
	HRV	Osijek	20	Local
1458	ALB	Lushnje	500	R Tirana
	ROU	Constantza	50	R Romania 2
	G	Brookmans Park	50	BBC GLR
	G	Birmingham	7	BBC R WM
	G	Manchester	5	BBC R Greater Manchester
	G	Newcastle-on-Tyne	2	BBC R Newcastle
	G	Torbay	1	BBC R Devon
	G	Whitehaven	0.5	BBC R Cumbria
	D	Weida	5	Thuringen Eins
1467	MCO	Monte Carlo	1000/400	R Monte Carlo/TWR
1476	AUT	Vienna Bisamberg	600	ORF 1/2/3
	UKR	Lvov	120	Ukrainian R 3/ R Liberty
	G	Guildford	0.5	County Sound
	E	Bilbao	10	RNE 5
1485	I	Bolzano	2	R Due
	G	Hull	1.5	BBC R Humberside
	G	Wallasey	2	BBC R Merseyside
	G	Bournemouth	2	BBC R 1
	G	Carlisle	1	BBC R 4
	G	Shoreham	1	BBC 2 Counties R
	G	Oxford	0.5	BBC R Oxford
	POL	Gizycko	1	Warsaw 4
	E	Gerona	2	R Gerona
	E	Santander	2	R Santander
1494	RUS	St Petersburg	1000	Ostankino 2/ R Moscow
	F	Bastia	20	R France Bastia
	CTI	Abidjan	20	
1503	POL	Stargard	300	Warsaw 4
	G	Stoke-on-Trent	1	BBC R Stoke
	E	Burgos	10	RNE 5
	BOS	Zavidovici	1	R Bosnia-Hercegovina
1512	BEL	Wolvertem	600	BRT2/ R Vlaanderen Intl
	GRC	Chania	50	Regional Prog
	RUS	Sotchi	30	Ostankino 1
	I	Palermo	2	R Tre
	ARS	Jeddah	1200	Call of Islam

Freq. [kHz]	Country	Station Site	Power [kW]	Programme/ Network
1521	TCH	Kosice	600	Radiozurnal
	G	Reigate	0.74	County Sound
	E	Oveido	5	R Asturias
	ARS	Duba	2000	
1530	CVA	Vatican City	450	Vatican R
	ROU	Mahmudia	15	R Romania 1
	UKR	Vinnytsya	5	Ukrainian R 1
	G	Halifax	1	Great Yorkshire R
	G	Southend-on-Sea	0.1	BBC R Essex
	G	Worcester	0.5	R Wyvern
1539	D	Mainflingen	450	DLF
	RUS	Borovitchi	150	Independent
	E	Valladolid	5	R Valladolid
1548	G	London	27.5	Capital Gold
	G	Bristol	5	BBC R Bristol
	G	Liverpool	1.2	City Gold
	G	Sheffield	0.3	Great Yorkshire R
	G	Edinburgh	2	Max AM
1557	MLT	Cyclops	600	DW/R Medi
	F	Nice	300	R France Nice
	G	Northampton	0.76	Northants R
	G	Lancaster	0.25	BBC R Lancashire
	G	Southampton	0.5	South Coast
	G	Tendring	0.1	Mellow 1557
1566	TUN	Sfax Sidi Mansour	1200	Arabic Network
	SUI	Monte Ceneri	300	DRS 1
	UKR	Odessa	5	Ukrainian R 3
	SLO	Smarje	2	R Slovenia
	POR	Covilha	1	Antena 1
1575	D	Burg	250	DS Kultur
	I	Genova	50	R Uno
	POR	Canidelo	10	R Comercial
	E	Cordoba	5	R Cordoba
	UAE	Sharjah	50	
1584	POL	Ostoda	1	Warsaw 4
	D	Cottbus	1	R Mecklenburg
	G	Mansfield	1	BBC R Nottingham
	G	Woofferton	0.3	BBC R Shropshire
	G	Perth	0.2	R Tay
	E	Pamplona	2	
	BOS	Mostar	1	R Bosnia-Hercegovina

Freq. [kHz]	Country	Station Site	Power [kW]	Programme/ Network
1593	D	Langenburg	800	WDR
	ROU	Baneasa	14	Bucharest 1
1602	I	Bolzano	2	R Tre
	POL	Gorzow Wielk	1	Warsaw 4
	D	Bautzen	1	R Mecklenburg
	G	Rusthall	0.25	BBC R Kent
	E	Lugo	2	R Lugo
1611	CVA	Vatican City	5	Vatican R

Section 9

CANADIAN MEDIUM WAVE RADIO STATIONS

Frequency [kHz]	Station Site	Province	Power [kW]	Call Sign
530	High Level	AB	0.25	CKHL
	Brampton	ON	1	CIAO
540	Grand Falls	NF	10	CBT
	Windsor	ON	2.5	CBEF
	New Carlisle	PQ	10	CBGA1
	Ottawa	ON	50	CJSB
	Watrous	SK	50	CBK
550	Kamloops	BC	25	CFJC
	Prince George	BC	10	CKPG
	Fredricton	NB	50	CFNB
	Sudbury	ON	10	CHNO
	Trois Rivieres	PQ	10	CHLN
560	Fort St John	BC	1	CKNL
	Prince Rupert	BC	1	CHTK
	Carbonear	NF	5	CHVO
	Kirkland Lake	ON	5	CJKL
	Owen Sound	ON	7.5	CFOS
	Sept Iles	PQ	10	CKCN
570	Cranbrook	BC	10	CKEK
	Williams Lake	BC	1	CKWL
	Edmundston	NB	5	CJEM
	Corner Brook	NF	1	CFCB
	Kitchener	ON	10	CKGL
	Swift Current	SK	10	CKSW
	Whitehorse	YT	5	CFWH
580	Edmonton	AB	10	CKUA
	Salmon Arm	BC	10	CKXR
	Winnipeg	MB	50	CKY
	Antigonish	NS	25	CJFX
	Kapuskasing	ON	10	CKAP
	Ottawa	ON	50	CFRA
	Thunder Bay	ON	5	CKPR
	Baie-Comeau	PQ	10	CHLC
590	Terrace	BC	1	CFTK
	Flin Flon	MB	10	CFAR
	Sussex	NB	1	CJCW
	St John's	NF	20	VOCM

Frequency [kHz]	Station Site	Province	Power [kW]	Call Sign
590 (cont)	Toronto	ON	50	CKYC
	Jonquiere	PQ	25	CKRS
600	Vancouver	BC	10	CHRX
	St Anthony	NF	10	CBNA
	Truro	NS	10	CKCL
	North Bay	ON	10	CFCH
	Montreal	PQ	10	CIQC
	Saskatoon	SK	10	CFQC
610	Peace River	AB	10	CKYL
	Kamloops	BC	25	CHNL
	Trail	BC	10	CJAT
	Thompson	MB	1	CHTM
	St Catherines	ON	10	CKTB
	Mont Laurier	PQ	1	CFLO
	New Carlisle	PQ	10	CHNC
	Whitehorse	YT	1	CKRW
620	Prince George	BC	10	CJCI
	Grand Falls	NF	10	CKCM
	Timmins	ON	10	CKOY
	Forestville	PQ	1	CFRP
	Regina	SK	10	CKCK
630	Edmonton	AB	50	CHED
	Kelowna	BC	5	CKOV
	Winnipeg	MB	10	CKRC
	Chatham	ON	10	CFCO
	Smiths Falls	ON	10	CJET
	Charlottetown	PEI	10	CFCY
	Sherbrooke	PQ	10	CHLT
640	St John's	NF	10	CBN
	Fort Frances	ON	1	CFOB
	Toronto	ON	50	CHOG
650	Richmond	BC	10	CISL
	Saskatoon	SK	10	CKOM
	Gander	NF	5	CKGA
660	Calgary	AB	50	CFFR
670	Musgravetown	NF	10	CKXB
680	Edmonton	AB	10	CHFA
	Winnipeg	MB	50	CJOB
	Grand Falls	NF	10	CKXG
	Toronto	ON	50	CFTR
690	Vancouver	BC	50	CBU

Frequency [kHz]	Station Site	Province	Power [kW]	Call Sign
690 (cont)	Montreal	PQ	50	CBF
	Gravelborg	SK	5	CBKF-1
700	Red Deer	AB	50	CKRD
	St John	NB	25	CHSJ
710	Clarenville	NF	10	CKVO
	Niagara Falls	ON	10	CJRN
	Port Cartier	PQ	1	CIPC
	Ville Marie	PQ	10	CKVM
720	Charlottetown	PEI	10	CHTN
730	Vancouver	BC	50	CKLG
	Dauphin	MB	10	CKDM
	Blind River	ON	1	CJNR
	Montreal	ON	50	CKAC
740	Edmonton	AB	50	CBX
	Toronto	ON	50	CBL
	Marystown	NF	10	CHCM
750	Bonavista	NF	10	CBGY
	Timmins	ON	10	CKGB
	Saskatoon	SK	10	CJWW
760	Burns Lake	BC	1	CFLD
	Castlegar	BC	20	CKQR
770	Calgary	AB	50	CHQR
780	Dartmouth	NS	50	CFDR
790	Camrose	AB	50	CFCW
	Newcastle	NB	5	CFAN
	Port au Choix	NF	1	CFNW
	Sudbury	ON	50	CIGM
800	Penticton	BC	10	CKOR
	St John's	NF	10	VOWR
	Belleville	ON	10	CJBQ
	Windsor	ON	50	CKLW
	Dryden	ON	1	CKDR
	Montreal	PQ	50	CJAD
	Quebec	PQ	50	CHRC
	Moose Jaw	SK	10	CHAB
810	Winnipeg	MB	10	CKJS
	Caraquet	NB	10	CJVA
820	Hamilton	ON	50	CHAM
830	Wainwright	AB	10	CKKY
	Brockville	ON	5	CFJR

171

Frequency [kHz]	Station Site	Province	Power [kW]	Call Sign
840	100 Mile House	BC	1	CKBX
	North Bay	ON	10	CHUR
	Grand Prairie	AB	25	CJXX
850	Abbotsford	BC	10	CFVR
	Montreal	PQ	50	CKVL
	Athabasca	AB	1	CKBA
860	Prince Rupert	BC	10	CFPR
	Inuvik	NWT	1	CHAK
	Toronto	ON	50	CJBC
	Saskatoon	SK	10	CBKF-2
870	Invermere	BC	1	CKIR
	Smithers	BC	1	CFBV
880	Edmonton	AB	50	CHQT
	Nelson	BC	1	CKKC
	Brandon	MB	25	CKLQ
890	Dawson Creek	BC	10	CJDC
900	Victoria	BC	10	CJVI
	Amherst	NS	1	CKDH
	Hamilton	ON	50	CHML
	Sudbury	ON	10	CHYC
	Rimouski	PQ	10	CJBR
	Saint Jerome	PQ	1	CJER
	Sherbrooke	PQ	10	CKTS
	Val d'Or	PQ	10	CKVD
	Prince Albert	SK	10	CKBI
910	Drumheller	AB	50	CKDQ
	Lindsay	ON	10	CKLY
	Roberval	PQ	10	CHRL
920	Quesnel	BC	10	CKCQ
	Portage la Prairie	MB	25	CFRY
	Woodstock	NB	10	CJCJ
	Halifax	NS	25	CJCH
	Wingham	ON	10	CKNX
930	Edmonton	AB	50	CJCA
	St John	NB	50	CFBC
	St John's	NF	50	CJYQ
	Espanola	ON	10	CKNS
940	Vernon	BC	10	CJIB
	Montreal	PQ	50	CBM
	Yorkton	SK	10	CJGX

Frequency [kHz]	Station Site	Province	Power [kW]	Call Sign
950	Altona	MB	10	CFAM
	Campbellton	NB	10	CKNB
	Sydney	NS	10	CHER
	Barrie	ON	10	CKBB
960	Calgary	AB	50	CFAC
	Halifax	NS	10	CHNS
	Cambridge	ON	1	CIAM
	Kingston	ON	10	CFFX
970	Edson	AB	10	CJYR
	Hull	PQ	10	CKCH
980	New Westminster	BC	50	CKNW
	London	ON	10	CFPL
	Peterborough	ON	10	CKRU
	Quebec	PQ	5	CBV
	Regina	SA	10	CKRM
990	Winnipeg	MB	50	CBW
	Corner Brook	NF	10	CBY
	Montreal	PQ	50	CKIS
1000	Bridgewater	NS	10	CKBW
	Rimouski	PQ	10	CFLP
1010	Calgary	AB	50	CBR
	Gander	NF	1	CKXD
	Toronto	ON	50	CFRB
1020	High Prairie	AB	1	CKVH
1040	Langley	BC	10	CKST
1050	Grande Prairie	AB	10	CFGP
	Vernon	BC	10	CICF
	Winnipeg	MB	10	CKSB
	Toronto	ON	50	CHUM
	North Battleford	SK	10	CJNB
1060	Calgary	AB	50	CFCN
	Quebec	PQ	50	CJRP
1070	Victoria	BC	10	CFAX
	Moncton	NB	50	CBA
	Sarnia	ON	10	CHOK
1080	Lloydminster	AB	50	CKSA
1090	Lethbridge	AB	10	CKRX
	Kitchener	ON	10	CKKW
1110	Sarnia	ON	10	CKTY
1130	Vancouver	BC	50	CKWX

Frequency [kHz]	Station Site	Province	Power [kW]	Call Sign
1140	Calgary	AB	50	CFXL
	Sydney	NS	10	CBI
	Trois Rivieres	PQ	50	CJTR
1150	Kelowna	BC	10	CKIQ
	Brandon	MB	50	CKX
	Hamilton	ON	50	CKOC
	Ottawa	ON	50	CJRC
	Gaspé	PQ	5	CHGM
1170	Red Deer	AB	50	CKGY
1190	Weyburn	SK	10	CFSL
1200	Victoria	BC	50	CKDA
	Ottawa	ON	50	CFGO
	St Albert	AB	25	CHMG
	Tilsonburgh	ON	10	CKOT
1210	Slave Lake	AB	1	CKWA
	St John's	NF	10	VOAR
	Kindersley	SK	1	CFYM
1220	Lethbridge	AB	10	CJOC
	Boissevain	MB	10	CJRB
	Moncton	NB	25	CKCW
	Cornwall	ON	1	CJSS
	Kenora	ON	5	CJRL
	St Catherines	ON	10	CHSC
	Amqui	PQ	10	CFVM
	Shawinigan	PQ	10	CKSM
1230	Iqaluit	NWT	4	CFFB
	Thunder Bay	ON	4	CJLB
	Dolbeau	PQ	10	CHVD
1250	Steinbach	MB	10	CHSM
	Oakville	ON	10	CHWO
	Matane	PQ	10	CBGA
1260	Edmonton	AB	50	CFRN
	Fredericton	NB	10	CIHI
1270	Medicine Hat	AB	10	CHAT
	Chilliwack	BC	10	CHWK
	Sydney	NS	10	CJCB
	Trenton	ON	1	CJTN
	Alma	PQ	10	CFGT
1280	High River	AB	10	CHRB
	Powell River	BC	1	CHQB
	Montreal	PQ	50	CJMS
	Estevan	SK	10	CJSL

Frequency [kHz]	Station Site	Province	Power [kW]	Call Sign
1290	Winnipeg	MB	10	CIFX
	London	ON	10	CJBK
	Matane	PQ	10	CHRM
1300	Regina	SK	10	CJME
1310	St Paul	AB	10	CHLW
	Ottawa	ON	50	CIWW
	La Pocatiere	PQ	10	CHGB
1320	Vancouver	BC	50	CHQM
	New Glasgow	NS	25	CKEC
	Mississauga	ON	20	CJMR
1330	Thetford Mines	PQ	10	CKLD
	Rosetown	SK	10	CJYM
1340	Cornerbrook	NF	10	CKXX
	Yellowknife	NWT	2.5	CFYK
	Yarmouth	NS	5	CJLS
1350	Nanaimo	BC	10	CKEG
	Middleton	NS	1	CKAD
	Oshawa	ON	10	CKDO
	Pembroke	ON	1	CHVR
	St Pamphile	PQ	1	CHAL
1360	Bathurst	NB	10	CKBC
	Ste Marie de Beauce	PQ	10	CJVL
1370	Westlock	AB	10	CFOK
	Parksville	BC	1	CHPQ
	Valleyfield	PQ	10	CKOD
	Ville Dégelis	PQ	1	CFVD
1380	Brantford	ON	25	CKPC
	Kingston	ON	10	CKLC
	Victoriaville	PQ	10	CFDA
1390	Medicine Hat	AB	10	CJCY
	Ajax	ON	10	CHOO
1400	Gander	NF	4	CBG
	Riviere du Loup	PQ	20	CJFP
1410	Vancouver	BC	50	CFUN
	Port Hawkesbury	NS	10	CIGO
	London	ON	10	CKSL
	Montreal	PQ	10	CFMB
1420	Digby	NS	1	CKDY
	Peterborough	ON	10	CKPT
	Chicoutimi	PQ	10	CJMT

Frequency [kHz]	Station Site	Province	Power [kW]	Call Sign
1420	Plessisville	PQ	1	CKTL
(cont)	Melfort	SA	10	CJVR
1430	Toronto	ON	50	CJCL
1440	Wetaskiwin	AB	10	CJOI
	Courtenay	BC	1	CFCP
1450	Coburg	ON	8	CHUC
	Granby	PQ	20	CHEF
1460	Medicine Hat	AB	10	CJMH
	Guelph	ON	50	CJOY
	St George de Beauce	PQ	10	CKRB
1470	Vancouver	BC	50	CJVB
	Welland	ON	10	CHOW
1480	Newmarket	ON	10	CKDX
	Edmonton	AB	10	CKER
	Drummondville	PQ	10	CHRD
1500	Duncan	BC	10	CKAY
1540	Toronto	ON	50	CHIN
1550	Windsor	ON	10	CBE
1570	Taber	AB	10	CFEZ
	Nanaimo	BC	10	CHUB
	St Thomas	ON	10	CHLO
	Montreal	PQ	50	CKLM
	Winkler	MB	10	CKMW
1580	Chicoutimi	PQ	50	CBJ
1600	Simcoe	ON	10	CHNR

Section 10

UNITED STATES OF AMERICA
MEDIUM WAVE RADIO STATIONS

Frequency [kHz]	Station Site	State	Power [kW]	Call Sign
540	Costa Mesa	CA	25	KOJY
	Columbus	GA	5	WSTH
	Fort Dodge	IA	5	KWMT
	Monroe	LA	5	KNOE
	Las Vegas	NM	5	KNMX
	Wendell	NC	5	WETC
	Hesperia	CA	25	KKJZ
	Salinas	CA	10	KIEZ
	Pine Hills	FL	50	WGTO
	Canonsberg	PA	7.5	WWCS
550	Atmore	AL	25	WASG
	Anchorage	AK	5	KENI
	Phoenix	AZ	5	KOY
	Bakersfield	CA	5	KCWR
	Craig	CO	5	KRAI
	Orange Park	FL	5	WAYR
	Gainesville	GA	5	WDUN
	Salina	KS	5	KFRM
	St Louis	MO	5	KUSA
	Butte	MT	5	KBOW
	Buffalo	NY	5	WGR
	Bismarck	ND	5	KFYR
	Cincinnati	OH	5	WLWA
	Corvallis	OR	5	KOAC
	Bloomsburg	PA	1	WJMW
	Pawtucket	RI	4.6	WICE
	Midland	TX	5	KCRS
	San Antonia	TX	5	KTSA
	Waterbury	VT	5	WDEV
	Harrisonburg	VA	5	WSVA
	Blaine	WA	5	KARI
	Wassau	WI	5	WSAU
560	Dotham	AL	5	WOOF
	Kodiak	AK	1	KVOK
	Yuma	AZ	1	KBLU
	San Francisco	CA	5	KSFO
	Denver	CO	5	KLZ

Frequency [kHz]	Station Site	State	Power [kW]	Call Sign
560	Miami	FL	5	WQAM
(cont)	Chicago	IL	5	WIND
	Portland	ME	5	WGAN
	Frostburg	MD	5	WFRB
	Springfield	MA	5	WHYN
	Duluth	MN	5	WEBC
	Springfield	MO	5	KWTO
	Great Falls	MT	5	KMON
	Philadelphia	PA	5	WBEB
	Columbia	SC	5	WVOC
	Memphis	TN	5	WHBQ
	Beaumont	TX	5	KLVI
	Wenatchee	WA	5	KPQ
	Beckley	WV	5	WJLS
570	Gadsden	AL	5	WAAX
	Alturas	CA	5	KCNO
	Los Angeles	CA	5	KLAC
	Pinellas Park	FL	5	WHNZ
	Waycross	GA	5	WACL
	Bethesda	MD	5	WTEM
	Biloxi	MS	5	WVMI
	Las Cruces	NM	5	KGRT
	New York	NY	5	WMCA
	Syracuse	NY	5	WSYR
	Asheville	NC	5	WWNC
	Youngstown	OH	5	WKBN
	Yankton	SD	5	WNAX
	Dallas	TX	5	KLIF
	Salt Lake City	UT	5	KISN
	Seattle	WA	5	KVI
580	Petersburg	AK	5	KRSA
	Marana	AZ	5	KSAZ
	Fresno	CA	5	KMJ
	Montrose	CO	5	KUBC
	Orlando	FL	5	WDBO
	Augusta	GA	5	WGAC
	Nampa	ID	5	KFXD
	Urbana	IL	5	WILL
	Manhattan	KS	5	KKSU
	Topeka	KS	5	WIBW
	Alexandria	LA	5	KALB
	Worcester	MA	5	WTAG
	Traverse City	MI	5	WTCM
	Ashland	OR	1	KCMX

Frequency [kHz]	Station Site	State	Power [kW]	Call Sign
580	Harrisburg	PA	5	WHP
(cont)	Charleston	WV	5	WCHS
	LaCrosse	WI	5	WKTY
590	Anchorage	AK	5	KHAR
	Hot Springs	AR	5	KBHS
	San Bernardino	CA	1	KRSO
	South Lake Tahoe	CA	2.5	KTHO
	Pueblo	CO	1	KCSJ
	Panama City	FL	2.5	WGNE
	Atlanta	GA	5	WKHX
	Idaho Falls	ID	5	KID
	Wood River	IL	1	KFNS
	Lexington	KY	5	WVLK
	Boston	MA	5	WEEI
	Ironwood	MI	5	WJMS
	Kalamazoo	MI	5	WKZO
	Omaha	NE	5	WOW
	Albany	NY	5	WROW
	Wilson	NC	5	WGTM
	Eugene	OR	5	KUGN
	Scranton	PA	5	WARM
	Uniontown	PA	1	WMBS
	Austin	TX	5	KLBJ
	Cedar City	UT	5	KSUB
	Lynchburg	VA	5	WLVA
	Spokane	WA	5	KAQQ
600	Flagstaff	AZ	5	KCLS
	Redding	CA	5	KHTE
	San Diego	CA	5	KKLQ
	Fort Collins	CO	5	KIIX
	Jacksonville	FL	5	WOKV
	Cedar Rapids	IA	5	WMT
	Paintsville	KY	5	WKLW
	Caribou	ME	5	WFST
	Baltimore	MD	5	WCAO
	Kalispell	MT	5	KGEZ
	Winston-Salem	NC	5	WSJS
	Jameston	ND	5	KSJB
	Memphis	TN	5	WREC
	El Paso	TX	5	KROD
	Tyler	TX	5	KTBB
610	Birmingham	AL	5	WZZK
	Lancaster	CA	5	KAVL
	San Francisco	CA	5	KFRC

Frequency [kHz]	Station Site	State	Power [kW]	Call Sign
610	Vail	CO	5	KSKE
(cont)	Miami	FL	10	WIOD
	Russellville	KY	2.5	WRUS
	Duluth	MN	5	KDAL
	Kansas City	MO	5	WDAF
	Havre	MT	1	KOJM
	Manchester	NH	5	WGIR
	Albuquerque	NM	5	KZSS
	Charlotte	NC	5	WAQS
	Columbus	OH	5	WTVN
	Medford	OR	5	KYJC
	Philadelphia	PA	5	WIP
	Houston	TX	5	KILT
	Logan	UT	5	KVNU
	Roanoke	VA	5	WSLC
	Tri-Cities	WA	5	KONA
620	Homer	AK	5	KGTL
	Lexington	AL	5	WKNI
	Phoenix	AZ	5	KTAR
	Hanford	CA	1	KIGS
	Grand Junction	CO	5	KSTR
	St Petersburg	FL	10	WSUN
	Wallace	ID	1	KWAL
	Sioux City	IA	1	KMNS
	Bangor	ME	5	WZON
	Jackson	MS	5	WJDS
	Newark	NJ	5	WSKQ
	Syracuse	NY	5	WHEN
	Durham	NC	5	WDNC
	Portland	OR	5	KINK
	Knoxville	TN	5	WRJZ
	Wichita Falls	TX	5	KWFT
	Burlington	VT	5	WVMT
	Milwaukee	WI	5	WTMJ
630	Juneau	AK	5	KJNO
	Nenana	AK	5	KIAM
	Monterey	CA	1	KIDD
	Denver	CO	5	KHOW
	Washington	DC	5	WMAL
	Savannah	GA	5	WBMQ
	Boise	ID	5	KIDO
	Lexington	KY	5	WLAP
	St Paul	MN	5	WDGY
	St Louis	MO	5	KXOK

Frequency [kHz]	Station Site	State	Power [kW]	Call Sign
630	Reno	NV	5	KOH
(cont)	Wilmington	NC	1	WMFD
	Coquille	OR	5	KWRO
	East Providence	RI	5	WPRO
	San Antonio	TX	5	KSLR
	Seattle	WA	39	KCIS
640	Bethel	AK	10	KYUK
	Los Angeles	CA	50	KFI
	West Palm Beach	FL	10	WLVJ
	Atlanta	GA	50	WGST
	Ames	IA	5	WOI
	Thibodeaux	LA	5	KTIB
	Westfield	MA	50	WNNZ
	Belgrade	MT	10	KGVW
	Mt Holly	NJ	5	WWJZ
	Fayetteville	NC	10	WFNC
	Akron	OH	5	WHLO
	Moore	OK	1	WWLS
	Blountsville	TN	5	WGOC
	Collierville	TN	10	WCRV
650	Anchorage	AK	50	KYAK
	Christmas	FL	10	WORL
	Hibbing	MN	10	WKKQ
	Junction City	OR	10	KZTU
	Nashville	TN	50	WSM
	Rancho Cordova	CA	25	KSTE
	Manti	UT	10	KMTI
	Cheyenne	WY	8.6	KUUY
660	Fairholpe	AL	22	WBLX
	Fairbanks	AK	10	KFAR
	Window Rock	AZ	50	KTNN
	Orcutt	CA	10	KGDP
	Saulk Rapids	MN	10	WVAL
	New York	NY	50	WFAN
	Williston	ND	5	KEYZ
	Greenville	SC	50	WESC
	Dallas	TX	10	KSKY
	Mount Vernon	WA	10	KAPS
670	York	AL	5	WYLS
	Dillingham	AK	10	KDLG
	Glenwood	AR	5	KWXI
	Simi Valley	CA	1	KWNK
	Commerce City	CO	5	KMVP

Frequency [kHz]	Station Site	State	Power [kW]	Call Sign
670	Miami	FL	50	WWFE
(cont)	Boise	ID	50	KBOI
	Chicago	IL	50	WMAQ
	Lewiston	PA	6	WIEZ
	Claremont	VA	20	WARO
680	Barrow	AK	10	KBRW
	San Francisco	CA	50	KNBR
	North Atlanta	GA	50	WCNN
	Baltimore	MD	10	WCBM
	Boston	MA	50	WRKO
	Escanaba	MI	10	WDBC
	St Joseph	MO	5	KFEQ
	Raleigh	NC	50	WPTF
	Memphis	TN	10	WOGY
	San Antonio	TX	50	KKYX
	Omak	WA	5	KOMW
	Charlestown	WV	50	WCAW
	Helena	MT	5	KVCM
690	Birmingham	AL	50	WJOX
	Jacksonville	FL	50	WPDQ
	Coffeyville	KS	10	KGGF
	New Orleans	LA	10	WTIX
	El Paso	TX	10	KHEY
	Bristol	VA	10	WZAP
700	Anchorage	AK	1	KBYR
	Walkersville	MD	5	WWTL
	Cincinnati	OH	50	WLW
	Winston	OR	25	KGRV
	Tomball	TX	2.5	KSEV
	Salt Lake City	UT	50	KFAM
	Newport	WA	10	KJMY
710	Mobile	AL	1	WKRG
	Black Canyon City	AZ	50	KUET
	Carmichael	CA	10	KFIA
	Los Angeles	CA	50	KMPC
	Denver	CO	5	KNUS
	Miami	FL	50	WAQI
	Shreveport	LA	50	KEEL
	Kansas City	MO	10	WHB
	New York	NY	50	WOR
	Amarillo	TX	10	KGNC
	Christianburg	VA	5	WFNR
	Seattle	WA	10	KIRO

Frequency [kHz]	Station Site	State	Power [kW]	Call Sign
710 (cont)	Superior	WI	10	WDSM
	Monticello	ME	5	WREM
	Bismarck	ND	50	KBMR
720	Kotzebue	AK	10	KOTZ
	Hogansville	GA	10	WMXY
	Chicago	IL	50	WGN
	Richland	MS	5	WWDF
	Pisgah Forest	NC	10	WGCR
	Las Vegas	NV	50	KDWN
	Universal City	TX	10	KSAH
	Hernando	FL	10	WRZN
	Tuckahoe	VA	10	WGNZ
730	Thomasville	GA	5	WSNI
	Vancleve	KY	5	WMTC
	Springfield	MA	5	WACE
	Billings	MT	5	KURL
	Pittsburgh	PA	5	WPIT
	Alexandria	VA	5	WCPT
740	Montgomery	AL	50	WLWI
	Avalon	CA	10	KBRT
	San Francisco	CA	50	KCBS
	Colorado Springs	CO	3.3	KSSS
	Orlando	FL	5	WWNZ
	Long Island	NY	25	WGSM
	Mount Airey	NC	10	WPAQ
	Tulsa	OK	50	KRMG
	Chester	PA	50	WVCH
	Houston	TX	50	KTRH
	Texarkana	TX	1	KCMC
	Buckley	WA	5	KWNT
750	Anchorage	AK	50	KFQD
	Atlanta	GA	50	WSB
	Polson	MT	50	KERR
	Grand Island	NE	10	KMMJ
	Canton	NY	5	WNYS
	Portland	OR	50	KXL
	El Paso	TX	10	KAMA
	Price	UT	10	KOAL
	Carson City	NV	10	KKNK
	Lebanon	MO	5	KJEL
760	Sherwood	AR	10	KMTL
	San Diego	CA	50	KFMB
	Thornton	CO	5	KRZN

Frequency [kHz]	Station Site	State	Power [kW]	Call Sign
760	Brandon	FL	5	WBDN
(cont)	Leicester	MA	5	WVNE
	Detroit	MI	50	WJR
	Champlain	NY	25	WCHP
	San Antonio	TX	50	KZXS
	Overland Park	KS	6	KCCV
770	Athens	AL	10	WVNN
	Valdez	AK	9.7	KCHU
	Riverbank	CA	50	KCBC
	North Fort Myers	FL	10	WWCN
	Lynn Haven	FL	5	WFBN
	Minneapolis	MN	5	KUOM
	Miles City	MT	10	KATL
	Albuquerque	NM	50	KKOB
	New York	NY	50	WABC
	Youngstown	NY	5	WTOR
	Rockingham	NC	5	WLWL
	Garland	TX	10	KPBC
	Cedar Bluff	VA	5	WYRV
	Seattle	WA	50	KULL
780	Lineville	AL	5	WZZX
	Nome	AK	10	KNOM
	Sedona	AZ	5	KAZM
	Chicago	IL	50	WBBM
	Ridgeland	MS	5	WLRM
	Norfolk	NE	1	WJAG
	Reno	NV	50	KROW
	Arlington	VA	5	WABS
790	Tuscaloosa	AL	5	WTSK
	Glenallen	AK	5	KCAM
	Tucson	AZ	5	KNST
	Rogers	AR	5	KURM
	Clovis	CA	2.5	KOQO
	Eureka	CA	5	KWSW
	Los Angeles	CA	5	KABC
	Leesburg	FL	5	WLBE
	South Miami	FL	25	WMRZ
	Atlanta	GA	5	WQXI
	Soda Springs	ID	5	KBRV
	Colby	KS	5	KXXX
	Louisville	KY	5	WWKY
	Saginaw	MI	5	WSGW
	Billings	MT	5	KGHL

Frequency [kHz]	Station Site	State	Power [kW]	Call Sign
790	Watertown	NY	1	WTNY
(cont)	Fargo	ND	5	KFGO
	Albany	OR	1	KWIL
	Allentown	PA	3.8	WAEB
	Providence	RI	5	WLKW
	Johnson City	TN	5	WETB
	Memphis	TN	5	WMC
	Houston	TX	5	KKBQ
	Lubbock	TX	5	KFYO
	Norfolk	VA	5	WTAR
	Bellingham	WA	5	KGMI
	Spokane	WA	5	KJRB
	Eau Claire	WI	5	WEAQ
800	Juneau	AK	10	KINY
	Camden	NJ	5	WTMR
	Crewe	VA	5	WSVS
	Huntington	WV	5	WKEE
	Waupaca	WI	5	WDUX
810	Jacksonville	AL	50	WJXL
	San Francisco	CA	50	KGO
	Kansas City	MO	50	KCMO
	Magee	MS	50	WSJC
	Santa Fe	NM	5	KSWV
	Schenectady	NY	50	WGY
	St George	SC	5	WQIZ
	Sturgis	SD	5	KBHB
	Murfreesboro	TN	5	WMTS
	Ephrata	WA	41	KTBI
	Tomahawk	WI	10	WJJQ
	Jackson	KY	5	WEKG
820	Fairbanks	AK	50	KCBF
	Largo	FL	50	WRFA
	Chicago	IL	5	WSCR
	New York	NY	50	WNYC
	Columbus	OH	5	WOSU
	Fort Worth	TX	50	WBAP
	Chester	VA	10	WGGM
	Seattle	WA	50	KGNW
830	Tucson	AZ	50	KFLT
	Grass Valley	CA	5	KNCO
	Orange	CA	2.5	KPLS
	Hialeah	FL	1	WRFM
	Norco	LA	5	WADU
	Minneapolis	MN	50	WCCO

Frequency [kHz]	Station Site	State	Power [kW]	Call Sign
830 (cont)	Kennett	MO	10	KBOA
	Eden	NC	1	WWMO
	Evansville	WY	10	KUYO
	Sand Point	AK	1	KSDP
	Cherry Valley	MA	3	WCRN
840	Mobile	AL	10	WBHY
	Sand Point	AK	10	KSDP
	Thomasville	GA	10	WHGH
	Louisville	KY	50	WHAS
	Ball	LA	10	KWDF
	West Point	NE	5	KWPN
	North Las Vegas	NV	50	KVEG
	Columbia	SC	50	WCTG
	Pharr	TX	5	KVJY
	Earlysville	VA	8.2	WKTR
	Opportunity	WA	50	KKPL
850	Birmingham	AL	50	WYDE
	Nome	AK	10	KICY
	Denver	CO	50	KOA
	Gainesville	FL	5	WREF
	West Palm Beach	FL	5	WEAT
	Statesboro	GA	1	WPTB
	Boston	MA	50	WHDH
	Muskegon	MI	1	WKBZ
	Duluth	MN	10	WWJC
	Forest	MS	10	WQST
	Clayton	MO	5	KFUO
	Raleigh	NC	50	WKIX
	Cleveland	OH	10	WRMR
	Johnston	PA	10	WJAC
	Reading	PA	1	WEEU
	Knoxville	TN	50	WUTK
	Houston	TN	10	KEYH
	Norfolk	VA	5	WNIS
	Tacoma	WA	10	KMTT
860	Phoenix	AR	1	KVVA
	Modesto	CA	50	KTRB
	Dunedin	FL	2	WGUL
	Atlanta	GA	5	WAEC
	Douglas	GA	5	WDMG
	Pittsburgh	KS	10	KKOW
	Troutdale	OR	20	KZTW
	Philadelphia	PA	10	WTEL
	San Antonio	TX	5	KONO

Frequency [kHz]	Station Site	State	Power [kW]	Call Sign
860 *(cont)*	Salt Lake City	UT	10	KLZX
	Oak Hill	WV	10	WOAY
870	McGrath	AK	10	KSKO
	Glendale	CA	10	KIEV
	New Orleans	LA	50	WWL
	East Lansing	MI	10	WKAR
	Park Rapids	MN	25	KPRM
	East Las Vegas	NV	5	KOWA
	Ithaca	NY	5	WHCU
	Colonial Heights	TN	10	WZMC
	Tri-Cities	WA	10	KORD
	Valley Head	AL	10	WQRX
	Gorham	ME	5	WLAM
880	Sheridan	AR	50	KGHT
	Gonzales	CA	5	KKMC
	Jefferson	GA	5	WBKZ
	Whitefish	MT	10	KJJR
	Lexington	NE	50	KRVN
	Tse Bonito	NM	10	KHAC
	New York	NY	50	WCBS
	Columbus	OH	9	WRFD
	Dallas	OR	5	KWIP
	Phoenix	OR	1	KTMT
	Conroe	TX	10	KJOJ
	Hamby	TX	2.5	KEIO
	Seattle	WA	50	KIXI
	Menomonie	WI	10	WMEQ
890	Homer	AK	10	KBBI
	Citrus Heights	CA	50	KPTO
	Chicago	IL	50	WLS
	Dedham	MA	10	WBMA
	Laurel	MS	10	WQIS
	Laredo	TX	10	KVOZ
	St George	UT	10	KDXU
900	Fort Yuko	AK	5	KZPA
	West Covina	CA	5	KGRB
	Georgetown	DE	10	WSSR
	Savannah	GA	5	WEAS
	Pikeville	KY	5	WLSI
	Minneapolis	MN	25	KTIS
910	Galena	AK	5	KIYU
	Phoenix	AZ	5	KFYI
	Blytheville	AR	5	KLCN

Frequency [kHz]	Station Site	State	Power [kW]	Call Sign
910	El Cajon	CA	5	KECR
(cont)	Oakland	CA	5	KNEW
	Oxnard	CA	5	KOXR
	Denver	CO	5	KPOF
	New Britain	CT	5	WNEZ
	Plant City	FL	1	WFNS
	Valdosta	GA	5	WFVR
	Iowa City	IA	5	WSUI
	Baton Rouge	LA	1	WNDC
	Bangor	ME	5	WABI
	Flint	MI	5	WFDF
	Meridian	MS	5	WALT
	Roswell	NM	5	KBIM
	Jacksonville	NC	5	WLAS
	Minot	ND	5	KCJB
	Marietta	OH	5	WBRJ
	Miami	OK	1	KVIS
	Apollo	PA	5	WAVL
	York	PA	5	WSBA
	Volga	SD	1	KJJQ
	Johnson City	TN	5	WJCW
	South Pittsburg	TN	5	WEPG
	McAllen	TX	5	KRIO
	Sherman	TX	1	KXEB
	Salt Lake City	UT	5	KALL
	Richmond	VA	5	WRVH
	Vancouver	WA	5	KKSN
	Hayward	WI	5	WHSM
920	Andalusia	AL	5	WKYD
	Soldotna	AK	5	KSRM
	Little Rock	AR	5	KARN
	Modesto	CA	2.5	KLOC
	Palm Springs	CA	5	KDES
	Lamar	CO	5	KLMR
	Melbourne	FL	1	WMEL
	Atlanta	GA	5	WAFS
	West Lafayette	IN	5	WBAA
	Shenandoah	IA	5	KYFR
	Whitesburg	KY	5	WTCW
	Bogalusa	LA	1	WBOX
	Lexington Park	MD	5	WPTX
	Faribault	MN	5	KDHL
	Wadena	MN	1	KWAD
	Las Vegas	NV	5	KORK

Frequency [kHz]	Station Site	State	Power [kW]	Call Sign
920	Reno	NV	5	KQLO
(cont)	Trenton	NJ	1	WTTM
	Kingston	NY	5	WGHQ
	Lake Placid	NY	5	WIRD
	Burlington	NC	5	WBBB
	Lebanon	OR	1	KSHO
	Providence	RI	5	WHJJ
	Manning	SC	5	WYMB
	Rapid City	SD	5	KKLS
	Texas City	TX	5	KYST
	Vernal	UT	5	KVEL
	Olympia	WA	5	KCPL
	Spokane	WA	5	KXLY
	Fairmont	WV	5	WMMN
	Milwaukee	WI	5	WOKY
930	Rainbow City	AL	5	WJBY
	Monroeville	AL	5	WYNI
	Ketchikan	AK	5	KTKN
	Unalakleet	AK	2.5	KNSA
	Flagstaff	AZ	5	KAFF
	Los Angeles	CA	5	KKHJ
	Durango	CO	5	KIUP
	Jacksonville	FL	5	WNZS
	Sarasota	FL	5	WKXY
	Bainbridge	GA	5	WMGR
	Pocatello	ID	5	KSEI
	Quincy	IL	5	WTAD
	Sandwich	IL	2.2	WAUR
	Bowling Green	KY	5	WKCT
	Frederick	MD	5	WFMD
	Battle Creek	MI	5	WBCK
	Jackson	MS	5	WSLI
	Poplar Bluff	MO	5	KWOC
	East Missoula	MT	5	KLCY
	Ogallala	NE	2.5	KOGA
	Rochester	NH	5	WZNN
	Paterson	NJ	5	WPAT
	Buffalo	NY	5	WBEN
	Charlotte	NC	5	WYFQ
	Washington	NC	5	WRRF
	Elyria	OH	1	WEOL
	Oklahoma City	OK	5	WKY
	Grants Pass	OR	5	KAGI
	Aberdeen	SD	5	KSDN

Frequency [kHz]	Station Site	State	Power [kW]	Call Sign
930 (cont)	Sevierville	TN	5	WSEV
	San Antonio	TX	5	KLUP
	Lynchburg	VA	5	WLLL
	Huntington	WV	5	WTKZ
	Auburndale	WI	5	WLBL
	Sheridan	WY	5	KROE
940	Tucson	AZ	5	KWFM
	Fresno	CA	50	KFRE
	Miami	FL	50	WINZ
	Macon	GA	50	WMAZ
	Mount Vernon	IL	5	WMIX
	Des Moines	IA	10	KIOA
	New Orleans	LA	10	WYLD
	St Ignace	MI	5	WIDG
	Houston	MS	50	WCPC
	Valentine	NE	5	KVSH
	Burnsville	NC	5	WKYK
	Bend	OR	10	KGRL
	Wartburg	TN	5	WECO
	Amarillo	TX	5	KIXZ
	Cedar City	UT	10	KBRE
	Grundy	VA	5	WNRG
	Smithfield	VA	10	WKGM
950	Seward	AK	1	KSWD
	Forrest City	AR	5	KXJK
	Fort Smith	AR	1	KFSA
	Auburn	CA	5	KAHI
	Denver	CO	5	KYGO
	Orlando	FL	5	WOMX
	Summerville	GA	5	WGTA
	Valdosta	GA	5	WGOV
	Lewiston	ID	5	KOZE
	Boise	ID	5	KKIC
	Chicago	IL	1	WJPC
	Indianapolis	IN	5	WXLW
	Oelwein	IA	5	KOEL
	Boston	MA	5	WROL
	Detroit	MI	5	WWJ
	St Louis Park	MN	1	KJJO
	Hattiesburg	MS	5	WBKH
	Jefferson City	MO	5	KLIK
	Helena	MT	5	KMTX
	Bayard	NM	5	KNFT
	Rochester	NY	1	WBBF

Frequency [kHz]	Station Site	State	Power [kW]	Call Sign
950	Utica	NY	5	WIBX
(cont)	Philadelphia	PA	5	WPEN
	Spartanburg	SC	5	WSPA
	Watertown	SD	1	KWAT
	Houston	TX	5	KPRC
	Lubbock	TX	5	KXTQ
	Richmond	VA	5	WXGI
	Seattle	WA	5	KJR
	Charleston	WV	5	WQBE
	Kemmere	WY	5	KMER
960	Birmingham	AL	5	WERC
	Pritchard	AL	2.5	WLPR
	Phoenix	AZ	5	KOOL
	Apple Valley	CA	5	KZXY
	San Francisco	CA	5	KABL
	Marshall	AR	5	KCGS
	New Haven	CT	5	WELI
	Lake City	FL	1	WGRO
	Sebring	FL	5	WJCM
	Albany	GA	5	WJYZ
	Athens	GA	5	WRFC
	South Bend	IN	5	WSBT
	Shenandoah	IA	5	KMA
	Prestonburg	KY	5	WPRT
	Salisbury	MD	5	WLVW
	Fitchburg	MA	1	WFGL
	Rogers City	MI	5	WHAK
	Little Falls	MN	5	KLTF
	Cape Girardeau	MO	5	KZIM
	Baker	MT	5	KFLN
	Farmington	NM	5	KNDN
	Plattsburgh	NY	5	WEAV
	Kinston	NC	5	WRNS
	Enid	OK	1	KGWA
	Klamath Falls	OR	5	KLAD
	Carlisle	PA	5	WHYL
	Sayre	PA	5	WATS
	San Angelo	TX	5	KGKL
	Provo	UT	5	KOVO
	Richland	WA	5	KALE
	Shawano	WI	5	WTCH
	Roanoke	VA	5	WFIR
970	Hamilton	AL	5	WERH
	Troy	AL	5	WTBF

Frequency [kHz]	Station Site	State	Power [kW]	Call Sign
970	Fairbanks	AK	5	KIAK
(cont)	Show Low	AZ	5	KVWM
	Bakersfield	CA	1	KAFY
	Coachella	CA	5	KCLB
	Modesto	CA	1	KBEE
	Tampa	FL	5	WFLA
	Atlanta	GA	5	WNIV
	Vidalia	GA	5	WVOP
	Harlan	KY	5	WFSR
	Louisville	KY	5	WAVG
	Alexandria	LA	1	KSYL
	Southbridge	ME	5	WESO
	Portland	ME	5	WZAN
	Ispheming	MI	5	WMVN
	Jackson	MI	1	WKHM
	Austin	MN	5	KQAQ
	Billings	MT	5	KCTR
	North Platte	NE	5	KJLT
	Paradise	NV	5	KNUU
	Hackensack	NJ	5	WWDJ
	Buffalo	NY	5	WNED
	Canton	NC	5	WWIT
	Fargo	ND	5	WDAY
	Ashtabula	OH	5	WFUN
	Tulsa	OK	2.5	KCFO
	Portland	OR	5	KBBT
	Pittsburgh	PA	5	WWSW
	Florence	SC	5	WJMX
	Del Valle	TX	1	KIXL
	Waynesboro	VA	5	WANV
	Spokane	WA	5	KTRW
	Madison	WI	5	WHA
980	Kenai	AK	1	KZXX
	Dardanelle	AR	5	KCAB
	Eureka	CA	5	KINS
	Los Angeles	CA	5	KFWB
	Washington	DC	5	WWRC
	Gainesville	FL	5	WLUS
	Pompano Beach	FL	5	WWNN
	Perry	GA	5	WPGA
	Ammon	ID	5	KUPI
	Danville	IL	1	WITY
	Shreveport	LA	5	KOKA
	Lowell	MA	5	WCAP

Frequency [kHz]	Station Site	State	Power [kW]	Call Sign
980 (cont)	Richfield	MN	5	KRXX
	McComb	MS	5	WAPF
	Kansas City	MO	5	KMBZ
	Fallon	NV	5	KVLV
	Clovis	NM	1	KICA
	Grants	NM	1	KMIN
	Troy	NY	5	WTRY
	Wilmington	NC	5	WAAV
	Dayton	OH	5	WONE
	Wilkes-Barre	PA	5	WILK
	Deadwood	SD	5	KDSJ
	Nashville	TN	5	WYFN
	Richfield	UT	5	KSVC
	Bristol	VA	5	WXBQ
	Selah	WA	5	KUTI
	Manitovoc	WI	5	WCUB
990	Tucson	AZ	10	KTKT
	Pittsburg	CA	5	KKIS
	Santa Barbara	CA	5	KQSB
	Denver	CO	5	KRKS
	Miami	FL	5	WFBA
	Orlando	FL	50	WHOO
	Rochester	NY	5	WCMF
	Southern Pines	NC	10	WEEB
	Philadelphia	PA	50	WZZD
	Somerset	PA	10	WVSC
	Providence	RI	50	WALE
	Knoxville	TN	10	WIVK
	Memphis	TN	10	KWAM
	Beaumont	TX	1	KZZB
	Wichita Falls	TX	10	KNIN
	Narrows	VA	5	WNRV
1000	Huntsville	AL	5	WTAK
	Bullhead City	AZ	5	KFLG
	Hayden	CO	10	KIDN
	Eagle	ID	10	KIDH
	Chicago	IL	50	WLUP
	Lexington	MS	5	WXTN
	Albuquerque	NM	10	KKIM
	Horseheads	NY	5	WLNL
	Oklahoma City	OK	5	KTOK
	Hemingway	SC	10	WKYB
	Sioux Falls	SD	10	KXRB

Frequency [kHz]	Station Site	State	Power [kW]	Call Sign
1000	Paris	TN	5	WMUF
(cont)	Seattle	WA	50	KOMO
1010	Dora	AL	5	WPYK
	Phoenix	AR	7.5	KXEG
	Little Rock	AR	10	KBIS
	Delano	CA	5	KCHJ
	San Francisco	CA	10	KIQI
	Brush	CO	5	KSIR
	Crestview	FL	10	WCNU
	Jacksonville	FL	70	WXTL
	Seffner	FL	50	WQYK
	Decatur	GA	50	WGUN
	Meridian	MS	10	WMOX
	St Louis	MO	50	KXEN
	New York	NY	50	WINS
	Black Mountain	NC	50	WFGW
	Gallatin	TN	5	WHIN
	Amarillo	TX	5	KDJW
	Houston	TX	5	KLAT
	Waco	TX	10	KBBW
	Tooele	UT	50	KTUR
	Portsmouth	VA	5	WPMH
1020	Eagle River	AK	10	KFFR
	Hollywood	CA	50	KTNQ
	Ochlocknee	GA	10	WJEP
	Newport	NH	10	WNTK
	Roswell	NM	50	KCKN
	Pittsburgh	PA	50	KDKA
	Selah	WA	5	KYXE
	Moses Lake	WA	5	KWIQ
	Anderson	SC	10	WRIX
1030	Fayetteville	AR	10	KFAY
	Cortaro	AZ	10	KEVT
	Folsom	CA	50	KKSA
	San Luis Obispo	CA	2.5	KJDJ
	Oviedo	FL	25	WONQ
	Holcomb	KS	25	KBUF
	Boston	MA	50	WBZ
	Indian Head	MD	50	WNTL
	Sterling Heights	MI	5	WUFL
	Maplewood	MN	50	WCTS
	Mint Hill	NC	10	WNOW
	Wake Forest	NC	35	WFTK
	Memphis	TN	50	WXSS

Frequency [kHz]	Station Site	State	Power [kW]	Call Sign
1030	Corpus Christi	TX	50	KCTA
(cont)	Shelton	WA	10	KMAS
	Casper	WY	50	KTWO
	Reedsport	OR	10	KDUN
1040	Boynton Beach	FL	10	WYFX
	Pinellas Park	FL	5	WMTX
	Des Moines	IA	50	WHO
	Lewisville	NC	9.1	WSGH
	North Ridgeville	OH	5	WJTB
	Everett	PA	10	WSKE
	Powell	TN	10	WQBB
	Flemington	NJ	4.7	WJHR
1050	Tuba City	AZ	5	KTBA
	Jacksonville	FL	5	WROS
	Frazier Park	CA	10	KNOB
	San Mateo	CA	50	KOFY
	Augusta	GA	5	WFAM
	Ann Arbor	MI	5	WTKA
	Kinsey	MT	10	KMTA
	New York	NY	50	WEVD
	Conway	SC	5	WJXY
	Norfolk	VA	5	WCMS
	Dishman	WA	5	KEYF
	Seattle	WA	5	KBLE
	Parkersburg	WV	5	WADC
	Springfield	OR	5	KORE
1060	Tempe	AZ	5	KUKQ
	Chico	CA	10	KPAY
	Longmont	CO	10	KLMO
	Titusville	FL	10	WAMT
	Tallapoosa	GA	5	WKNG
	Caldwell	ID	10	KBGN
	New Orleans	LA	50	WNOE
	Natick	MA	25	WBIV
	Benton Harbor	MI	5	WHFB
	Las Vegas	NV	5	KKVV
	Canton	OH	5	WRCW
	Philadelphia	PA	50	KYW
	Pierre	SD	10	KGFX
	El Paso	TX	10	KFNA
	Gilmer	TX	10	KHYM
	Farwell	TX	5	KIJN
	Salt Lake City	UT	10	KKDS

Frequency [kHz]	Station Site	State	Power [kW]	Call Sign
1070	Birmingham	AL	50	WAPI
	Los Angeles	CA	50	KNX
	Tallahassee	FL	10	WANM
	Indianapolis	IN	50	WIBC
	Wichita	KS	10	KFDI
	Monticello	MN	10	KMOM
	Hannibal	MO	5	KHMO
	Plentywood	MT	5	KATQ
	Plattsburgh	NY	5	WNWX
	Greenville	NC	10	WNCT
	Sunbury	PA	10	WKOK
	Greenville	SC	50	WHYZ
	Lookout Mountain	TN	50	WFLI
	Memphis	TN	50	WDIA
	Alice	TX	1	KDSI
	Houston	TX	10	KRBE
	Charlottesville	VA	5	WINA
	Beckley	WV	10	WIWS
	Madison	WI	10	WTSO
1080	Athens	AL	5	WKAC
	Anchorage	AK	10	KKSD
	Santa Cruz	CA	10	KSCO
	Hartford	CT	50	WTIC
	Coral Gables	FL	50	WVCG
	Kissimmee	FL	10	WFIV
	Marietta	GA	10	WFTD
	Coeur d'Alene	ID	10	KVNI
	Louisville	KY	10	WDJX
	Carthage	MS	5	WSSI
	Lenoir	NC	5	WKGX
	St Pauls	NC	50	WKKE
	Portland	OR	50	KWJJ
	Pittsburgh	PA	50	WEEP
	Dallas	TX	50	KRLD
	Price	UT	10	KRPX
	Hurricane	WV	5	WVKV
1090	Little Rock	AR	50	KAAY
	Fortuna	CA	10	KAJK
	Aurora	CO	50	KYBG
	Port Charlotte	FL	5	WKII
	Cantonment	FL	5	WNVY
	Lake Tahoe	CA	5	KJRC
	Gonzales	LA	10	WSLG

Frequency [kHz]	Station Site	State	Power [kW]	Call Sign
1090 (cont)	Baltimore	MD	50	WBAL
	Boston	MA	5	WILD
	Bozeman	MT	5	KBOZ
	Kingsport	TN	10	WKCV
	Plainview	TX	5	KKYN
	Seattle	WA	50	KING
	Rice Lake	WI	5	WAQE
1100	Cave Creek	AZ	25	KCCF
	Bakersfield	CA	10	KZPM
	San Francisco	CA	50	KFAX
	Grand Junction	CO	50	KNZZ
	Woodbine	GA	10	WCGA
	Webb City	MO	5	KKLL
	Hempstead	NY	10	WHLI
	Cleveland	OH	50	WWWE
	Alamo Heights	TX	10	KDRY
	Hudson	TX	10	KWXL
	Wells River	VT	5	WYKR
1110	Bay Minette	AL	10	WBCA
	Clinton	AR	5	KGFL
	Dermott	AR	10	KGPL
	Pasadena	CA	50	KRLA
	Roseville	CA	5	KRCX
	Tampa	FL	10	WTIS
	Chicago	IL	5	WMBI
	Pittsfield	MA	5	WUHN
	Petoskey	MI	10	WJML
	Omaha	NE	50	KFAB
	Salem	NH	5	WNNW
	Humble City	NM	5	KYKK
	Charlotte	NC	50	WBT
	Atoka	OK	5	KEOR
	Bend	OR	25	KBND
	East Providence	RI	5	WHIM
	Norfolk	VA	50	WZAM
1120	San Martin	CA	10	KSJI
	Gordon	GA	10	WBNM
	Washington	DC	20	WUST
	Concord	MA	5	WADN
	Clinton	MS	5	WTWZ
	St Louis	MO	50	KMOX
	Eugene	OR	50	KPNW
	Roy	UT	10	KANN

Frequency [kHz]	Station Site	State	Power [kW]	Call Sign
1130	Dinuba	CA	5	KRDU
	San Diego	CA	50	KSDO
	Dillon	CO	5	KHTH
	Bartow	FL	2.5	WWBF
	Gainesville	GA	10	WLBA
	Murray	KY	2.5	WSJP
	Shreveport	LA	50	KWKH
	Detroit	MI	50	WWWW
	Minneapolis	MN	50	KFAN
	Milan	NM	5	KOFK
	New York	NY	50	WBBR
	Lincoln	ND	50	KBMR
	Brownsville	PA	5	WASP
	Edna	TX	10	KTMR
	Milwaukee	WI	50	WISN
1140	Hazel Green	AL	15	WBXR
	Soldotna	AK	10	KSLD
	Palm Springs	CA	10	KCMJ
	Sacramento	CA	50	KRAK
	Miami	FL	50	WQBA
	Boise	ID	10	KGEM
	Pekin	IL	5	WVEL
	Kentwood	MI	5	WKWM
	Senatobia	MS	5	WSAO
	Las Vegas	NV	10	KXNO
	Sioux Falls	SD	10	KSOO
	Concord	NH	10	WNHA
	Conroe	TX	5	KSSQ
	Richmond	VA	50	WRVA
	Greybull	WY	10	KZMQ
1150	Tuscaloosa	AL	5	WSPZ
	Coolidge	AZ	5	KCKY
	Little Rock	AR	5	KLRG
	Los Angeles	CA	5	KIIS
	Morro Bay	CA	5	KBAI
	Santa Rosa	CA	5	KMXN
	Englewood	CO	5	KCUV
	Wilmington	DE	5	WDEL
	Daytona Beach	FL	1	WNDB
	Tampa	FL	5	WTMP
	Valdosta	GA	5	WJEM
	Marion	IL	5	WGGH
	Des Moines	IA	1	KWKY
	Salina	KS	5	KSAL

Frequency [kHz]	Station Site	State	Power [kW]	Call Sign
1150	Baton Rouge	LA	5	WJBO
(cont)	Boston	MA	5	WMEX
	Shelby	MT	5	KSEN
	Albuquerque	NM	5	KDEF
	Utica	NY	5	WRUN
	Goldsboro	NC	5	WGBR
	Lima	OH	1	WIMA
	Cuyahoga Falls	OH	5	WCUE
	McAlester	OK	1	KNED
	Klamath Falls	OR	5	KAGO
	Portland	OR	5	KKEY
	Huntingdon	PA	5	WHUN
	Orangeburg	SC	5	WJZS
	Rapid City	SD	5	KIMM
	Chattanooga	TN	5	WGOW
	Morristown	TN	5	WCRK
	Seattle	WA	5	KEZX
	Welch	WV	5	WELC
	Kimberley	WI	5	WHBY
	Chippewa Falls	WI	5	WAYY
1160	Mobile	AL	10	WKWA
	East Point	GA	10	WMLD
	Chicago	IL	50	WJJD
	Hawesville	KY	2.5	WKCM
	Skowhegan	ME	10	WSKW
	Fenton	MI	1	WWON
	Virginia City	NV	5	KNKQ
	Lakewood	NJ	5	WOBM
	Oakland	NJ	10	WVNJ
	Mechanicville	NY	5	WMVI
	Trumansburg	NY	1	WPIE
	Red Springs	NC	5	WYRU
	Tryon	NC	10	WTYN
	Homer City	PA	10	WCCS
	Lehighton	PA	4.4	WYNS
	Donelson	TN	50	WAMB
	San Antonio	TX	10	KENS
	Salt Lake City	UT	50	KSLJ
	Fieldale	VA	5	WODY
1170	Montgomery	AL	10	WACV
	North Pole	AK	50	KJNP
	San Diego	CA	50	KCBQ
	San Jose	CA	50	KLOK
	Davie	FL	5	WAVS

Frequency [kHz]	Station Site	State	Power [kW]	Call Sign
1170	Cumming	GA	5	WHNE
(cont)	Mattoon	IL	5	WLBH
	Davenport	IA	1	KSTT
	Claremont	NC	7.7	WCXN
	Clinton	NC	5	WCLN
	Tulsa	OK	5	KVOO
	Lexington	SC	10	WLGO
	Bellingham	WA	10	KPUG
	Wheeling	WV	50	WWVA
1180	Williams	AZ	10	KYET
	Wasco	CA	50	KERI
	Trion	GA	5	WSAF
	Pearl	MS	10	WJNT
	Kalispell	MT	50	KOFI
	Bellevue	NE	5	KOIL
	Rochester	NY	50	WHAM
	Humble	TX	10	KGOL
	Lakewood	WA	2.4	KLAY
	Carolina Beach	NC	10	WMYT
	Knoxville	TN	10	WHJM
	Marathon Key	FL	50	VoA/R Marti
1190	Tolleson	AZ	5	KRDS
	Anaheim	CA	10	KORG
	Kensett	AR	10	KMOA
	Boulder	CO	5	KBCO
	Pine Castle	FL	5	WAJL
	Royal Palm Beach	FL	1	WOEQ
	Atlanta	GA	10	WGKA
	Fort Wayne	IN	50	WOWO
	Annapolis	MD	10	WANN
	Jackson	MN	5	KKOJ
	Bay St Louis	MS	5	WBSL
	De Soto	MO	5	KHAD
	Kansas City	MO	5	KFEZ
	New York	NY	10	WLIB
	Portland	OR	50	KEX
	Albuquerque	NM	10	KXKS
	Dunlap	TN	5	WSDQ
	Dallas	TX	50	KGBS
	Bluefield	VA	10	WBDY
1200	Ozark	AL	10	WQLS
	Eureka	CA	10	KTCD
	Pismo Beach	CA	5	KRDE
	Soquel	CA	25	KOQI

Frequency [kHz]	Station Site	State	Power [kW]	Call Sign
1200	Pine Island Center	FL	10	WDCQ
(cont)	Chicago	IL	10	WOPA
	Brewer	ME	10	WNSW
	Framingham	MA	10	WKOX
	Taylor	MI	50	WCHB
	Newburgh	NY	10	WGNY
	Graham	NC	10	WSML
	West Fargo	ND	10	KFNW
	New Castle	PA	5	WBZY
	Lebanon	TN	10	WQDQ
	Mt Carmel	TN	10	WRVX
	San Antonio	TX	50	WOAI
	Leesburg	VA	5	WAGE
1210	Sahuarita	AZ	10	KQTL
	Fowler	CA	10	KRGO
	Rocklin	CA	5	KEBR
	San Marcos	CA	20	KPRZ
	Miami Springs	FL	25	WCMQ
	Dahlonega	GA	10	WDGR
	Denham Springs	LA	10	WBIU
	Saginaw	MI	10	WKNX
	Guymon	OK	10	KGYN
	Philadelphia	PA	50	WOGL
	Arlington	TN	10	WGSF
	San Juan	TX	50	KUBR
	Washington	UT	10	KONY
	Auburn	WA	10	KBSG
	Sunnyside	WA	10	KREW
	Afton	WY	5	KRSV
	Laramie	WY	10	KLDI
	Huron	SD	10	KOKK
1220	Palo Alto	CA	5	KDFC
	Salem	IN	5	WSLM
	Stillwater	MN	5	WTCN
	Newburgh	NY	5	WGNY
	Whiteville	NC	5	WENC
	Cleveland	OH	50	WKNR
	Falls Church	VA	5	WFAX
1250	Fort Payne	AL	5	WZOB
	Wetumpka	AL	5	WAPZ
	Willcox	AZ	5	KHIL
	Little Rock	AZ	2	KURB
	Santa Barbara	CA	2.5	KTMS
	Willits	CA	5	KLLK

Frequency [kHz]	Station Site	State	Power [kW]	Call Sign
1250	Fraser	CO	5	KGRJ
(cont)	Tampa	FL	5	WDAE
	Fort Wayne	IN	1	WGL
	Lawrence	KS	5	KFKU
	Topeka	KS	5	WREN
	Ware	MA	5	WARE
	Fergus Falls	MN	5	KBRF
	McComb	MS	5	WHNY
	Forsyth	MT	5	KIKC
	Manchester	NH	5	WKBR
	Morristown	NJ	5	WMTR
	Farmville	NC	5	WGHB
	Pittsburgh	PA	5	WTAE
	Charleston	SC	5	WTMA
	Port Arthur	TX	5	KALO
	San Antonio	TX	1	KZEP
	Roosevelt	UT	5	KNEU
	Danville	VA	5	WDVA
	Pullman	WA	5	KWSU
	Warrenton	VA	5	WPRZ
	Seattle	WA	5	KKDZ
	Rupert	WV	5	WYKM
	Milwaukee	WI	5	WEMP
	Bangor	ME	5	WARP
	Marion	NC	5	WBRM
1260	Birmingham	AL	5	WCEO
	San Fernando	CA	5	KJQI
	San Francisco	CA	5	KOIT
	Aspen	CO	5	KRKE
	Washington	DC	5	WWDC
	Miami	FL	5	WSUA
	Baxley	GA	5	WUFE
	East Point	GA	5	WTJH
	Idaho Falls	ID	5	KTICN
	Belleville	IL	5	WIBV
	Indianapolis	IN	5	WNDE
	Boone	IA	5	KFGQ
	Boston	MA	5	WEZE
	Zeeland	MI	5	WWJQ
	Springfield	MO	5	KTTS
	Trenton	NJ	5	WBUD
	Santa Fe	NM	5	KVSF
	Syracuse	NY	5	WNDR
	Asheboro	NC	5	WKXR

Frequency [kHz]	Station Site	State	Power [kW]	Call Sign
1260	Cleveland	OH	5	WRDZ
(cont)	Portsmouth	OH	5	WNXT
	Wewoka	OK	1	KWSH
	McMinnville	OR	1	KLCY
	Erie	PA	5	WRIE
	Philipsburg	PA	5	WPHB
	Greenville	SC	5	WMUU
	Lake City	SC	5	WRIP
	Winner	SD	5	KWYR
	Chattanooga	TN	5	WNOO
	Dickson	TN	5	WDKN
	Charlottesville	VA	5	WCHV
	Amery	WI	5	WXCE
	Powell	WY	5	KPOW
1270	Prichard	AL	5	WKSJ
	Holbrook	AZ	5	KDJI
	Pine Bluff	AR	5	KPBA
	Tulare	CA	5	KJUG
	Thousand Palms	CA	5	KNWZ
	Naples	FL	5	WNOG
	Eatonville	FL	5	WHBS
	Tallahassee	FL	5	WNLS
	Columbus	GA	5	WHYD
	Commerce	GA	5	WJJC
	Twin Falls	ID	5	KTFI
	Rock Island	IL	5	WKBF
	Elkhart	IN	5	WFRN
	Gary	IN	2.5	WWCA
	Cumberland	MD	5	WCBC
	Fairhaven	MA	5	WLAW
	Springfield	MA	5	WSPR
	Charlevoix	MI	5	WMKT
	Detroit	MI	5	WXYT
	Baxter	MN	5	WJJY
	Rochester	MN	5	KWEB
	Sparks	NV	5	KPLY
	Dover	NH	5	WTSN
	Niagara Falls	NY	5	WHLD
	Walton	NY	5	WDLA
	Belmont	NC	5	WCGC
	Smithfield	NC	5	WMPM
	Claremore	OK	1	KTRT
	Grants Pass	OR	5	KAJO
	Lebanon	PA	5	WLBR

Frequency [kHz]	Station Site	State	Power [kW]	Call Sign
1270	Surfside Beach	SC	5	WYAK
(cont)	Sioux Falls	SD	2.5	KNWC
	Newport	TN	5	WLIK
	Bay City	TX	1	KIOX
	Fort Worth	TX	5	KESS
	Newport News	VA	1	WTJZ
	Stuart	VA	5	WHEO
	Longview	WA	5	KBAM
	Gillette	WY	5	KIML
1280	Tuscaloosa	AL	5	WWPG
	Arroyo Grande	CA	5	KKAL
	Long Beach	CA	1	KFRN
	Stockton	CA	1	KJAX
	Denver	CO	5	KXKL
	DeFuniak Springs	FL	5	WGTX
	Jacksonville	FL	5	WSVE
	Macon	GA	5	WKXK
	Aurora	IL	1	WBIG
	Evansville	IN	5	WWOK
	New Orleans	LA	5	WQUE
	Gardiner	ME	5	WABK
	Fitchburg	MA	5	WEIM
	Minneapolis	MN	5	WWTC
	Moorehead	MN	5	KVOX
	Henderson	NV	5	KDOL
	Farmington	NM	5	KRZE
	New York	NY	5	WADO
	Rochester	NY	5	WPXY
	Salisbury	NC	1	WSAT
	Scotland Neck	NC	5	WYAL
	Eugene	OR	5	KDUK
	Hanover	PA	5	WHVR
	New Castle	PA	5	WKST
	Anderson	SC	5	WANS
	Columbia	TN	5	WMCP
	Salt Lake City	UT	5	KDYL
	Spokane	WA	5	KUDY
	Yakima	WA	5	KIT
	Neenah	WI	5	WNAM
1290	Opp	AL	2.5	WOPP
	Tucson	AZ	5	KCUB
	El Dorado	AR	5	KDMS
	Siloam Springs	AR	5	KUOA

Frequency [kHz]	Station Site	State	Power [kW]	Call Sign
1290	Chico	CA	5	KHSL
(cont)	San Jose	CA	5	KAZA
	San Bernadino	CA	5	KMEN
	Ocala	FL	5	WTMC
	West Palm Beach	FL	5	WBTZ
	Canton	GA	5	WCHK
	Savannah	GA	5	WCHY
	Peoria	IL	5	WIRL
	New Albany	IN	1	WDGS
	Pratt	KS	5	KWLS
	Benton	KY	5	WCBL
	Manchester	KY	5	WKLB
	Houghton Lake	MI	5	WHGR
	Missoula	MT	5	KGVO
	Omaha	NE	5	KKAR
	Keene	NH	5	WKNE
	Binghamton	NY	5	WNBF
	Hickory	NC	5	WHKY
	Dayton	OH	5	WHIO
	Pendleton	OR	5	KUMA
	Lake Oswego	OR	5	KPHP
	Altoona	PA	5	WFBG
	Providence	RI	5	WRCP
	Sumter	SC	1	WQMC
	Oak Ridge	TN	5	WATO
	Weslaco	TX	5	KRGE
	Wichita Falls	TX	5	KLLF
	Colonial Heights	VA	5	WSTK
	Logan	WV	5	WVOW
	Milwaukee	WI	5	WMVP
	Sparta	WI	5	WKLJ
	Laramie	WY	5	KOWB
1300	Winfield	AL	5	WKXM
	Fairbanks	AK	5	KAKQ
	Searcy	AR	5	KWCK
	Fresno	CA	5	KYNO
	Mendocino	CA	5	KPMO
	Pasadena	CA	5	KAZN
	Colorado Springs	CO	5	KVOR
	New Haven	CT	1	WAVZ
	Cocoa	FL	5	WXXU
	Marathon	FL	2.5	WFFG
	Tampa	FL	5	WQBN
	Moultrie	GA	5	WMTM

Frequency [kHz]	Station Site	State	Power [kW]	Call Sign
1300	Orofino	ID	5	KLER
(cont)	La Grange	IL	5	WTAQ
	Mason City	IA	5	KGLO
	Lexington	KY	2.5	WLXG
	Baton Rouge	LA	5	WIBR
	Shreveport	LA	5	KFLO
	Baltimore	MD	5	WJFK
	Grand Rapids	MI	5	WOOD
	Jackson	MS	5	WKXI
	McCook	NE	5	KBRL
	Carson City	NV	5	KPTL
	Plymouth	NH	5	WPNH
	Trenton	NJ	3.2	WIMG
	Lancaster	NY	2.5	WXRL
	Rensselaer	NY	5	WQBK
	Mount Airey	NC	5	WSYD
	Cleveland	OH	5	WERE
	Tulsa	OK	5	KAKC
	Phoenix	OR	5	KDOV
	West Hazelton	PA	5	WXPX
	Mobridge	SD	5	KOLY
	Morristown	TN	5	WMTN
	Nashville	TN	5	WNQM
	Austin	TX	5	KVET
	Harrisonburg	VA	5	WKCY
	Seattle	WA	5	KMPS
1310	Marion	AL	5	WAJO
	Mesa	AZ	5	KXAM
	Barstow	CA	5	KIQQ
	Oakland	CO	5	KDIA
	Greeley	CO	5	KFKA
	Norwich	CT	5	WICH
	DeLand	FL	5	WYND
	Wauchula	FL	5	WAUC
	Twin Falls	ID	5	KEZJ
	Indianapolis	IN	5	WTLC
	Prestonburg	KY	5	WDOC
	West Monroe	LA	5	KMBS
	Portland	ME	5	WLOB
	Worcester	MA	5	WORC
	Dearborn	MI	5	WMTG
	Traverse City	MI	5	WCCW
	Joplin	MO	5	KFSB
	Great Falls	MT	5	KEIN

Frequency [kHz]	Station Site	State	Power [kW]	Call Sign
1310	Asbury Park	NJ	2.5	WJLK
(cont)	Corrales	NM	5	KIVA
	Mount Kisco	NY	5	WVIP
	Utica	NY	5	WTLB
	Canandaigua	NY	2.5	WCGR
	Asheville	NC	5	WISE
	Charlotte	NC	1	WGSP
	Durham	NC	5	WTIK
	Grand Forks	ND	5	KNOX
	Newport	OR	5	KNPT
	Bedford	PA	5	WAYC
	Warren	PA	5	WNAE
	Kingstree	SC	5	WDKD
	Chattanooga	TN	5	WDOD
	Jackson	TN	5	WDXI
	Dallas	TX	5	KAAM
	San Antonio	TX	5	KXTN
	Fairfax	VA	5	WDCT
	Newport News	VA	5	WGH
	Prosser	WA	5	KARY
	White Sulphur Springs	WV	5	WSLW
	Madison	WI	5	WIBA
1320	Birmingham	AL	5	WAGG
	Dothan	AL	1	WAGF
	Fort Smith	AR	5	KWHN
	Sacramento	CA	5	KCTC
	Farmerville	CA	5	KQIQ
	Waterbury	CT	5	WATR
	Hollywood	FL	5	WLQY
	Jacksonville	FL	5	WQIK
	Venice	FL	5	WAMR
	Griffin	GA	5	WHIE
	Vivian	LA	5	KNCB
	Attleboro	MA	5	WARA
	Lansing	MI	5	WILS
	Marquette	MI	5	WDMJ
	Grand Rapids	MN	5	KOZY
	Picayune	MS	5	WRJW
	St Louis	MO	5	KSIV
	Scottsbluff	NE	5	KOLT
	Derry	NH	5	WDER
	Hornell	NY	5	WHHO
	Greensboro	NC	5	WGLD
	Murphy	NC	5	WKRK

Frequency [kHz]	Station Site	State	Power [kW]	Call Sign
1320	Oberlin	OH	1	WOBL
(cont)	Allentown	PA	5	WKAP
	Pittsburgh	PA	5	WJAS
	Columbia	SC	5	WOMG
	Sioux Falls	SD	5	KELO
	Kingsport	TN	5	WKIN
	Manchester	TN	5	WMSR
	Houston	TX	5	KXYZ
	Salt Lake City	UT	5	KCNR
	Richmond	VA	5	WLEE
	Aberdeen	WA	5	KXRO
	Wisconsin Rapids	WI	5	WFHR
1330	Butler	AL	5	WPRN
	Scottsboro	AL	5	WZCT
	Tucson	AZ	2	KHYT
	Los Angeles	CA	5	KWKW
	Redding	CA	5	KRDG
	Los Banos	CA	5	KLBS
	Fort Pierce	FL	5	WJNX
	Milton	FL	5	WEBY
	Tallahassee	FL	5	WCVC
	Dublin	GA	3.4	WMLT
	Evanston	IL	5	WKTA
	Evansville	IN	5	WVHI
	Waterloo	IO	5	KWLO
	Wichita	KS	5	KFH
	Corbin	KY	5	WKDP
	Lafayette	LA	5	KVOL
	Havre de Grace	MD	5	WASA
	Waltham	MA	5	WRCA
	Flint	MI	5	WDLZ
	St Paul	MN	5	KNOW
	Fulton	MS	5	WFTO
	Gallup	NM	5	KGAK
	New York	NY	5	WWRV
	Owego	NY	5	WEBO
	Springville	NY	1	WFWC
	Wishek	ND	5	KDRQ
	Youngstown	OH	1	WZKC
	Portland	OR	5	KUPL
	Erie	PA	5	WEYZ
	Somerset	PA	5	WADJ
	Conway	SC	5	WPJS
	Greenville	SC	5	WFBC

Frequency [kHz]	Station Site	State	Power [kW]	Call Sign
1330 *(cont)*	Monahans	TX	5	KLBO
	Danville	VA	5	WBTM
	Marion	VA	5	WOLD
	Onley	VA	5	WESR
	Spokane	WA	5	KMBI
	Sheboygan	WI	5	WHBL
	Lander	WY	5	KOVE
1350	Gadsden	AL	5	WGAD
	San Bernardino	CA	5	KCKC
	Santa Rosa	CA	5	KSRO
	Pueblo	CO	5	KGHF
	Norwalk	CT	1	WNLK
	Norwalk	CT	2.5	WNLK
	Putnam	CT	5	WINY
	Cocoa	FL	1	WWHL
	Fort Myers	FL	5	WCRM
	Blackshear	GA	5	WGIA
	Warner Robins	GA	5	WCOP
	Lewiston	ID	5	KRLC
	Peoria	IL	1	WXCL
	Kokom	IN	5	WIOU
	Des Moines	IA	5	KRNT
	Louisville	KY	5	WLOU
	New Orleans	LA	5	WSMB
	Laconia	NH	5	WLNH
	Princeton	NJ	5	WHWH
	Albuquerque	NM	5	KABQ
	Akron	OH	5	WSLR
	York	PA	5	WOYK
	Jasper	TX	5	KXTJ
	San Antonio	TX	5	KCOR
	Norton	VA	5	WNVA
	Norfolk	VA	5	WSVY
1360	Mobile	AL	5	WMOB
	Glendale	AZ	5	KNNS
	Helena	AR	1	KFFA
	Modesto	CA	5	KFIV
	San Diego	CA	5	KPOP
	Hartford	CT	5	WDRC
	Cypress Gardens	FL	5	WHNR
	Jacksonville	FL	5	WCGL
	Miami Beach	FL	5	WKAT
	Bainbridge	GA	5	WYSE

Frequency [kHz]	Station Site	State	Power [kW]	Call Sign
1360 (cont)	Sioux City	IA	5	KSCJ
	Baltimore	MD	5	WWLG
	Caro	MI	1	WKYO
	Kalamazoo	MI	5	WKMI
	Bemidji	MN	5	KKBJ
	Washington Township	NJ	5	WNJC
	Ruidoso	NM	5	KBUY
	Binghamton	NY	5	WKOP
	Chapel Hill	NC	5	WCHL
	Cincinnati	OH	5	WSAI
	Hermiston	OR	1	KOHU
	Hillsboro	OR	1	KUIK
	McKeesport	PA	5	WIXZ
	Pottsville	PA	5	WPPA
	Milan	TN	1	WWHY
	Baytown	TX	1	KWWJ
	Corpus Christi	TX	1	KRYS
	Fort Worth	TX	5	KNRB
	Galax	VA	5	WBOB
	Harrisonburg	VA	5	WHBG
	Tacoma	WA	5	KKMO
	Green Bay	WI	5	WGEE
	Rock Springs	WY	5	KRKK
1370	Corona	CA	5	KWRM
	Quincy	CA	5	KPCO
	San Jose	CA	5	KEEN
	Deer Trail	CO	5	KTMG
	Ocala	FL	5	WOCA
	Pensacola	FL	5	WCOA
	Jessup	GA	5	WLOP
	Bloomington	IN	5	WGCL
	Gary	IN	1	WLTH
	Dubuque	IA	5	KDTH
	Dodge City	KS	5	KGNO
	Grayson	KY	5	WGOH
	Ellsworth	ME	5	WDEA
	Leonardtown	MD	1	WKIK
	Cadillac	MI	5	WKJF
	Fairmont	MN	1	KSUM
	Butte	MT	5	KXTL
	Manchester	NY	5	WFEA
	Ellenville	NU	5	WELV
	Rochester	NY	5	WXXI
	Gastonia	NC	5	WLTC

Frequency [kHz]	Station Site	State	Power [kW]	Call Sign
1370	Lillington	NC	5	WLLN
(cont)	Tabor City	NC	5	WTAB
	Toledo	OH	5	WSPD
	Astoria	OR	1	KAST
	Corry	PA	1	WWCB
	Roaring Spring	PA	5	WKMC
	Santee	SC	5	WMNY
	Chattanooga	TN	5	WDEF
	Longview	TX	1	KFRO
	Salt Lake City	UT	5	KSOP
	Martinsville	VA	5	WHEE
	Frost	WV	5	WVMR
	Moundsville	WV	5	WZAO
	Neillsville	WI	5	WCCN
1380	Vernon	AL	5	WVSA
	North Little Rock	AR	1	KPAL
	Sacramento	CA	5	KSMJ
	Salinas	CA	5	KTOM
	Waterbury	CT	5	WFNW
	Wilmington	DE	5	WAMS
	Ormond Beach	FL	5	WELE
	St Petersburg	FL	5	WRBQ
	Atlanta	GA	5	WAOK
	Ocilla	GA	5	WSIZ
	South Beloit	IL	5	WBEL
	Fort Wayne	IN	5	WQHK
	Carroll	IA	1	KCIM
	Baton Rouge	LA	5	WYNK
	Port Huron	MI	5	WPHM
	Brainerd	MN	5	KLIZ
	St Louis	MO	5	KASP
	Portsmouth	NH	1	WCQL
	Bath	NY	5	WAHB
	New York	NY	5	WKDM
	Asheville	NC	5	WKJV
	New Bern	NC	5	WSFL
	Winston-Salem	NC	5	WTOB
	Lawton	OK	1	KSWO
	Ontario	OR	5	KSRV
	Rapid City	SD	5	KOTA
	Franklin	TN	5	WIZO
	Millington	TN	2.5	WMPS
	El Paso	TX	5	KTSM
	Rutland	VT	5	WSYB

Frequency [kHz]	Station Site	State	Power [kW]	Call Sign
1380 *(cont)*	Richmond	VA	5	WTVR
	Everett	WA	5	KRKO
	Cliftonville	WI	3.9	WFCL
1390	Anniston	AL	5	WHMA
	Fields Landing	CA	5	KKDV
	Long Beach	CA	5	KGER
	Turlock	CA	5	KMIX
	Denver	CO	5	KJME
	Gainesville	FL	5	WAJD
	Americus	GA	5	WISK
	Chicago	IL	5	WGCI
	Des Moines	IA	1	KKSO
	Hazard	KY	5	WKIC
	Presque Isle	ME	5	WTMS
	Plymouth	MA	5	WPLM
	Charlotte	MI	5	WLCM
	Waite Park	MN	2.5	KXSS
	Gulfport	MS	5	WROA
	Meridian	MS	5	WMER
	Farmington	NM	5	KENN
	Hobbs	NM	5	KHOB
	Poughkeepsie	NY	5	WEOK
	Syracuse	NY	5	WDCW
	Rocky Mount	NC	5	WEED
	Minot	ND	5	KRRZ
	Middleport	OH	5	WMPO
	Youngstown	OH	5	WHOT
	Enid	OK	1	KCRC
	Salem	OR	5	KSLM
	Lancaster	PA	5	WLAN
	State College	PA	2	WRSC
	Charleston	SC	5	WXTC
	Jackson	TN	5	WTJS
	Logan	UT	5	KLGN
	Burlington	VT	5	WKDR
	Arlington	VA	5	WMZQ
	Lynchburg	VA	5	WWOD
	Yakima	WA	5	KBBO
	Schofield	WI	5	WRIG
1410	Mobile	AL	5	WLVV
	Prattville	AL	5	WRNB
	Bakersfield	CA	1	KERN
	Carmel	CA	5	KRML
	Marysville	CA	5	KMYC

Frequency [kHz]	Station Site	State	Power [kW]	Call Sign
1410	Redlands	CA	5	KCAL
(cont)	Fort Collins	C0	5	KCOL
	Hartford	CT	5	WPOP
	Dover	DE	5	WDOV
	Fort Myers	FL	5	WMYR
	Leesburg	FL	5	WQBQ
	Tallahassee	FL	5	WHBT
	Rome	GA	1	WLAQ
	Leavenworth	KS	5	KKLO
	Wichita	KS	5	KQAM
	Bowling Green	KY	5	WLBJ
	Harlan	KY	5	WHLN
	Roseau	MN	5	KRWB
	Boyle	MS	5	WDTL
	Cuba	MO	5	KGNN
	North Platte	NE	5	KOOQ
	Las Vegas	NV	5	KFMS
	Elmira	NY	2.5	WELM
	Watertown	NY	5	WNCQ
	Durham	NC	5	WSRC
	Dayton	OH	5	WING
	Portland	OR	5	KBNP
	Lansford	PA	5	WLSH
	Pittsburgh	PA	5	KQV
	Cleveland	TX	1	KLEV
	Odessa	TX	1	KRIL
	Roanoke	VA	5	WRIS
	South Charleston	WV	5	WSCW
	LaCrosse	WI	5	WIZM
	Sheridan	WY	5	KWYO
1420	Tuscaloosa	AL	5	WACT
	Bethel	AK	1	KSKM
	Hot Springs	AR	5	KXOW
	Stockton	CA	5	KSTN
	Old Saybrook	CT	5	WLIS
	Delray Beach	FL	5	WDBF
	Palmetto	FL	2.5	WBRD
	Columbus	GA	5	WRCG
	Toccoa	GA	5	WLET
	Michigan City	IN	5	WIMS
	Davenport	IA	5	WOC
	Owensboro	KY	5	WVJS
	New Bedford	MA	5	WBSM
	Pittsfield	MA	1	WBEC

Frequency [kHz]	Station Site	State	Power [kW]	Call Sign
1420	Mankato	MN	5	KTOE
(cont)	Wiggins	MS	5	WIGG
	Wolfeboro	NH	5	WASR
	Newark	NY	5	WACK
	Peekskill	NY	5	WLNA
	Cleveland	OH	5	WHK
	Coatesville	PA	5	WCOJ
	DuBois	PA	5	WCED
	Erwin	TN	5	WEMB
	Pulaski	TN	1	WKSR
	Lufkin	TX	5	KSRK
	Warrenton	VA	5	WKCW
	Centralia	WA	5	KITI
	Walla Walla	WA	5	KUJ
	Kenova	WV	5	WTCR
1430	Pell City	AL	5	WFHK
	Fresno	CA	5	KFIG
	San Gabriel	CA	5	KALI
	Santa Clara	CA	1	KNTA
	Aurora	CO	5	KEZW
	Homestead	FL	5	WOIR
	Lakeland	FL	5	WLKF
	Panama City	FL	5	WLTG
	Covington	GA	5	WGFS
	Tifton	GA	5	WWGS
	Highland Park	IL	1	WEEF
	Indianapolis	IN	5	WCKN
	Mayfield	KY	1	WYMC
	Annapolis	MD	5	WNAV
	Amherst	MA	5	WTTT
	Everett	MA	5	WXKS
	Ionia	MI	5	WION
	Laurel	MS	5	WLAU
	St Louis	MO	5	WRTH
	Grand Island	NE	5	KRGI
	Newark	NJ	5	WNJR
	Roswell	NM	5	KCRX
	Endicott	NY	5	WMRV
	Monroe	NC	2.5	WDEX
	Moranton	NC	5	WMNC
	Minot	ND	5	KTYN
	Fostoria	OH	1	WFOB
	Tulsa	OK	5	KQLL
	Keizer	OR	5	KYKN

Frequency [kHz]	Station Site	State	Power [kW]	Call Sign
1430	Altoona	PA	5	WVAM
(cont)	Batesburg	SC	5	WBLR
	Germantown	TN	2.5	WNWZ
	Knoxville	TN	5	WEMG
	Madison	TN	5	WHNK
	Gladewater	TX	5	KEES
	Houston	TX	5	KCOH
	Ogden	UT	5	KLO
	Ashland	VA	5	WPES
	Clintwood	VA	5	WDIC
	Mount Vernon	WA	5	KBRC
	Asotin	WA	5	KCLK
	Weirton	WV	1	WEIR
	Beaver Dam	WI	1	WBEV
1440	Montgomery	AL	5	WHHY
	Scottsdale	AZ	5	KOPA
	Little Rock	AR	5	KITA
	Napa	CA	5	KVON
	Riverside	CA	1	KDIF
	Santa Maria	CA	5	KUHL
	Wray	CO	5	KRDZ
	Lehigh Acres	FL	5	WWCL
	Winter Park	FL	5	WWZN
	Brunswick	GA	5	WGIG
	Quincy	IL	5	WGEM
	Rockford	IL	5	WROK
	Topeka	KS	5	KMAJ
	Monroe	LA	5	KMLB
	Glasgow	KY	5	WCDS
	Portland	ME	5	WLPZ
	Worcester	MA	5	WVEI
	Bay City	MI	5	WMAX
	Inkster	MI	1	WMKM
	Minneapolis	MN	5	KQRS
	Lucedale	MS	5	WRBE
	Elizabethtown	NC	5	WBLA
	Lexington	NC	5	WLXN
	Warren	OH	5	WRRO
	Medford	OR	5	KMED
	The Dalles	OR	5	KODL
	Carbondale	PA	5	WCDL
	Greenville	SC	5	WSSL
	Cowan	TN	5	WZYX
	Amarillo	TX	5	KPUR

Frequency [kHz]	Station Site	State	Power [kW]	Call Sign
1440 (cont)	Corpus Christi	TX	1	KEYS
	Denton	TX	5	KDNT
	Livingston	TX	5	KETX
	Blackstone	VA	5	WKLV
	Bluefield	WV	5	WHIS
	Morgantown	WV	5	WAJR
	Green Bay	WI	5	WNFL
	Puyallup	WA	5	KJUN
1460	Cullman	AL	5	WFMH
	Phoenix City	AL	5	WPNX
	Inglewood	CA	5	KTYM
	Salinas	CA	5	KRQC
	Colorado Springs	CO	5	KKCS
	DeFuniak Springs	FL	5	WZEP
	Jacksonville	FL	5	WZNZ
	Lake Mary	FL	5	WOLM
	Buford	GA	5	WXEM
	Des Moines	IA	5	KGGO
	Elkhorn City	KY	5	WBPA
	Baton Rouge	LA	5	WXOK
	Brockton	MA	5	WBET
	Big Rapids	MI	5	WBRN
	Montevideo	MN	1	KDMA
	St Charles	MO	5	KIRL
	Kearney	NE	5	KKPR
	Las Vegas	NV	5	KENO
	Florence	NJ	5	WIFI
	Albany	NY	5	WGNA
	Rochester	NY	5	WWWG
	Fuquay-Varina	NC	5	WCRY
	Laurinburg	NC	5	WEWO
	Dickinson	ND	5	KLTC
	Columbus	OH	1	WBNS
	Harrisburg	PA	5	WIMX
	Tunkhannok	PA	5	WEMR
	Union	SC	1	WBCU
	Waco	TX	1	WACO
	Manassas	VA	5	WKDV
	Radford	VA	5	WRAD
	Kirkland	WA	5	KARR
	Yakima	WA	5	KMWX
	Buckhannon	WV	5	WBUC
1470	Palmdale	CA	5	KUTY
	Sacramento	CA	5	KXOA

Frequency [kHz]	Station Site	State	Power [kW]	Call Sign
1470	Meriden	CT	2.5	WMMW
(cont)	Clearwater	FL	5	WLVU
	Fort Lauderdale	FL	5	WRBD
	Rome	GA	5	WRGA
	Chicago Heights	IL	1	WCFJ
	Peoria	IL	5	WMBD
	Sioux City	IA	5	KWSL
	Atchison	KS	1	KERE
	Lake Charles	LA	5	KLCL
	Lewiston	ME	5	WZOU
	Salisbury	MD	5	WJDY
	Westminster	MD	1	WTTR
	Marlboro	MA	5	WSRO
	Flint	MI	5	WKMF
	Kalamazoo	MI	5	WQSN
	Brooklyn Park	MN	5	KBCW
	Ithaca	NY	5	WTKO
	Greensboro	NC	5	WWBG
	Plymouth	NC	5	WPNC
	Spruce Pine	NC	5	WTOE
	Toledo	OH	1	WWWM
	Allentown	PA	5	WXKW
	Columbia	SC	5	WQXL
	Berry Hill	TN	5	WVOL
	Abilene	TX	5	KNTS
	Henderson	TX	5	KWRD
	Tremonton	UT	5	KNFL
	Broadway	VA	5	WBTX
	Chehalis	WA	5	KELA
	Moses Lake	WA	5	KBSN
	Huntington	WV	5	WHRD
	West Bend	WI	2.5	WBKV
1480	Irondale	AL	5	WLPH
	Mobile	AL	5	WABB
	Phoenix	AZ	5	KPHX
	Berryville	AR	5	KTHS
	Concord	CA	5	KWUN
	Eureka	CA	5	KRED
	Merced	CA	5	KYOS
	Santa Ana	CA	5	KWIZ
	Marco Island	FL	1	WODX
	Atlanta	GA	5	WYZE
	Augusta	GA	5	WRDW
	Terre Haute	IN	5	WTHI

Frequency [kHz]	Station Site	State	Power [kW]	Call Sign
1480	Wichita	KS	5	KZSN
(cont)	Neon	KY	5	WNKY
	Fall River	MA	5	WSAR
	Kentwood	MI	5	WGVU
	Ypsilanti	MI	3.8	WSDS
	Austin	MN	1	KAUS
	Fosston	MN	5	KKCQ
	Sidney	MT	5	KGCX
	Lincoln	NE	5	KMEM
	Hobbs	NM	5	KKEL
	New York	NY	5	WZRC
	Remsen	NY	5	WADR
	Charlotte	NC	5	WCNV
	Franklin	NC	5	WAJA
	Canton	OH	5	WHBC
	Cincinnati	OH	5	WCIN
	Latrobe	PA	1	WCNS
	Philadelphia	PA	5	WDAS
	Shamokin	PA	1	WISL
	Memphis	TN	5	WBBP
	Dallas	TX	5	KMRT
	Springfield	VT	5	WCFR
	Salem	VA	5	WTOY
	Vancouver	WA	1	KBMS
	Madison	WI	5	WTDY
1500	Burbank	CA	50	KRCK
	San Jose	CA	50	KSJX
	Milford	CT	5	WFIF
	Washington	DC	50	WTOP
	Indianapolis	IN	5	WBRI
	Detroit	MI	50	WLQV
	St Paul	MN	50	KSTP
	Winston-Salem	NC	10	WSMX
	Pawhuska	OK	5	KXVQ
1510	Mesa	AZ	10	KFNN
	Fresno	CA	10	KIRV
	Ontario	CA	10	KNSE
	Littleton	CO	10	KDKO
	New London	CT	10	WNLC
	Boston	MA	50	WSSH
	Jackson	MI	5	WJCO
	Independence	MO	10	KJLA
	Dover	NJ	10	WMHQ
	Annville	PA	5	WAHT

Frequency [kHz]	Station Site	State	Power [kW]	Call Sign
1510 *(cont)*	Milbank	SD	5	KMSD
	Nashville	TN	50	WLAC
	Nederland	TX	10	KQHN
	West Jordan	UT	10	KLLB
	Spokane	WA	50	KGA
	Waukesha	WI	10	WAUK
1520	Opelika	AL	5	WZMG
	Hollister	CA	5	KMPG
	Oxnard	CA	10	KTRO
	Orlando	FL	5	WTLN
	Clinton	IL	5	WHOW
	Greenup	KY	5	WTCV
	Lafayette	LA	10	KACY
	Greenfield	MA	10	WGAM
	Brunswick	MD	9.3	WTRI
	Muskegon	MI	10	WQWQ
	St Louis	MI	1	WMLM
	Rochester	MN	10	KOLM
	Sikeston	MO	5	KMPL
	Buffalo	NY	50	WWKB
	Mocksville	NC	5	WDSL
	Warrenton	NC	5	WARR
	Toledo	OH	1	WVOI
	Oklahoma City	OK	50	KOMA
	Portland	OR	50	KFXX
	Myrtle Beach	SC	5	WKZQ
	Dayton	TN	5	WREA
	Sequim	WA	20	KSJM
1530	Sacramento	CA	50	KFBK
	Moreno Valley	CA	50	KHPY
	Bridgeport	CT	10	WDJZ
	Jacksonville	FL	50	WCRJ
	Dalton	GA	10	WTTI
	Lapeer	MI	5	WWGZ
	Shakopee	MN	8	KKCM
	Poplarville	MS	10	WRPM
	Lincoln	NE	5	KHAT
	Durham	NC	10	WRTP
	Cincinnati	OH	50	WCKY
	Harlingen	TX	50	KGBT
	Wagoner	OK	5	KXTD
	Ralls	TX	5	KCLR
	Fox Farm	WY	10	KSHY

Frequency [kHz]	Station Site	State	Power [kW]	Call Sign
1540	Phoenix	AZ	10	KASA
	Aptos	CA	10	KLAU
	Los Angeles	CA	50	KXED
	Waterloo	IA	50	KXEL
	Wheaton	MD	5	WMDO
	Exeter	NH	5	WMYF
	Albany	NY	50	WPTR
	Charlotte	NC	10	WOGR
	Philadelphia	PA	50	WPGR
	Punxsutawney	PA	5	WECZ
	Pickens	SC	10	WTBI
	San Antonio	TX	5	KEDA
	Richmond	VA	10	WREJ
	Bellevue	WA	5	KBLV
1550	Huntsville	AL	50	WLOR
	Tucson	AZ	50	KUAT
	Apple Valley	CA	5	KAPL
	Fresno	CA	5	KXEX
	San Francisco	CA	10	KKHI
	Arvada	CO	10	KQXI
	Bloomfield	CT	5	WRDM
	Miami	FL	10	WRHC
	Tampa	FL	10	WAMA
	Augusta	GA	5	WTHB
	Smyrna	GA	50	WAZX
	Port Allen	LA	5	WLUX
	Shreveport	LA	10	KVKI
	Newton	MA	10	WNTN
	Springfield	MO	5	KLFJ
	Cape Girardeau	MO	5	KAPE
	St Joseph	MO	5	KSFT
	Fargo	ND	10	KQWB
	Pittston	PA	5	WARD
	Bennettsville	SC	5	WBSC
	Bristol	TN	5	WBCV
	Clarksville	TN	2.5	WCTZ
	Granger	UT	10	KRGQ
	Vinton	VA	10	WKBA
	Virginia Beach	VA	5	WVAB
	Ferndale	WA	10	KNTR
	Spokane	WA	10	KSVY
	Vancouver	WA	10	KVAN
	Charles Town	WV	5	WXVA
	Madison	WI	5	WHIT

Frequency [kHz]	Station Site	State	Power [kW]	Call Sign
1560	Daleville	AL	5	WTKN
	Bakersfield	CA	10	KNZR
	Inverness	FL	5	WINV
	Miami	FL	10	WRHC
	Melbourne	FL	5	WTAI
	Iowa City	IA	1	KCJJ
	Paducah	KY	10	WPAD
	Joplin	MO	10	KQYX
	New York	NY	50	WQEW
	Warsaw	NC	10	WTRQ
	Fairfield	OH	5	WCNW
	Toledo	OH	5	WTOD
	Lancaster	SC	50	WAGL
	Aberdeen	SD	10	KKAA
	Nashville	TN	10	WWGM
	West Lake Hills	TX	2.5	KTXZ
1570	Selma	AL	5	WTQX
	Lodi	CA	5	KCVR
	Riverside	CA	5	KPRO
	Salinas	CA	5	KTGE
	Auburndale	FL	5	WTWB
	Fernandina Beach	FL	5	WQAI
	Morrow	GA	5	WSSA
	Freeport	IL	5	WFRL
	Baltimore	MD	5	WFEL
	Bay Springs	MS	5	WIZK
	Penn Yan	NY	5	WFLR
	Doylestown	PA	5	WBUX
	Centerville	TN	5	WNKX
	Cleveland	TN	5	WCLE
	Ripley	TN	28	WTRB
	Minocqua	WI	5	WMQA
1580	Tempe	AZ	50	KCWW
	Santa Monica	CA	50	KBLA
	Colorado Springs	CO	10	KWYD
	Chattahoochee	FL	5	WTCL
	Fort Lauderdale	FL	10	WSRF
	Mount Dora	FL	5	WBGD
	Columbus	GA	2.3	WEAM
	Georgetown	KY	10	WBBE
	Lake Charles	LA	1	KXZZ
	Morningside	MD	50	WPGC
	Pascagoula	MS	5	WZZJ
	Albuquerque	NM	10	KZKL

Frequency [kHz]	Station Site	State	Power [kW]	Call Sign
1580 (cont)	Patchogue	NY	10	WLIM
	Icard Township	NC	5	WUIV
	Travelers Rest	SC	5	WBBR
	Knoxville	TN	5	WDMF
	Pulaski	VA	5	WPUV
1590	Atmore	AL	5	WGYJ
	Tuscumbia	AL	5	WVNA
	Pine Bluff	AR	5	KYDE
	San Jose	CA	5	KLIV
	Ventura	CA	5	KOGO
	Waterbury	CT	5	WQQW
	Port St Lucie	FL	5	WPSL
	St Petersburg Beach	FL	5	WRXB
	Albany	GA	5	WALG
	La Fayette	GA	5	WQCH
	Evanston	IL	1	WONX
	Galesburg	IL	5	WAIK
	Beach Grove	IN	5	WNTS
	Great Bend	KS	5	KVGB
	Gorham	ME	5	WASY
	Glen Burnie	MD	1	WJRO
	Coldwater	MI	5	WTVB
	East Grand Forks	MN	5	KCNN
	Jackson	MS	5	WZRX
	Sun Valley	NV	5	KHIT
	Nashua	NH	5	WSMN
	Auburn	NY	0.5	WAUB
	Brockport	NY	1	WASB
	Salamanca	NY	5	WGGO
	Clayton	NC	5	WHPY
	Akron	OH	5	WAKR
	Tillamook	OR	5	KTIL
	Chambersburg	PA	5	WCBG
	Chester	PA	1	WCZN
	Warwick	RI	5	WARV
	Jonesboro	TN	5	WKTP
	El Paso	TX	5	KELP
	Houston	TX	5	KYOK
	Lubbock	TX	1	KLLL
	Richmond	VA	5	WFTH
	Seattle	WA	5	KZOK
	New Richmond	WI	5	WIXK
1600	Huntsville	AL	5	WEUP
	Montgomery	AL	5	WXVI

Frequency [kHz]	Station Site	State	Power [kW]	Call Sign
1600	South Tucson	AZ	2.5	KXEW
(cont)	Bellefonte	AR	5	KNWA
	Fresno	CA	5	KGST
	Pomona	CA	5	KMNY
	Yuba City	CA	5	KUBA
	Lakewood	CO	5	KWMX
	Dover	DE	5	WKEN
	Atlantic Beach	FL	5	WNCM
	West Palm Beach	FL	5	WPOM
	Orlando	FL	5	WXTO
	Austell	GA	5	WAOS
	Algona	IA	5	KGLA
	Cedar Rapids	IA	5	KCRG
	Rockville	MD	1	WINX
	Boston	MA	5	WUNR
	East Longmeadow	MA	5	WAQY
	Ann Arbor	MI	5	WAAM
	Muskegon	MI	5	WSFN
	Watertown	MN	5	KWOM
	St Louis	MI	5	KATZ
	New York	NY	5	WWRL
	Charlotte	NC	2.5	WGIV
	Hendersonville	NC	5	WTZQ
	Eugene	OR	5	KEED
	Bedford	PA	5	WBFD
	Borger	TX	5	KBBB
	Brownsville	TX	1	KBOR
	Cockrell Hill	TX	5	KRVA
	Orange	TX	5	KOGT
	Centerville	UT	5	KCOX
	Chesapeake	VA	5	WJQI
	Saltville	VA	5	WXMY
	Milton	WV	5	WNST
	Wheeling	WV	5	WBBD
	Ripon	WI	5	WCWC

Section 11

INTERNATIONAL RADIO BROADCASTS IN ENGLISH

This chapter details the main international service broadcasts in English beamed throughout the world.

Time	Station	Frequencies [kHz]
0000–0030	R Prague	7345, 9485
0000–0030	R Yugoslavia	9580, 11870
0000–0100	R Ukraine Intl	4825, 6020, 7285, 9685, 11720, 12030, 15180, 15580
0000–0200	REE	9540
0000–0200	Monitor R Intl	5850, 9430
0003–0005	RAI	846, 900, 6060
0030–0100	HCJB	9745, 11925, 17490-usb, 21455-usb
0030–0100	R Sweden	6065, 9810
0030–0325	R Netherlands	9840 (to 0130), 9860, 12025
0100–0120	RAI	7275, 11800
0100–0130	R Norway Intl	9560, 11925 [Monday]
0100–0130	Swiss R Intl	5905, 6135, 9885
0100–0130	R Slovakia Intl	5930, 7310, 9810
0100–0130	R Prague Intl	7345, 9485
0100–0150	DW	6040, 6085, 6145, 9700, 11740, 11865
0100–0200	R Korea	7550, 15575
0100–0200	HCJB	9745, 11925, 17490-usb, 21455-usb
0100–0200	RCI	6120, 9535, 9755, 11845, 11940
0100–0200	R Tashkent	7190, 7250, 9715, 9740
0103–0105	RAI	846, 900, 6060
0130–0200	R Tirana	9580, 11840
0130–0200	R Sweden	9695, 11695
0130–0140	Vo Greece	9380, 9420, 9460, 11645
0130–0200	R Austria Intl	9655, 9870, 13730
0130–0325	R Netherlands	9860, 12025
0200–0250	DW	7285, 9580, 9615, 9690, 11865, 11945, 11965, 12045, 15185
0200–0300	R Romania Intl	6155, 9510, 9570, 11830, 11940
0200–0300	RAE Buenos Aires	11710 [Tuesday–Saturday]
0200–0330	R Cairo	9475, 11600
0200–0300	HCJB	9745, 11925, 17490-usb, 21455-usb
0200–0400	Monitor R Intl	5850, 9430
0203–0205	RAI	846, 900, 6060
0230–0300	R Sweden	6155, 9850

Time	Station	Frequencies [kHz]
0230–0300	R Portugal	9570, 9705 [Tuesday–Saturday]
0230–0245	R Tirana	9580, 11840
0230–0300	R Budapest	5970, 9835, 11910
0250–0315	Vatican R	7305, 9605
0300–0330	R Prague	5930, 7345
0300–0330	NHK R Japan	11880, 11885, 15230
0300–0350	DW	6085, 6185, 9535, 9640, 11750
0300–0430	HCJB	9745, 11925, 17490-usb, 21455-usb
0300–0400	RAE Buenos Aires	9690, 11710
0300–0400	R Ukraine Intl	4825, 6020, 7285, 9685, 11720, 12030, 15180
0300–0500	Channel Africa	3220, 5955
0300–0400	TRT Vo Turkey	9445
0303–0305	RAI	846, 900, 6060
0320–0335	Vatican R	7360, 9725
0330–0400	R Sweden	6155, 9850
0330–0400	R Prague	5930, 9440, 11640
0330–0425	R Netherlands	6165, 9590
0330–0400	UAE R Dubai	11945, 13675, 15400, 17890
0330–0430	R Bulgaria	9700, 11720
0340–0350	Vo Greece	9380, 9420, 9460, 11645
0350–0410	RAI	11905, 15330, 17795
0400–0415	Kol Israel	9435, 11605, 17545
0400–0415	R Latvia	5935 [Sunday only]
0400–0430	R Romania Intl	6155, 9510, 9570, 11830, 11940
0400–0430	RCI	9650, 11905, 11925, 15275
0400–0430	Swiss R Intl	6135, 9860, 9885
0400–0430	R Yugoslavia	9580, 11870
0400–0450	DW	5980, 6015, 6185, 7150, 7225, 9565, 9765
0400–0450	R Pyongyang	15180, 15230, 17765
0400–0500	Monitor R Intl	7465, 9840
0400–0500	WYFR	11825
0403–0405	RAI	846, 900, 6060
0415–0440	RAI	7275, 9575
0430–0445	R Latvia	5935 [Saturday]
0430–0450	R Finland	11755, 15440
0500–0515	Vatican R	9725, 11625, 15570
0500–0515	Swiss R Intl	3985, 6165
0500–0520	Vatican R	527, 1530, 3945, 6245
0500–0530	R Norway Intl	7165, 9560, 9590, 11865 [Sunday]
0500–0530	RCI	6050, 6150, 7295, 9740, 15430, 17840 [Mon–Fri]

Time	Station	Frequencies [kHz]
0500–0550	DW	5960, 9515, 9670, 11705
0500–0600	REE	9540
0500–0600	WYFR	9870, 11580
0500–0600	Channel Africa	5955, 9695
0500–0600	NHK R Japan	5975, 7230
0500–0600	Vo Mediterranean	9765
0500–0700	HCJB	11925, 21455-usb
0530–0600	UAE R Dubai	13675, 15435, 21605
0530–0600	R Romania Intl	15250, 15380, 17720, 17745, 17790
0530–0600	R Austria Intl	6015
0600–0630	Swiss R Intl	3985, 6165
0600–0630	R Latvia	5935 [Sunday]
0600–0630	R Prague	5930, 7345, 9505
0600–0630	Swiss R Intl	9885, 13635, 15430
0600–0650	R Pyongyang	15180, 15230
0600–0650	DW	11915, 13790, 15185, 15205, 17820, 17875, 21680
0600–0700	R Korea	11945, 15155
0600–0700	Channel Africa	5955, 15220
0600–0800	WYFR	7355, 11770, 13695
0600–0800	Monitor R Intl	9840, 9870 (to 0700)
0630–0645	Vatican R	527, 1530, 3945, 6245, 7250, 9645, 11740, 15210
0630–0655	R Vlaanderen Intl	1512, 6015, 9925
0630–0700	R Austria Intl	6015
0630–0640	R Romania Intl	7225, 9550, 9665, 11810
0640–0820	TWR	7385
0645–0700	YLE R Finland	558, 963, 6120, 9560, 11755
0645–0715	R Romania Intl	15250, 15335, 17720, 17805
0700–0730	ICRC	6165 [last Sunday]
0700–0750	R Pyongyang	15340, 17765
0700–0800	NHK R Japan	5975, 7230, 11740, 15380, 15410, 17810
0700–0830	HCJB	6205, 9600, 11835, 17490-usb, 21455-usb
0730–0753	R Georgia	11910
0730–0800	R Prague	15605, 17535, 21705
0730–0930	R Netherlands	9630, 9810 (to 0825)
0740–0750	Vo Greece	9425, 11645, 15650
0800–0830	YLE R Finland	15445, 17800
0800–0845	R Pakistan	17900, 21520
0800–0850	R Pyongyang	15180, 15230
0800–0900	KNLS	9615
0800–0900	R Korea	7550, 13670, 15575
0800–0915	KTWR Guam	9785

Time	Station	Frequencies [kHz]
0800–1000	Monitor R Intl	13615
0830–0900	R Slovakia Intl	11990, 17535, 21705
0830–0930	AWR Europe	7180
0830–0900	R Austria Intl	15450, 17870
0830–1025	R Netherlands	5955, 9810
0855–0935	TWR Monte Carlo	7385 [Sunday]
0900–0925	R Vlaanderen Intl	1512, 6035, 13690, 17595
0900–0930	Swiss R Intl	9885, 13685, 17515
0900–0930	DW	6160, 9565, 11715, 12055, 15410, 17715, 21600
0900–1000	Monitor R Intl	7395, 9840, 13615, 17705
0930–1000	R Korea	13670
0930–1125	R Netherlands	9715, 9810 [to 1025], 12065, 15470
0940–0950	Vo Greece	15650, 17525
1000–1030	Kol Israel	15640, 15650, 17575
1000–1030	Swiss R Intl	6165, 9535
1000–1100	All India Radio	15050, 15180, 17387, 17895, 21735
1000–1100	Channel Africa	17810
1000–1200	Monitor R Intl	7395, 7465, 13625, 17555 (to 1100)
1020–1030	Vatican R	6245, 11740, 15210, 21730
1030–1100	R Korea	11715
1030–1100	UAE R Dubai	13675, 15320, 15395, 21605
1030–1100	R Austria Intl	15450, 17870
1030–1057	R Prague	7345, 9505, 11990
1100–1130	Swiss R Intl	6165, 9535, 13635, 15505, 17515
1100–1130	Vo Vietnam	9730
1100–1150	DW	15370, 15410, 17715, 17765, 17800, 17860, 21600
1100–1200	Channel Africa	9730
1100–1120	R Pakistan	17900, 21520
1130–1225	Vo Iran	9525, 11715, 11790, 11910, 11930
1130–1200	R Austria Intl	6155, 13730
1130–1200	R Sweden	13775, 15120, 15240
1130–1325	R Netherlands	5955, 9650
1200–1300	R Korea	7180
1200–1300	R France Intl	9805, 13325, 13640, 15155, 15195, 15530, 17575
1200–1300	R Bulgaria	17625
1200–1300	R Canada Intl	9635, 11855, 17820 [Monday–Friday]
1200–1300	R Jordan	9560
1200–1320	R Bras	15445
1200–1400	Monitor R Intl	7465, 9425, 9455 [to 1300], 13625

Time	Station	Frequencies [kHz]
1215–1330	R Cairo	17595
1230–1255	R Vlaanderen Intl	1512, 15545, 17775 [Sunday]
1230–1300	Swiss R Intl	6165, 9535
1230–1300	R Bangladesh	11895, 13620
1230–1300	Vo Vietnam	9840, 12020, 15010
1230–1300	R Sweden	15240, 17870
1230–1300	TRT Vo Turkey	9675
1240–1250	Vo Greece	11645
1300–1325	Kol Israel	15640, 15650 [Sunday–Thursday]
1300–1325	R Vlaanderen Intl	1512, 15545, 17775 [Monday–Saturday]
1300–1330	R Norway Intl	9590 [Sunday]
1300–1330	Swiss R Intl	7480, 11690, 13635, 15505
1300–1330	R Korea	9570, 13670
1300–1330	ICRC	6165 [last Sunday]
1300–1350	R Pyongyang	9345, 9640, 11740, 15230
1300–1400	R Romania Intl	11775, 11940, 15365, 17720, 17775
1300–1400	KNLS	7355
1300–1400	Vo Mediterranean	11925
1302–1502	WYFR	11550
1330–1400	R Sweden	15240, 17870
1330–1400	R Canada Intl	15315, 15325, 17820, 17895, 21455 [Monday–Saturday]
1330–1400	R Austria Intl	15450
1330–1400	R Tashkent	7285, 9175, 15295, 17745, 17815
1330–1400	UAE R Dubai	13675, 15320, 15395, 21605
1330–1400	Vo Vietnam	9840, 12020, 15010
1330–1500	AIR	11760, 15120
1330–1625	R Netherlands	9890, 13700, 15150
1335–1345	Vo Greece	15630, 17535
1400–1500	R France Intl	11910, 17560, 17695
1400–1500	AWR	7230
1400–1500	R Korea	5975
1400–1500	R Bulgaria	15460, 17705
1400–1500	Monitor R Intl	9355, 11900
1400–1700	R Iraq Intl	13680
1430–1500	R Austria Intl	6155, 9870, 13730, 15450
1430–1530	R Romania Intl	11810, 15335, 17720
1430–1625	R Netherlands	15150
1500–1600	Monitor R Intl	9355
1500–1530	R Prague	5930, 7345, 13580
1500–1530	Swiss R Intl	11960, 13635, 15505
1500–1530	DW	7185, 9735, 11965, 17800, 21600
1500–1530	R Pyongyang	9325, 9640, 9977, 13785

229

Time	Station	Frequencies [kHz]
1500–1555	Polish R Warsaw	7285, 9525
1500–1600	R Algiers	11715, 15205, 17745
1500–1635	KTWR Guam	12025
1500–1800	Channel Africa	4945, 11770
1500–1800	R Jordan	9560
1530–1600	R Tirana	7155, 9760
1530–1600	R Portugal	21515 [Monday–Friday]
1530–1600	R Austria Intl	11780
1530–1630	R Netherlands	5955
1530–1700	RTM Rabat	17595 [Monday–Friday]
1600–1620	Vatican R	12050, 15585
1600–1630	Vo Ethiopia	7165, 9560
1600–1630	R Pakistan	9470, 11570, 13587, 15555, 15660
1600–1630	Vo Vietnam	9840, 12020, 15010
1600–1645	UAE R Dubai	13675, 15320, 15395, 21605
1600–1650	DW	1548, 7225, 9875, 15595, 17810, 21680
1600–1700	R Korea	5975
1600–1700	R France Intl	3965, 6175, 11615, 11700, 12015, 15530, 17620, 17795, 17850
1600–1700	WYFR	15355, 21525, 21615
1600–1800	Monitor R Intl	9355
1600–2100	BSKSA	9705
1615–1630	Vatican R	527, 1530, 6245, 7250, 9645
1615–1645	R Sweden	1179, 6065
1630–1700	R Alma Ata	5915, 6135
1645–1700	HCJB	15270, 17790, 21455-usb [Monday–Friday]
1700–1730	R Prague	5930, 7345, 11640
1700–1730	Swiss R Intl	9885, 13635, 15635
1700–1730	R Alma Ata	5035, 5260, 5960, 5970, 6010, 15250, 15315, 15360, 17765
1700–1750	R Pyongyang	9325, 9640, 9977, 13785
1700–1755	Polish R Warsaw	5995, 7270, 7285
1700–1800	NHK R Japan	6150, 9580, 9535, 11930
1700–1800	R Dada Gorgud	7160, 15240
1700–1800	RTV Algiers	1422, 7145
1700–1900	WYFR	21500
1700–1800	R Pakistan	11570, 15675
1730–1745	Vatican R	9725, 11625, 15570
1730–1800	R Sweden	1179, 6065, 9655, 15390
1730–1800	R Latvia	5935 [Saturday]
1730–1925	R Netherlands	6020, 7120, 17655, 21590
1745–1945	AIR	7412, 9950, 11620, 11860, 11935, 15075

Time	Station	Frequencies [kHz]
1800–1825	R Vlaanderen Intl	1512, 5910, 15550
1800–1830	R Norway Intl	9560, 9590, 11745, 15220 [Sunday]
1800–1830	Vo Vietnam	9840, 12020, 15010
1800–1920	R Bras	15265
1800–2000	Monitor R Intl	9355, 13770, 21640
1800–2100	R Kuwait	11990
1815–1900	R Bangladesh	7190, 9680, 9700
1830–1855	R Finland	558, 963, 6120, 9730, 9770, 11755, 15440
1830–1900	R Austria Intl	5945, 6155, 9880, 13730
1830–1900	R Slovakia Intl	5915, 7345, 9440
1830–1900	R Yugoslavia	6100, 9720
1840–1850	Vo Greece	15650, 17525
1850–2135	R New Zealand Intl	11735 [Monday–Friday]
1900–1930	Swiss R Intl	3985, 6165
1900–1930	R Budapest	3955, 6110, 7220
1900–1930	Vo Vietnam	9840, 12020, 15010
1900–1930	Kol Israel	9435, 11603, 11675, 15640, 17575
1900–1930	R Portugal	9780, 9815, 11975, 15155 [Monday–Friday]
1900–1930	R Vilnius	666, 1557, 9400, 9710
1900–1950	DW	9670, 9735, 11740, 11765, 11785, 11810, 13690, 13790
1900–2000	RAE Buenos Aires	15345 [Monday–Friday]
1900–2000	REE	11775
1900–2000	HCJB	15270, 17490-usb, 17790, 21455-usb
1900–2000	WYFR	15355, 21615
1900–2000	R Bulgaria	9700, 11720
1900–2000	R Romania Intl	9690, 9750, 11810, 11940
1930–2000	R Romania Intl	15340, 15365, 17720
1930–2000	KFBS	9465 [Sunday]
1930–2025	Polish R Warsaw	1503, 5995, 6135, 7285
1930–2025	R Netherlands	17605, 17655
1930–2030	Vo Iran	9022, 11965
1935–1955	RAI	7275, 11800
1950–2015	Vatican R	527, 1530, 3945, 5882
2000–2015	Vo Greece	9395
2000–2030	Swiss R Intl	6135, 9885, 13635, 15505
2000–2030	R Norway Intl	9590, 15220 [Sunday]
2000–2030	Vatican R	9725, 11625, 15570
2000–2030	R Prague	5930, 7345, 9485
2000–2050	TRT Vo Turkey	9900
2000–2050	R Pyongyang	6576, 9345, 9640, 9977
2000–2050	DW	7170, 9615

Time	Station	Frequencies [kHz]
2000–2100	China R Intl	6950, 9920
2000–2100	AWR Europe	6055
2000–2100	Vo Indonesia	9675, 11752, 11785
2000–2120	SLBC	15120
2000–2200	WYFR	15355, 15566, 17612, 21525, 21615
2000–2200	Monitor R Intl	13770, 13840 [from 2100], 15665
2005–2105	R Damascus	12085, 15095
2025–2045	RAI	7275, 9575, 11800
2030–2100	R Yugoslavia	9620
2030–2100	R Korea	5965
2030–2100	Vo Vietnam	9840, 12020, 15010
2030–2100	R Latvia	5935 [Monday–Friday]
2030–2100	R Sweden	1179, 6065, 9655
2030–2130	RCI	5995, 7235, 13650, 13670, 15325, 17820, 17850, 17875
2045–2230	AIR	7412, 9910, 9950, 11620, 11715, 15265
2100–2125	R Prague	5930, 7345, 9485
2100–2125	R Vlaanderen Intl	1512, 5910
2100–2130	R Yugoslavia	7265, 9595
2100–2130	R Budapest	3955, 6110, 7220
2100–2130	China R Intl	3985
2100–2150	DW	9670, 9735, 9765, 11765, 11785, 13690, 15135
2100–2155	China R Intl	6950, 9920
2100–2200	R Romania Intl	7225, 9690, 9750, 11940
2100–2200	REE	6125
2100–2200	R Havana Cuba	17760
2100–2200	NHK R Japan	11925
2100–2200	R Korea	6480, 15575
2100–2200	R Bulgaria	9700, 11645, 11720
2100–2200	R Ukraine Intl	936, 4825, 6020, 6090, 7150, 7240, 7285, 11705, 12030
2100–2300	R Iraq Intl	11810
2115–2245	R Cairo	9900
2130–2200	HCJB	11835, 15270, 17490-usb, 21455-usb
2130–2200	R Vilnius	666, 1557, 9710
2130–2200	R Austria Intl	5945, 6155, 9880, 13730
2130–2200	Kol Israel	7465, 9435, 11603, 11675, 15575
2130–2200	R Sweden	1179, 6065
2130–2230	Vo Iran	11790
2200–2225	RAI	5990, 9710, 11800
2200–2230	R Korea	9640
2200–2300	VoFC	17750, 21720

Time	Station	Frequencies [kHz]
2200–2300	WYFR	17612, 2152
2200–2300	RCI	5960, 9755, 11705, 11845, 11875, 13670, 15305
2200–2300	TRT Vo Turkey	7185, 9445, 11710
2200–2400	UAE R Dubai	9770, 11885, 13605
2200–2400	Monitor R Intl	13625, 13770, 15405, 17555
2230–2300	R Sweden	1179, 6065
2230–2300	YLE R Finland	11755, 13750
2240–2250	Vo Greece	9425, 11645
2245–0045	AIR	7412, 9910, 9950, 11745, 11785, 15110, 15145
2245–2345	R Bulgaria	9700, 11720
2300–2315	R Tirana	1395, 9760, 11825
2300–2330	R Vilnius	7150 [Saturday–Sunday]
2300–2330	R Norway Intl	9655, 11860 [Sunday]
2300–2400	RCI	5960, 9755, 11940, 13670, 15235
2300–2400	NHK R Japan	5965, 6155, 6185, 9625
2330–2400	R Sweden	11910
2330–2355	R Vlaanderen Intl	11740, 13655
2330–0125	R Netherlands	6020, 6165
2330–2400	Vo Vietnam	9840, 12020, 15010
2335–2345	Vo Greece	9420, 11595, 11645

Section 12

MEDIA, SHORT WAVE LISTENER AND
DX PROGRAMMES

Many international radio broadcasters produce regular programmes for short wave listeners and DXers. A number of the programmes also include news about computers, and devlopments in all forms of electronic communications (including space). We have included a selection of the more popular programmes in this section, but it is by no means exhaustive. Frequencies for the programmes can be found in the section *Broadcasts in English.*

BBC World Service: *WAVEGUIDE*
News about developments in BBC World Service, advice for better listening, satellite information and regular reviews of new equipment for the short wave broadcast listener. Produced by Kip Meyers and presented by Simon Spanswick.

HCJB Quito Ecuador: *DX PARTY LINE*
The DX Party Line often concentrates on one subject each week, including reviews of individual stations, equipment news or listening tips.

Radio Netherlands: *MEDIA NETWORK*
A weekly magazine of world-wide communications and media news, with regular reviews of new equipment, reports on major short wave events around the world, and listening tips each week concentrating on a different part of the world. Produced and presented by Jonathan Marks.

Radio Sweden: *MEDIASCAN*
On Tuesdays on the Nordic station, produced by George Wood. The programme includes developments in the electronic media worldwide, with satellite and computer news.

Voice of America: *COMMUNICATIONS WORLD*
Produced and presented by Gene Reich, the programme features news about the electronic media in North America, together with technical features and news from the international broadcasting world.

WRNO: *WORLD OF RADIO*
With Glenn Hauser and his listening tips.

Monday
0000	WWCR Nashville
0100	WHRI South Bend
0125	Radio Japan
0135	Radio Korea
0342	Voice of Free China (last Monday in month)
0350	Radio Budapest
0430	Radio New Zealand (even weeks)
0635	Radio Korea
0700	Radio for Peace Intl, Costa Rica
0738	Radio Vlaanderen Intl
1008	Radio Vlaanderen Intl
1040	All India Radio (2nd and 4th Monday)
1345	Radio Sofia
1408	Radio Vlaanderen Intl
1415	Voice of the Mediterranean
1435	All India Radio (2nd and 4th Monday)
1545	Radio Sofia
1840	All India Radio (2nd and 4th Monday)
2020	Radio Budapest
2130	All India Radio (2nd and 4th Monday)
2200	Radio Sofia
2245	Israel Radio
2340	All India Radio (2nd and 4th Monday)
2345	Radio Sofia

Tuesday
0220	Radio Budapest
0247	Radio Bucharest
1100	Radio for Peace Intl
1245	Radio Sweden (1st and 3rd Tuesday)
1330	WWCR Nashville
1345	Radio Sweden (1st and 3rd Tuesday)
1445	Radio Sweden (1st and 3rd Tuesday)
1520	Polish Radio Warsaw
1730	Radio Sweden (1st and 3rd Tuesday)

1845	Radio Sweden (1st and 3rd Tuesday)
1900	Radio for Peace Intl
2020	Radio Budapest
2130	Radio Havana Cuba
2145	Radio Sweden (1st and 3rd Tuesday)
2245	Radio Sweden (1st and 3rd Tuesday)
2345	Radio Sweden (1st and 3rd Tuesday)

Wednesday
0030	Radio Havana Cuba
0045	Radio Sweden (1st and 3rd Wednesday)
0145	Radio Sweden (1st and 3rd Wednesday)
0220	Radio Budapest
0230	Radio Havana Cuba
0245	Radio Sweden (1st and 3rd Wednesday)
0300	Radio for Peace Intl
0345	Radio Sweden (1st and 3rd Wednesday)
0530	Radio Havana Cuba
0700	HCJB Quito
0800	HCJB Quito
1030	HCJB Quito
1100	Radio for Peace Intl
1220	Polish Radio Warsaw
1330	WWCR Nashville
1520	Polish Radio Warsaw
1545	FEBA Seychelles
1720	Polish Radio Warsaw
1730	HCJB Quito
1930	HCJB Quito
1950	Polish Radio Warsaw
2000	Deutsche Welle (fortnightly)
2020	Radio Budapest
2050	Radio Budapest
2100	HCJB Quito
2130	HCJB Quito
2230	WHRI South Bend

Thursday
0015	Radio Prague
0100	HCJB Quito

236

Thursday *(continued)*

0115	Radio Prague
0130	BBC World Service
0150	Radio Netherlands
0200	HCJB Quito
0220	Radio Budapest
0315	Radio Prague
0330	HCJB Quito
0345	Radio Prague
0350	Radio Budapest
0400	HCJB Quito
0750	Radio Netherlands
0830	Radio New Zealand (even weeks)
0950	Radio Netherlands
1150	Radio Netherlands
1350	Radio Netherlands
1540	FEBC Manila
1550	Radio Netherlands
1650	Radio Netherlands
1750	Radio Netherlands
1950	Radio Netherlands

Friday

0050	Radio Netherlands
0100	Radio Tashkent (3rd Friday)
0215	RAE Buenos Aires
0250	Radio Netherlands
0350	Radio Netherlands
1015	FEBC Manila
1348	Radio Yugoslavia (fortnightly)
1500	Radio Sofia
1545	Radio Portugal (every 3 weeks)
1930	Radio New Zealand (even weeks)
1948	Radio Yugoslavia (fortnightly)
2000	Radio for Peace Intl
2015	Radio Portugal (every 3 weeks)
2045	Radio Sofia
2215	WWCR Nashville
2218	Radio Yugoslavia (fortnightly)
2220	Radio Budapest
2300	WHRI South Bend

Saturday

0030	Radio Sofia
0100	FEBC Manila
0118	Radio Yugoslavia (fortnightly)
0245	Radio Portugal (every 3 weeks)
0350	Radio Budapest
0400	Radio for Peace Intl
0430	Radio Sofia
0430	HCJB Quito
0518	Radio Yugoslavia (fortnightly)
0600	WHRI South Bend
0700	WWCR Nashville
0715	BBC World Service
0737	HCJB Quito
0738	Radio Vlaanderen Intl
0935	Deutsche Welle (last Saturday)
1007	HCJB Quito
1008	Radio Vlaanderen Intl
1010	Voice of America
1030	BBC World Service
1135	Deutsche Welle (last Saturday)
1210	Voice of America
1300	Radio Sofia
1330	Radio Tashkent (2nd Saturday)
1400	FEBC Manila
1408	Radio Vlaanderen Intl
1500	Radio Sofia
1610	Voice of America
1800	Radio for Peace Intl
1907	HCJB Quito
1908	Radio Vlaanderen Intl
1910	Radio Exterior de Espana
1940	Radio Bucharest
2037	HCJB Quito
2100	Voice of Turkey (fortnightly)
2110	Voice of America
2110	Radio Exterior de Espana
2130	Radio Havana Cuba
2135	Deutsche Welle (last Saturday)
2140	Radio Bucharest
2208	Radio Vlaanderen Intl
2220	Radio Budapest

Saturday *(continued)*
2315 Voice of Turkey (fortnightly)
2315 AWR Asia Guam

Sunday
0010 Radio Exterior de Espana
0037 HCJB Quito
0038 Radio Vlaanderen Intl
0100 WWCR Nashville
0110 Voice of America
0110 Radio Exterior de Espana
0120 Deutsche Welle
      (following last Saturday)
0130 WHRI South Bend
0130 Radio Havana Cuba
0200 Radio for Peace Intl
0215 AWR Asia Guam
0220 Deutsche Welle
      (following last Saturday)
0240 Voice of Free China
      (last Sunday)
0245 Radio Bucharest
0300 WWCR Nashville
0307 HCJB Quito
0322 Deutsche Welle
      (following last Saturday)
0330 Radio Havana Cuba
0350 Radio Budapest
0410 Voice of Turkey (fortnightly)
0415 WWCR Nashville
0507 HCJB Quito
0510 Radio Exterior de Espana

0520 Deutsche Welle
      (following last Saturday)
0525 NHK Radio Japan
0630 Radio Havana Cuba
0700 WWCR Nashville
0720 AWR Europe Forli
0725 NHK Radio Japan
0740 Voice of Free China
      (last Sunday)
0805 Radio Korea
0835 Radio Korea
0935 Radio Korea
1000 Radio for Peace Intl
1135 Radio Korea
1235 Radio Korea
1305 Radio Korea
1400 Israel Radio
1425 NHK Radio Japan
1615 AWR Asia Guam
1725 NHK Radio Japan
1815 AWR Asia Guam
2024 Israel Radio
2035 Radio Korea
2125 NHK Radio Japan
2135 Radio Korea
2205 Radio Korea
2220 Radio Budapest
2240 Voice of Free China
      (last Sunday)
2245 Radio Sofia
2300 WWCR Nashville
2300 Radio for Peace Intl

Section 13

UK FM RADIO STATIONS

At the time of compilation, some stations are not yet on the air. These are indicated with an asterisk [*].

Some regional BBC stations in Scotland carry more than one service: for example Radio Nan Gaidheal will share with Radio Aberdeen or Radio Highland.

Frequency [MHz]	Station	Site
National Networks		
89.1-90.2	BBC Radio Two	Multiple Locations
90.3-9.26	BBC Radio Three	Multiple Locations
91.1	BBC Radio Two	Les Platons, CI
92.5-94.6	BBC Radio Four	Multiple Locations
92.5-94.6	BBC Radio Cymru	Multiple Locations
92.5-94.7	BBC Radio Scotland	Multiple Locations
92.6	BBC Radio Three	Pendle Forest
94.8	BBC Radio Three	Les Platons, CI
94.9	BBC Radio Four	Forfar; Londonderry
95.3	BBC Radio Four	Meldrum; Kirkconnel
95.8	BBC Radio Four	Black Hill
95.9	BBC Radio Four	Haverfordwest
96.8	BBC Radio Cymru	Wenvoe
97.1	BBC Radio Four	Les Platons, CI
97.7-99.7	BBC Radio One	Multiple Locations
99.9-101.9	Classic FM	Multiple Locations
103.6	BBC Radio Four	Anglesey; Rosemarkie
103.8	BBC Radio Four	Rosneath
103.9	BBC Radio Four	Ashkirk
104.0	BBC Radio Four	Blaenplwyf
104.3	BBC Radio Four	Darvel
104.9	BBC R Scotland	Port Ellen
Regional and Local Stations		
88.6	BBC R Sheffield	Sheffield City Centre
88.8	BBC R Jersey	Les Platons, CI
89.0	Manx Radio	Snaefell, IoM
92.4	BBC R Leeds	Holme Moss
92.5	BBC R Highland; Nan Gaidheal	Ballachulish; Mallaig
92.6	BBC R Highland	Knock More
92.7	BBC R Aberdeen; Orkney; Shetland	Bressay
92.8	BBC R Tweed	Peebles

239

Frequency [MHz]	Station	Site
92.9	BBC R Highland; Nan Gaidheal	Skriaig, Skye
93.0	BBC R Ulster	Rostrevor Forest
93.1	BBC R Aberdeen	Meldrum
	BBC R Solway	Cambret Hill
	BBC R Ulster/Foyle	Londonderry
93.2	BBC Guernsey	Les Touillets
93.3	BBC R Highland; Nan Gaidheal	Oban
93.5	BBC R Highland; Nan Gaidheal	Melvaig
	BBC R Tweed	Ashkirk
	BBC R Ulster	Larne
	BBC R Highland	Kingussie
93.7	BBC R Highland; Nan Gaidheal	Fort William
93.8	BBC R Ulster	Brougher Mountain; Kirkeel
	BBC R Aberdeen	Durris
93.9	BBC R Nan Gaidheal	Glengorm
	BBC R Ulster	Newry South
	BBC R Tweed	Innerleithen
	BBC R Highland; Nan Gaidheal	Penifiler
94.0	BBC R Highland	Rosemarkie
94.1	BBC R Solway	Stranraer
	BBC R Highland; Nan Gaidheal	Kinlochleven
94.2	BBC R Nan Gaidheal	Eitshal
	BBC R Derby	Derby City Centre
94.5	BBC R Ulster	Divis
	BBC R Aberdeen	Tullich
94.6	BBC R Highland	Grantown-on-Spey
	BBC Berks	Henley-on-Thames
	BBC Stoke	Alsagers Bank
94.7	BBC R Solway	Sandale
	BBC Hereford & Worcester	Ridge Hill
	BBC R Sheffield	Chesterfield
94.8	BBC CWR	Meriden
	BBC R Devon	Huntshaw Cross
94.9	BBC R Lincolnshire	Belmont
	BBC GLR	Crystal Palace
	BBC R Bristol	Ilchester Crescent
95.0	BBC R Cleveland	Bilsdale West Moor
	BBC R Shropshire	Ludlow
	BBC R Gloucestershire	Stroud
	BBC Southern Counties	Newhaven
95.1	BBC R Wales	Blaenavon
	BBC GMR	Holme Moss
	BBC R Norfolk	Tacolneston
	BBC R Ulster	Ballycastle
	BBC Southern Counties	Horsham

Frequency [MHz]	Station	Site
95.2	BBC R Cornwall	Caradon Hill
	BBC R Furness	Kendal
	BBC R Oxford	Oxford
95.3	BBC R Derby	Stanton Moor
	BBC R Essex	South Benfleet
	BBC R Leeds	Wharfedale
	BBC Southern Counties	Brighton
95.4	BBC R Newcastle	Pontop Pike
	BBC R Ulster	Limavady
	BBC R Berkshire	Windsor
95.5	BBC 3 Counties R	Sandy Heath
	BBC R Bristol	Mendip
	BBC R Nottingham	Mansfield
	BBC R Lancashire	Blackburn
	BBC R York	Scarborough
	BBC R Suffolk	Lowestoft
95.6	BBC R Cumbria	Sandale
	BBC R WM	Birmingham
95.7	BBC R Cambridgeshire	Peterborough
95.8	BBC R Cleveland	Whitby
	BBC R Devon	Exeter
	BBC R Gloucester	Cirencester
	BBC R Merseyside	Allerton Park
	Capital FM	London
95.9	BBC R Wales	Christchurch
	BBC R Humberside	Hull
	Invicta FM	Thanet
96.0	BBC R Cambridgeshire	Madingley
	BBC R Cornwall	Scilly Isles
	BBC R Devon	Okehampton
	BBC R Newcastle	Chatton
	BBC R Shropshire	The Wrekin
96.1	BBC R Furness	Morecambe Bay
	BBC R Solent	Rowridge
	Hallam FM	Rotherham
	Invicta FM	Ashford
	BBC R Cymru	Llandinam
96.2	Trent FM	Nottingham
	Lantern	North Devon
	SIBC	Shetland
	Yorkshire Coast	Olivers Mount
96.3	Aire FM	Morley, Leeds
	Essex R	Southend-on-Sea
	GWR FM (West)	Bristol
	Marcher Coast	North Wales

Frequency [MHz]	Station	Site
96.3 *(cont)*	Q96	Paisley
96.4	BRMB-FM	Sutton Coldfield
	Mercury	Guildford
	DevonAir	Torbay
	Downtown R	Limavady
	SGR FM	Bury St Edmunds
	Swansea Sound	Swansea
	R Tay	Perth
	Signal Radio	Sutton Common, Cheshire
	CFM	Carlisle
96.5	GWR FM	Marlborough
	RadioWave	Blackpool
	Trent FM	Mansfield
96.6	Northants	Northampton
	TFM	Teesside
	Downtown R	Brougher Mountain
	Ceredigion	Lampeter
	Tavistock	Tavistock
96.7	BBC R Kent	Wrotham
	City FM	Liverpool
	West Sound	Ayr
	Ocean FM	Winchester
	BCR	Belfast
	Central FM	Stirling
	KLFM	Kings Lynn
96.8	Borders	Selkirk
96.9	Chiltern	Bedford
	NorthSound	Aberdeen
	Viking FM	Humberside
	Signal One	Stafford
	Bay	Ulverston
	Choice FM	Brixton
	Southern FM	Newhaven
97.0	Mercia FM	Coventry
	DevonAir	Exeter
	Invicta FM	Dover
	Plymouth Sound	Plymouth
	2 Ten FM	Reading
97.1	Metro FM	Newcastle-on-Tyne
	SGR FM	Ipswich
	Orchard FM	Chedington, Somerset
	Mercury	Haslemere
	MFM	Moel-y-Parc
97.2	Beacon R	Wolverhampton
	Galaxy	Bristol

Frequency [MHz]	Station	Site
97.2 *(cont)*	GWR	Swindon
	Manx	Carnane, IoM
	West Sound	Dumfries
	Galaxy	Pur Down, Bristol
	Wessex FM	Weymouth
97.3	Forth FM	Edinburgh
	London News R	London
97.4	Cool FM	Belfast
	Moray Firth	Inverness
	Hallam FM	Sheffield
	Red Dragon FM	Newport
	Red Rose Rock	Winter Hill, Lancashire
	Fox FM	Banbury
	CNFM	Newmarket
97.5	Ocean FM	Portsmouth
	The Pulse	Bradford
	R Mercury	Horsham
	West Sound	Girvan
	Southern Sound	Hastings
	Borders	Berwick-on-Tweed
	Heartland FM	Pitlochry
97.6	Chiltern	Luton
	R Wyvern	Hereford
	Forth RFM	Black Hill
	BBC R Kent	Folkestone
97.9	BBC R Nan Ghaideal	Lochgilphead
100.0	Kiss FM	London
100.3	Scot FM	Glasgow Craig Kelly
100.4	JFM North West	Winter Hill
100.7	Century Radio	Bilsdale
100.7	Heart FM	Sutton Coldfield
101.0	Galaxy Radio	Mendip
101.1	Scot FM	Edinburgh Blackhills
101.6	Star FM	Slough
101.7	Ten 17	Rye Hill
101.8	Century Radio	Ben Hope
102.0	Sunset R	Manchester
	Southern FM	Hastings
	Wey Valley 102	Alton
102.2	JFM	London
	GWR FM	West Wiltshire
	Lincs FM	Lincoln
	Pirate FM	East Cornwall
	Spire FM	Salisbury
102.3	2CR FM	Bournemouth

Frequency [MHz]	Station	Site
102.4	Broadland	Norwich/Great Yarmouth
	Downtown	Londonderry
	Severn Sound	Gloucester
	Southern FM	Heathfield
	Buzz FM	Birmingham
102.5	Clyde 1	Glasgow
	The Pulse	Huddersfield
102.6	Essex R	Chelmsford
	Signal One	Stoke-on-Trent
	Fox FM	Oxford
	Orchard FM	Mendip
	Harmony	Coventry
102.7	Hereward	Peterborough
	Mercury	Reigate
	*BBC R Leeds	Keighley
102.8	Invicta FM	Canterbury
	Pirate FM	West Cornwall
	Tay	Dundee
	Trent FM	Derby
	Wyvern	Worcester
102.9	2 Ten FM	Hannington
	Hallam FM	Barnsley
	Mercia FM	Leamington Spa
	Q102	Londonderry
103.0	GWR FM	Bath
	Piccadilly 103	Manchester
	DevonAir	Stockland Hill, E Devon
	CN-FM	Madingley
	Severn Sound	Stroud
	Metro FM	Newcastle-on-Tyne
103.1	Beacon	Shrewsbury
	Invicta FM	Maidstone
	Borders	Peebles
103.2	Leicester Sound	Leicester
	Power FM	Southampton
	Sunrise	Bradford
	Red Dragon FM	Cardiff
	Bay	Kendal
103.3	Horizon R	Milton Keynes
	London Greek R/WNK	Haringey
	Ceredigion	Aberystwyth
103.4	BBC R Devon	North Hessary Tor
	MFM	Wrexham
	Hallam FM	Doncaster
	Borders	Eyemouth

Frequency [MHz]	Station	Site
103.4 *(cont)*	Wear FM	Sunderland
103.5	BBC R Essex	Great Braxted
	BBC Wiltshire Sound	Salisbury
	BBC R Suffolk	Manningtree
	Southern FM	Brighton
	East End R	Glasgow
103.6	BBC R Northampton	Geddington
	BBC Wiltshire Sound	Blunsdon
103.7	Manx	Jurby
	BBC R York	Acklam Wold
	BBC CWR	Lark Stoke
	Channel 103 FM	Jersey
103.8	BBC 3 Counties	Luton
	BBC R Nottingham	Colwick Park
	BBC Dorset FM	Dorchester
	RTM	London SE
103.9	BBC R Cornwall	Redruth
	BBC R Lancashire	Winter Hill
	BBC R Leeds	Beecroft Hill
104.0	BBC Southern Counties	Reigate
	BBC Hereford & Worcester	Great Malvern
	BBC CWR	Nuneaton
104.1	BBC R Berkshire	Hannington
	BBC R Sheffield	Holme Moss
104.2	BBC R Furness	Windermere
	BBC R Kent	Dover
	BBC R Northampton	Northampton
104.3	BBC R York	Woolmoor
	BBC Wiltshire Sound	Naish Hill
104.4	BBC R Berkshire	Reading
	BBC R Newcastle	Fenham
104.5	BBC R Derby	Sutton Coldfield
	BBC R Lancashire	Lancaster
	BBC R Sussex	Heathfield
	BBC Three Counties	Bow Brickhill
104.6	BBC R Bristol	Bath
	BBC R Hereford & Worcester	Kidderminster
	BBC R Suffolk	Great Barton
	BBC Southern Counties	Guildford
104.7	BBC R Gloucestershire	Churchdown Hill
	BBC R Leeds	Keighley
	*BBC R Lincolnshire	Grantham
	Island FM	Guernsey
	Minster FM	York
104.8	*BBC Southern Counties	Burton Down

Frequency [MHz]	Station	Site
104.9	BBC R Leicestershire	Copt Oak
	BBC Wiltshire Sound	Marlborough
	Melody R	Croydon

Section 14

TIME DIFFERENCES FROM GMT

North America

Newfoundland	$-3^1/_2$
Atlantic zone	-4
Eastern zone	-5
Central zone	-6
Mountain zone	-7
Pacific zone	-8

Central and South America

Argentina	-3
Bahamas	-5
Barbados	-4
Belize	-6
Bermuda	-4
Bolivia	-4
Brazil [east]	-3
Brazil [west]	-4
Chile	-4
Colombia	-5
Costa Rica	-6
Cuba	-5
Ecuador	-5
Falkland Islands	-4
Guatemala	-6
Guyana	-3
Honduras	-6
Jamaica	-5
Mexico	-6
Nicaragua	-6
Panama	-5
Paraguay	-4
Peru	-5
Trinidad	-4
Uruguay	-3
Venezuela	-4

Europe

Albania	$+1$
Austria	$+1$

Europe (cont'd)

Belgium	$+1$
Bulgaria	$+2$
Czech Republic	$+1$
Denmark	$+1$
Finland	$+2$
France	$+1$
Germany	$+1$
Gibraltar	$+1$
Greece	$+2$
Hungary	$+1$
Italy	$+1$
Luxembourg	$+1$
Malta	$+1$
Netherlands	$+1$
Norway	$+1$
Poland	$+1$
Portugal	gmt
Romania	$+2$
Slovakia	$+1$
Spain	$+1$
Sweden	$+1$
Switzerland	$+1$
Russia [Moscow]	$+3$

Africa and Middle East

Angola	$+1$
Botswana	$+2$
Cameroon	$+1$
Chad	$+1$
Congo	$+1$
Cyprus	$+2$
Djibouti	$+3$
Egypt	$+2$
Ethiopia	$+3$
Iran	$+3^1/_2$
Iraq	$+3$
Israel	$+2$
Jordan	$+2$

Africa and Middle East (cont'd)

Kenya	+3
Kuwait	+3
Lebanon	+2
Lesotho	+2
Libya	+1
Madagascar	+3
Malawi	+2
Mauritius	+4
Mozambique	+2
Nigeria	+1
Saudi Arabia	+4
Seychelles	+4
Somalia	+3
South Africa	+2
Sudan	+2
Syria	+2
Tanzania	+3
Tunisia	+1
Turkey	+2
Uganda	+3
Zaire	+1
Zambia	+2
Zimbabwe	+2

Near and Far East

Afghanistan	$+4^1/_2$
Bangladesh	+6
Brunei	+8
Burma	$+6^1/_2$

Near and Far East (cont'd)

China	+8
Hong Kong	+8
India	$+5^1/_2$
Indonesia	+7
Japan	+9
Kampuchea	+7
Korea	+9
Lao	+7
Malaysia	+8
Nepal	$+5^3/_4$
Pakistan	+5
Philippines	+8
Singapore	+8
Sri Lanka	$+5^1/_2$
Taiwan	+8
Thailand	+7
Vietnam	+7

Pacific

Australia [Canberra, New Sth Wales, Queensland, Victoria]	+10
[South Australia, Northern Territory]	$+9^1/_2$
[Western Australia]	+8
[Lord Howe Island]	$+10^1/_2$
[Tasmania]	+10
Fiji	+12
New Zealand	+12

Daylight saving time has not been taken into account in this table.

Section 15

WAVELENGTH/FREQUENCY CONVERSION

Wavelength in metres $\quad = \quad \dfrac{300,000}{\text{Frequency in kHz}}$ (a)

Wavelength in metres $\quad = \quad \dfrac{300}{\text{Frequency in MHz}}$ (b)

Frequency in kHz $\quad = \quad \dfrac{300,000}{\text{Wavelength in metres}}$ (c)

Frequency in MHz $\quad = \quad \dfrac{300}{\text{Wavelength in metres}}$ (d)

Examples:

No. 1   Convert 180kHz to wavelength in metres.
Using formula - (a)

$$\text{Wavelength} \quad = \quad \frac{300,000}{180} \quad = 1667 \text{ metres}$$

No. 2   Convert 91MHz to wavelength in metres.
Using formula - (b)

$$\text{Wavelength} \quad = \quad \frac{300}{91} \quad = 3.3 \text{ metres}$$

No. 3   Convert a wavelength of 1500 metres to frequency.
Using formula - (c)

$$\text{Frequency} \quad = \quad \frac{300,000}{1500} \quad = 200\text{kHz}$$

No. 4   Convert a wavelength of 4 metres to frequency.
Using formula - (d)

$$\text{Frequency} \quad = \quad \frac{300}{4} \quad = 75\text{MHz}$$

PLEASE NOTE

Babani books should be available from all good Booksellers, Radio Component Dealers and Mail Order Companies

However, should you experience difficulty in obtaining any title in your area, then please write directly to the publisher enclosing payment to cover the cost of the book plus adequate postage.

If you would like a complete catalogue of our entire range of Radio, Electronics and Computer Books then please send a Stamped Addressed Envelope to:

BERNARD BABANI (publishing) LTD
THE GRAMPIANS
SHEPHERDS BUSH ROAD
LONDON W6 7NF
ENGLAND